11

Born In Mississippi 'Raised In Buffalo, New York'

Curley & Gladys Holmes And Family

Edited by
SANCHO JOHNSON

by
Bettye Holmes Chansamone

Published by
UBUS COMMUNICATIONS SYSTEMS
206070 Barhams Hills - Barhams Hill Rd.
Drewryville, Virginia 23844
publish@khabooks.com – (704) 509-2226

FIRST EDITION – FIRST PRINTING

ISBN# 978-1-56411-548-5
YBBG# 0513

Published in the USA by:
KHA Books
210 East Arrowhead Drive, Suite #2
Charlotte, N. C. 28213
(704) 509-2226
www.khabooks.com

Acknowledgments

I love, honor and praise God! I would have not started nor completed this book without Him. Thank You! Thank You! Thank You!

I am most appreciative to my wonderful husband Sitthisak, (Jimmee) for encouraging me to be bold and make this happen. I am also appreciative for his love and moral support. Jimmee, you have done more for me than you will ever realize.

I am truly grateful to my son, Sancho Sereno for his honesty and valued information, and suggestions which I incorporated into this book. 'Peace and love be with you.'

Sacha and Malesha: (my daughters) your input and support in getting this book together was a treasure which will be treasured.

Doll: Your Knowledge and your recollection was essential in writing this book. I am delighted. Robert (Bob), my brother in law: Thank you for your support.

Charlie and Charlene: The information you shared with me for this book was a necessity. Without it, this book would be incomplete. Thank you so much!

Roy and Rochelle: My heartfelt thanks is extended to you, for your invaluable advice and for the defining moments we had concerning this book.

Paulette McKinnis: Your drawing for the back cover of this book is superb! It's exactly what I wanted! I simply love it. Thank you for all of the time and patience you put into this drawing.

I want to acknowledge Aunt Lottie Holmes Moore. She's Daddy's only living sibling. She's eighty two and some change. She looks much younger. She's sharp with a good sense of humor. We consider her as a 'precious jewel.'

I also want to mention Mama's first cousin 'Clare Henderson', who came into our lives ten months after Mama passed. (Mama didn't know she existed. She lives in Buffalo, NY too). Clara, as we say in Mississippi, 'Couldnt' Clara we are pleased to have you as part of the Holmes, Gilchrist, and Chansamone family! I truly thank you for your love and support.

You guys are unique. That's why I love you dearly. I wouldn't trade you for nothin!

Originally I wanted this book to be named: **'Curley, Gladys And Family'**

Dedication

I dedicate this book to my precious, loving, unforgettable family who have crossed over:

I am most appreciative to my parents for everything they did for my siblings and I!

* The discipline! *For closing the door when they had a dispute. Seeing our parents argue was something we never witnessed. I consider that a rare blessing.

A lot of emotion, stress, sweat, laughter, and tears was involved in writing this book.

Writing this book has been an outlet to help me put the heavy grieving, which had consumed me, in proper perspective.

This book is based on the real life stories of the Jackson / Stewart and Holmes family, including their friends and neighbors from Gloster, Mississippi and Buffalo, New York:

It consists of stories and events that occurred for the last four generations. (At the end of the book, the fifth generation merges in.)
It's a serious book with a unique touch of humor. It touches on the closeness of my fore-families, along with their acquaintances. When difficult times invaded their lives, no matter what differences may have existed between them, they put them aside. And their faith enabled them to come together, exhibiting their love and concern for one another, doing whatever was necessary to rectify those difficult situations.

I hope the reader enjoys this book as much as I've enjoyed writing it.

This book is based on a true story: It is written with love and precious memories straight from my heart about the life of my great grandparents 'Mr. and Mrs. Stewart', my grandparents, 'Smiley and Mary Ellen Jackson', my parents Curley and Gladys Stean Holmes', my siblings, myself and a variety of relatives and friends. The siblings: Edward Jean (June) Holmes, Dolly Mae (Doll) Holmes Gilchrist, Thomas James (T. J.) Holmes, (myself) Bettye Joe Holmes Chansamone, Richard Noble Holmes, Charlie Bruce Holmes, Robert Earl Holmes, Emerson Holmes and Roy Lane Holmes.

Part One

FAMILY HISTORY

Smiley Jackson And Mary Ellen Srewart's First Eighteen Years Together:

They were married on New Years Day 1917. Smiley Jackson was twenty-two years of age. He weighed one hundred and twenty pounds. His height was five feet eight inches. Mary Ellen Stewart was the age of fifteen. Her height was five feet and she weighed seventy five pounds. Smiley was an extremely quiet and shy person with a fantastic sense of humor. He was the youngest of ten brothers, whom raised him. His parents passed away when he was a child. Although he only had a second grade education, he was sharp when it came to mathematics. God gave him the gift to master mathematic and to utilize it to make a fair living through the selling of his produce. He was a farmer in Jackson, Mississippi. He met Mary Ellen at a church convention, in May of

1916. He almost lost his composure when he looked into her big, pretty, brown eyes. She had brought his favorite dish, chicken and dumplings. Smiley wanted to try that dish, but was too shy to go over and ask her to fix a plate for him. So he sent his brother 'Conley' over to get a plate for him. It was so good that Smiley didn't take the time to chew it.

Smiley just gulped it down: "My stomach is not full. I want some more of that chicken and dumplings. Autrey, go ask that lil ol pretty girl to put some more chicken and dumplings on this plate." After he gulped that down, he commented: "That taste better than the first plate." Then he sent his brother 'Dirty Red' over to get a third plate and to ask her to put more on the plate. Dirty Red wanted to help Smiley out. So he told Mary Ellen that Smiley liked her and wanted to come calling on her. He pointed Smiley out to her. She took the third plate to him herself: "Hello Smiley Jackson. My name is Mary Ellen Stewart. Your brother said you like my chicken and dumplings. And you like me too. And that you want to come-a-calling on me. Is that a fact?"

Although Smiley was lost for words and his face was a bit numb, he was happy and felt very special. So he managed to loosen up and nod his head indicating Yes! Yes! Yes! (Smiley was hooked and ready). He courted Mary Ellen for seven months before he gained the nerves to ask her to marry him. Every day after he came to the house from working in the field, he'd get in front of the mirror and practice saying these words; 'Mary Ellen will you marry me?'
He asked his brothers to ask Mary Ellen to marry him but they wouldn't do it. They said that was something he had to do for himself. After his proposal, they were married the next month. Mary Ellen was the tenth of eleven children. There were seven boys and four girls. She was an energetic, petite beauty, with big, pretty, brown eyes that a man could get lost in. She had long, thick, black, wavy hair, a small waist and large breasts. She had a strong personality. Being a superb homemaker was her passion. Mary Ellen was always well groomed, wearing the stunning outfits which she made. Smiley's nose was open wide enough for a train

to go through.

On the day of their marriage, Mary Ellen's brothers loaded her three trunks on the wagon. She stuffed her personal belongings in two pillow cases. With the help of her three sisters, she packed all that she owned. Mary Ellen found her parents sitting on a tree stump in the back yard. They had given their permission for the marriage. But it was hard to let go of their baby girl.

Mary Ellen talked: "Mama, Daddy, y'all is crying like somebody done died."

Mrs. Stewart responded: "We didn't mean for you to catch us like this baby girl. Things just won't be the same around here wit you gone. There is so many things that I didn't get a chance to teach you. You are still so young."

Mary Ellen hugged her parents and told her mother: "Mama you can still teach me whatever I need to know. I'm still your baby girl no matter what. I don't want all this crying to make you sick. Me and Smiley gon be back here every fourth Sunday to go to church wit y'all."

"Mary Ellen's mother spoke: "I been saving this here money for you. This handkerchief has two dollars and forty eight cents tied in it. Now stand still and let me pin hit to yo bosom. I want you to promise us that you won't go spend it on nothin foolish. Save hit for a rainy day. I ain't gon tell you not to tell Smiley. Cause he is yo husband now. I want you to promise us if things don't work out wit you and Smiley, you will hurry up and write so me and yo daddy can come and git you."

Mary Ellen: "I promise to do what y'all is asking me."

Mary Ellen's father said: "OK Mama. That's enough talking for now. We have to let Smiley and Mary Ellen go so they can get home before dark. Baby daughter, I think you got yourself a darn good husband. If I had to pick a husband for you, Smiley would have been the one. Y'all make a good match. He's quiet and you are a pretty good talker."

The whole family walked them out to the wagon and bid them farewell. They rushed back into the house. They watched Mary Ellen proudly and happily show her husband their wedding gifts. They realized that it was time to let her go, because she was on her way to assume the role of being a wife to her quiet handsome husband.

Mr. Stewart had an idea: "I figure we'll give them a week to be alone. Come Saturday morning, we'll load up the wagon and go stay the whole day wit them. We'll do this every second Saturday." Mrs. Stewart and the rest of the family agreed to that wonderful splendid suggestion.

Looking at the ground, Smiley said in a soft low tone: "Come here little girl."

Mary Ellen quickly responded, "Look-a-here, I ain't no little girl! I am your wife!"

Smiley kept looking at the ground as he talked: "OK Mrs. Jackson. Course I'll remember that from here on out. Are you ready to go home with Mr. Jackson?"

Mary Ellen responded: "Shucks! Been ready all day long. Do you suppose we'll get there before dark set in?"

Smiley answered: "I magine we will if we leave rat now. Come here lil woman and let me help you up on the wagon. Goodness gracious! Look at all them trunks. What you got in them pillow slips? Is yo whole family moving wit us?"

Mary Ellen talked: "Hush! Mr. Jackson! Ain't nobody moving wit you but me. Come over here Smiley. This here trunk (on the left hand side) has all of my clothes and some cloth to make some dresses and bonnets for church wearing. This here middle trunk has food. A pound cake and a coconut cake from Mama, twelve jars of canned fruit, four of each, peaches, pears and figs, which me and Mama canned back in September. These two hams and four dozens of eggs is from my grandmother and my five aunts. This here butter and cheese come from Miss Lucy Mae. And that basket of black walnuts come from the back yard. The two quilts that Mama and our four neighbors made, are in this trunk. Go on Smiley, open it and take a look at them."

Smiley smiled after he saw them saying: "Sho glad they made them quilts for us. Cause we need them awful bad. They is so pretty too. I love them for making a fuss over us."

They set out for home and darkness caught them before they arrived. They could hear the rumbling thunder in the distance. It was a cold black bitter winter night. Mary Ellen shivered and her teeth were chattering as Smiley raced his mule and wagon down the road.

Mary Ellen pleaded: "Smiley slow down. You are scaring me."

Smiley was an impatient nervous virgin, hotter than a two dollar pistol. He wanted to be home alone with his beautiful young bride. At her request, he slowed the mule down to a trot. They arrived home safe and sound in Jackson, Mississippi that evening close to seven.

THIRTEEN MONTHS AND TWENTY-FIVE DAYS LATER: February 25, 1918

Smiley and Mary Ellen Jackson my grandparents, (my siblings and I called them Papa and Big Mama) were blessed with a precious bundle, a beautiful daughter with big pretty brown eyes, just like her mother's. Gladys Stean Jackson, (my mother) was born February 25,1918. When Papa found out that he was going to be a father, he made a gorgeous crib for the baby. The baby brought a lot of pleasure, joy and happiness into their life and home, but Big Mama was afraid to handle and be alone with the baby, because she was extremely small. She had no confidence in herself as a mother. But my great grandmother 'Mrs. Stewart' was there by her side teaching her how to care for her new born baby. And when she left, Big Mama was highly confident and comfortable on every aspect of caring for Gladys on her own. Their neighbors were simply beautiful caring people. They came over daily, bringing all sorts of homemade gifts and offering their support. Big Mama became friends with the neighbors. They were sociable and caring towards Big Mama. Some of them had children older than Big Mama. Papa and Big Mama were hard working poor farmers on Brookfield's Plantation, living in a three room flat on one acre of land. They paid $8.00 a month for rent. Their hard work got them two horses, two broken down but strong mules, three cows, four pigs, thirty seven chickens, six roosters and twelve laying hens. Besides a vegetable garden, they raised cotton as well. Their transportation was a wagon that seated six people (depending on their size). Times were simply hard but they managed. The money was tight and scarce. Papa and Big Mama were soul mates and they stuck together, working diligently as they kept their faith in God and in themselves intact. They were proud people who loved God, each other and their daughter. They acknowledged, accepted and respected the fact that it was necessary to work hard in order to make a decent living. God, faith and their strong love for each other, kept them high spirited and energetic. Before retiring to bed each evening, they would get on their knees and thank God for the prosperous day which they encountered. They earned a living by selling milk, butter, eggs, vegetables, fruit and cotton. Other products they made and sold were molasses, syrup, jellies and jams.

During the off season months from October to March, Papa worked a job at Jenny's Cafe as a cook. Big Mama worked for Professor and Mrs. Heddington as a cook. She was welcome at their home anytime. They truly loved her cooking. They swore she was the best cook in the whole state of Mississippi. Gladys (Mama) was walking and very active by the age of eleven months. So to keep up with her during work hours, Big Mama would sit her in a chair and tie a diaper around her waist and around the back of the chair to keep her from falling or trying to get out. She would put the chair by the window where Gladys could see the birds and the squirrels, dancing among the leaves and branches as the wind rushed through them. She gave her play pretties to play with. Contented, Gladys snacked on homemade tea cakes. On occasions, Big Mama would give Gladys store bought things, for special treats. Such as Stage Planks.

During the Autumn season, Big Mama always canned enough peaches, figs, plums and apples to last through the winter. She also made apple, peach and plum jam. Papa dug potatoes and peanuts and put them in cool dry dark places to keep them fresh, until the spring season. They had a variety of meat in the smoke house: smoked ham, sausage, bacon, neck bones, pig feet and salt pork for the seasoning of their vegetables. They had a relatively comfortable winter as far as food was concerned.

As Gladys grew older she helped Big Mama with all the chores. They were very close, kind of like sisters. Big Mama taught Gladys everything that she knew; how to cook, sew and straighten her hair by the age of twelve. Like Big Mama, she became quite independent and sufficient. She was known for saying 'I can do that by myself, cause Im-ma big girl!'

She and Big Mama were inseparable, except when Gladys was in school. They were a team at all of the church ground socials and were always being complimented for having the best tasting chicken pies, biscuits, egg custard pies, red beans and rice and pound cake. People would often invite themselves to dinner at Papa and Big Mama's house, especially the preacher, 'Reverend Cole'.

Papa and Big Mama couldn't afford to give Gladys a lot of frilly material things, but Gladys was a happy-go-lucky girl. Since she was an only child, she had all of Papa and Big Mama's attention and they loved her so much. Gladys was secure and content.

She made two best friends on her first day of school. Maggie Chatman and Martha Berry were their names. Big Mama took Gladys to school for her first day in preprimer (kindergarten) Gladys cried. Martha Berry and Maggie Chatman consoled her: "If you stop crying, we will be your friends and give you some peanut candy."

Gladys immediately dried her tears up. From then, through school and beyond they were a threesome, growing up and walking to and from school, sitting with each other in class, studying, and doing their school work.

One day Mrs. Demos (her teacher) wrote a chess pie recipe on the black board and told the class to bake one. She said the recipe was from her sister-in-law in Baton Rouge. The sister-in-law got it from her friend who lived in Tennessee. This recipe became an instant hit in the community. Mrs. Demos said it tasted better than any other pie.

Big Mama wanted to know: "What is in that pie that make hit taste better than all the other pies?"

"Just six things. Butter, eggs, sugar, corn meal, vinegar and flavoring." Gladys told her.

"Mercy. I ain't never had a pie this good." Big Mama said.

"We'll make another one for supper tomorrow." Gladys promised.

But today she had something else to tell Big Mama. "Mama, guess what! Today I dropped my book in class and ol ugly nappy head, buckteeth, Nathan picked it up for me. Now everybody is teasing me and saying he is my boyfriend. I didn't ask him to pick up my book. Ain't nothin wrong wit me, I could've picked it up my self. I can take the teasing from the others, but it hurt me when Martha and Maggie teased me. I hate them too. I walked home by myself today. They ain't my friends and I ain't talking to them no more. I don't tease them about boys. I ain't going to school tomorrow."

"Now don't you go fretting. They were just having fun that's all. Tomorrow is another day and it will all be forgotten. And everybody will be talking about something else. The next time somebody tease you and believe me, God knows they will, just laugh rat along wit them. That will almost always wipe the smile off their face." Big Mama assured Gladys.

"I don't understand! Why should I laugh Mama?" Gladys asked.

"Cause some children are devilish and they get a kick out of teasing people just to make them mad. But if you laugh rat along wit them they will feel like a fool. And sometimes they will get mad because their crooked, underhanded plotting and scheming backfired on them. And that gives you the upper hand. Gladys you are blessed to have Martha and Maggie as friends. Friends don't just fall off trees every day. They come over here three or four times a week and go straight to the kitchen and get the pail and go to the barn and milk the cows. Just to remind you, they do that after milking their own cows. Gladys it's not their job to milk our cows. That's your job. Y'all have been friends since your first day of school. Why don't you make up with them before this day is over? You ain't supposed to go to bed mad at anybody."

Gladys was confused: "Why I gotta be the one to make up when they started it?"

"Who started it ain't important. But it is important not to let a small foolish thing separate you from your friends. Take heed to what I'm telling you Girl!" Big Mama explained.

Gladys somewhat understood what Big Mama was saying.

"OK! I think I kind-a-understand what you are saying. I'll make up with them. And know what? In the morning, I will take some ham and biscuits so we can eat it on the way to school. But if they ever tease me about that ugly boy again I will bash both of them in the mouth."

Gladys made up with Martha and Maggie and they made a pact that there wouldn't be any more teasing among them about boys.

1932 - Two Years Later

Maggie and Martha are at the age of fifteen. Gladys is fourteen. On a gorgeous, extremely warm spring day in May, the three girls were on their way home from school and decided to savor the day by taking the long way home. They walked through the woods along the creek. The sun was shining and the creek was as clear as a crystal. The floor of the creek was visible, with rocks of multi colors and sizes laying on it. The water was decorated with tadpoles dancing through it, accompanied by many different fish swimming forward and backwards. There was surely a heavenly sense of serenity as the girls gazed into the water as though seeing it for the first time.

Maggie broke the silence: "Hey y'all! Come on. Let's wade in the water."

Martha disagreed: "We can't. Not today. We have chores to do. And you know that."

Maggie argued the issue: "So what! Chores, chores, chores, I'm tired of chores. Them chores ain't going nowhere. They were there when we left and they will be there when we get back. Besides ain't nobody else gon do um. What difference do it make if we do um now or later on? Im-ma have me some fun today. And if I get a whoopin when we get home, I don't care."

Gladys motioned: "I guess we can wade. We got four or five hours before it get dark. And y'all will have the chores finished way before then."

"OK. I'm going in the water too, but I ain't gon get no whoopin. And Martha, you gon be the one who tell why we are late from school. And I do mean that. You ain't nothin but a chicken, always quacking. You're scared of everything." Said Maggie.

Martha shouted: "You better shut your big mouth. You talk too much. One day I'm going to slap you."

Maggie threw her shoe at Martha and hit her in the corner of the mouth causing it to bleed profusely. Then she snapped: "You heffer. That's what you git. Don't mess with me girl! I will put a hurtin on you."

"You shouldn't have did that! Im-ma tell what you been doing. Having Clifton Taylor come to the house at night after everybody don went to bed, beating on the window and waking me up. Yeah. Im-ma tell everything. I ain't leaving nohtin out."

Maggie: "Yea he come to the house at night cause he is my boyfriend. He can't come in the day time cause he is working in the field wit his daddy and mama. You can tell if you want to. I don't care. You jealous anyhow. You ain't even got no boyfriend. You are almost an old maid."

Gladys: (Splashing water on them), "Cut it out before you start fighting. You two should be ashamed of yourselves for talking to one another like that. Life is too precious to be carrying on like wild fools. Y'all need to appreciate each other. Pretty soon you will be going your own separate ways and you will want to look back at happy times and laugh, not cry and feel bad for something stupid you said or did to each other."

"Alright, Miss level headed Gladys." Said Maggie.

Maggie uttered in a low tone, "Martha I'm sorry that my shoe hit you. I chunked it but I didn't think it would hit you. Blood is all over your dress. Let's wash it out before it get dry."

The cool water was refreshing to them. And while playing, talking and having fun, Martha heard something: "Be quiet y'all! I hear somebody whistling. Do y'all hear anything?"

Gladys: "Nope."

Maggie: "Gal I declare you are hearing things. Two of us don't hear nothin. And one of us hear something. That's spooky. Maybe it's a ghost and you are the only one that can hear it."

Gladys: "Be quiet! Y'all be quiet! It is somebody whistling. I can hear them now. See it's getting closer."

Maggie: "I can hear it now."

Being cautious they joined hands and tried to find shelter under a tree branch hanging over the creek, where the shallow waters began.

As Gladys peeped through one of the branches she saw the tall figure: "Oh goodness! It's a man. A white man. And he is some kind of handsome! What is he doing over here whistling like he's so happy for?"

The whistling man 'Curley Holmes' (my father). thought he was all alone out there in the woods.

He stopped whistling and pulled both legs of his britches up and said to himself: "Hot dam! My legs are covered with ticks."

As he scratched his little hairy legs, he continued to talk to himself: "These bastards are making my legs itch something fierce."
Then he began to stomp his feet trying to shake those little creatures off his legs. That's when he found out that he had an audience. And they were laughing.

After looking in all directions and not seeing a soul, he said:

20

"Hey. Who is there? Show yourself!"

Then there was silence. His mind told him that the noise came from the creek. So he headed in that direction and found them standing under the branch. He was stunned, out done, surprised, shocked and embarrassed, and didn't know what to do. So he laughed and looked away for a while trying to be cool. But with those biting bastards he couldn't be still. So he did what he had to do. He stomped and scratched until he finally felt some relief.

Then he began to talk: "Excuse me! But if I had known that y'all were hiding behind those bushes looking at me, y'all would have never got that treat."

The girls looked at each other with question marks on their faces.

Curley explained: "Well I'm talking about setting your eyes on these big, beautiful, legs."

The girls laughed.

Martha said: "Either he's kidding or he need a darn good thick pair of eye glasses. Cause them is some lil biddy legs."

Then Curley told them: "Ah y'all frightened me for a minute. What are you girls doing out here? Where y'all from? Do y'all live around here?"

Maggie pointed: "We live about a mile over yonder. What are you doing over this way? I ain't never seen you before?"

Curley: "Oh I live on the other side of town. I am out this way visiting my grandmother. Hey girl. You in the green plaid dress. What is your name?"

"Gladys Stean Jackson!" She answered. (my mother).

"Yeah? Ah. I'm Curley Holmes. Ah. Hey, anybody ever told you that you have big, beautiful, brown eyes?"

Gladys: "No!"

Curley: "Well allow me to be the first one to tell you that you have the most beautiful, big, brown eyes that I have ever seen in my whole life."

Gladys never bit her finger nails before. But it would have been unbelievable if you'd of seen her left hand. She bit those nails down to the nub in a matter of seconds before she responded to Curley's compliment: "Thank you!"

Curley: "Ah, ah, how old are you?"

Gladys : "fourteen."

Curley: (Tossing his hat from one hand to another). "Young lady you just stole something from me!"

Gladys: (pausing) "Mister I didn't steal nothin from you."

Curley: "You just stole my heart! Right now I'm getting ready to go to the Army. But when I get back I'm going to marry you. I want to have a house full of children. And I want you to be their mother. Who are your people?"

Gladys: "Smiley and Marry Ellen Jackson."

Curley: "What? I know them. Been knowing them for years. They are very nice people. I didn't know they had a daughter. Come on out of that water. I want to have a talk with your father and mother. I'm walking you home!"

The girls came out of the water. Maggie and Martha sat on the ground and put their shoes on. Gladys stood there holding her books as she tied her shoe strings together so she could throw the shoes over her shoulders.

Curley untied the strings and said: "Give me your books and put these shoes on."

Gladys put her shoes on and the four of them were on their way. They reached Martha and Maggie's house first. They said 'bye' to Curley and Gladys and told Gladys they would pick her up for school the next morning. Then they were off to find out if they were going to get a whoopin for being late. Curley and Gladys took the opportunity to be by themselves and chat as they slowly walked to her house.

Gladys: "Curley what is your age?"

Curley: "I am twenty one years old. I turned twenty one on March 10. I was born on March 10,1911. Ah you have dimples too. We're going to have some beautiful children. Im-ma build you and our children a house from the ground up. And one day I will put you in a brand new car. I like that green plaid dress you wearing. It looks good on you."

Gladys: "Thank you. I made this dress."

Curley: "What? You made it? You did a darn good job. It looks like a store bought dress. How bout making me a shirt out of that same cloth?"

Gladys: "There's only scraps left and Mama is going to use that to put in a quilt."

Curley: "That's OK." Then he put his hand in his pocket and brought out a quarter.

As he gave it to her he said: "Take this. The next time you are in town buy that same cloth and make me a shirt. You don't have to rush or anything cause I won't be back here for a couple of years. That's going to be the first shirt I put on after I take off my uniform shirt."

Curley continued to ask questions: "Do you know how to cook?"

Gladys: "Yes. I been cooking for quite some time."

Curley smiled and asked: "Can you make banana puddin? That's my favorite sweet."

Gladys, smiling and blushing as she looked away saying: "I make banana puddin real good. Oh there's Daddy sittin on the garret. I know he's wondering why I'm late from school. (Waving as she spoke to him from a distance). "Hi Daddy. I'm home from school now. I'm late because I was at the creek with Martha and Maggie. Do you know who this is?"

Papa got out of his rocking chair, took a good look and said: "You bet your britches I know who that is. Hey Curley! Happy to see you. What brings you out this way?"

Gladys excused herself: "I'm going in the house to help Mama with supper."

Curley: "Mr. Jackson, You know Miss Hattie is my grandmother Well, she's been under the weather lately. So I came out here to pay her a visit and see what I could do for her. She wanted a blackberry cobbler. I decided to take a stroll through the woods in search of blackberries. That's when I stumbled upon my future wife; your daughter. I fell in love with her the very first time I laid eyes on her. That's why I'm over here, to ask you and Mrs. Jackson for Gladys' hand in marriage."

Papa: "I declare! Curley you done caught me by surprise! Gladys is our only child! And we ain't quite ready to part wit her just yet! Me and my wife will have to discuss this very important subject for many hours! My wife ain't gon be tickled about this one bit! I tell you, why don't you come over here in a month or so for supper. We can sit at the table and talk on this some more.

24

Now answer this question for me. You say you love Gladys. I believe you. I can hear it in your voice. I can see it in your face. But how do you know she will feel the same for you Curley?"

Curley: "She already do! My heart is strongly telling me that! And I always go with my gut feeling. Well, I will be here a month from Sunday for supper at 4:00. Six days after that I have to leave for the Army. I will see you all then. Bye."

Papa: "Wait a minute Curley. Don't run off yet. We have a blackberry patch rat over yonder by the fence. Come. I'll help you pick some."

At supper that evening, Papa, Big Mama and Gladys had a conversation going on. It lasted through supper, clearing the table, washing the dishes and two hours beyond that. Papa: (cleared his throat several times, trying to get Gladys attention. But it didn't work).

"Gladys? Do you feel alright? You have been quiet since you got home from school" Big Mama asked as she looked at Papa.

Big Mama: "Her face is real red. I hope she ain't comin down wit nothin."

Papa: "Ha, ha, ha. Oh Lord! I think its too late for that. She done caught it already! This gal done fell head over hills in love wit that fellow. I'm talkin bout Curley Holmes."

Big Mama: "You mean pretty boy Holmes? What you talkin bout? Gladys don't know him! Do you Gladys?"

Gladys: "I met him at the creek today. While we were wading in the water. He carried my books and walked me home. Daddy? What did he say to you?"

Big Mama: "Gladys, you didn't mention Curley walking you home! Not a word! Smiley what did that man want with you?

Speak up! I can't hear you. This ain't no time to be quiet!"

Papa: "Curley, that boy, bless his heart. Ah, I like Curley a lot. He came to ask us for Gladys' hand in marriage rat after school today."

Big Mama: "Wait just a darn minute! I was here all day long. Why didn't you fetch me?"

Papa: "Hold your horses Mary Ellen! I told Curley that me and you will talk on it, then give him an answer come a month from this Sunday at supper time."

Big Mama calmed down a bit and after thinking she sadly said: "I knew that day would come when a man would fall for Gladys and want to marry her and take her away. But I didn't expect it to happen so soon. Smiley, she is the only child we got! I can't bare for her to get married and leave us! What if Curley ain't nice like you? A good man is hard to find!"

Papa: "He gon be in the Army for four years. I ain't for Gladys getting married and leaving us either! But that boy said something to me. He said he would make her a good husband and will love and respect her for the rest of his life! Say he ain't gon never hit her! His plan is to save his money while he's in the army and use it towards making a life for him and Gladys! He want to build a house for her and fill it up with chillens! Now that was pleasing to my heart! Ain't no way you can tell me that you don't want a house full of grand chillens. As for Curley being a good caring husband, my instincts tell me that he will make a rat fine husband for our daughter! And he will make us a rat fine son-in-law too! Of course he is a good looker, but you can't hold that against him. He didn't have nothin to do with that. You remember when I fell off the wagon in town and sprang my ankle last year?

"Boy. I had wasted that whole tub of snap beans on the ground. I was hopping around trying to pick all of them beans up. Some of them town people came around, just to see what happened and to

26

steal some of that fruit and other stuff from the wagon.

" That boy Curley came up and told them: 'If you ain't over here to help, get the hell out of the way.'

"Curley was the only one that stayed and helped me. My ankle was swollen and it was paining me too. He picked me up and sat me on the wagon and told me to stay there while he finished cleaning up that mess. Then he took me to Dr. Murphy's office and stayed there with me until Dr. Murphy put that wide bandage on my ankle. He helped me get back on the wagon. I offered to pay him for his kindness, he told me to put my money back in my pocket and said it was his pleasure to help me. He stood there and we chatted for a while. Said his mother died when he was ten years old and he will always remember her saying: 'Every day of your life, treat people like you want to be treated.' Then he grabbed four peaches off the wagon and left whistling."

Big Mama: "I have always liked Curley. I have the highest respect for him. He had a pretty good schooling (pausing) just look at Gladys she is in a daze and tickled pink. She ain't touched nothin on her plate. I bet her food is good and cold by now."

Big Mama Remembers:

"Girl, just to see you in this predicament, is bringing back memories, memories, memories. Child, let me tell you bout the things that happened the day that me and yo daddy got married! First of all as soon as the wagon turned onto the road from Mama and Daddy's house and we were out of the sight of my family, I took Smiley's hand and laid my head on his shoulder. (laughing) He snatched his hand back talking bout:

'What is you doing?'

I told him: 'Baby I just wanted to be a little romantic! That's all.'

27

"That's what I had been daydreaming about every day since the day he asked me to marry him. The night before we got married; I was some kind of jittery. I couldn't sleep for the jitters. That man would not leave my mind for nothin. Well anyhow, he told me right off: 'I ain't no baby! I am a man! I cannot steer this wagon and hold yo hand wit yo head on my shoulder all at the same time. That is too many things to do at one time. You are moving way too fast. You needs to slow down! If its alright wit you, we can hold hands when we get home and be romantic. But rat now I need both of my hands to steer this wagon.'

"I told him to hush! After all I didn't think that jack ass needed that much steering. Shucks. He had been hitched to that wagon bringing Smiley to see me for months. I didn't think he was so dumb, that he couldn't remember his way back home. Anyhow, on the way home from Mama and Daddy's house, Smiley's jack ass 'Ol Buddy' stopped in the middle of the road, raised his tail and did his business rat there. Yeah, he dropped about twenty-five golf ball size turds. That tired him out for a good forty five minutes or so. I mean he wouldn't even budge."

"It was bout rat then when I developed a dislike for that old grey jack ass. Smiley was shame cause that jack ass was showing his ass. He got off the wagon and told me to stay where I was at, cause it might be snakes out there. Well, I sat there for five minutes or so. Smiley's back was turned to me and it sounded like he was talking. Yeah. I was nosey! Trying to hear. I leaned over the wagon so far that I almost fell head over heels. So I said to myself: 'I ain't staying on this wagon. I got a mind of my own.' So I got off the wagon to see just what Smiley was doing. What I'm bout to tell you, is gon shock you."

"Gladys, yo daddy was sho nough talking to that stubborn jack ass. He was saying: 'I know that I been working you hard. And I am very sorry. I'm jusa-a-beggin you to please take us home. If you do that, I won't never hitch you to another plow or wagon. You got my word on it. I'll put you in the pasture and you can eat all the grass and clover you want.'

28

"I didn't want him to know that I was eaves-dropping while he talked to Buddy the Jack Ass, therefore I climbed back upon the wagon. Before Smiley could sit down, the jack ass started off trotting, then the speed picked up to the point that the wagon was just a bouncing. I had to ask Smiley to slow that wagon down. He slowed down, I calmed down and being a bit confused, I wondered; 'Did that jack ass really understand what Smiley was saying to him?' I thought it was a peculiar thing for a man to talk to a jack ass. 'What had I got myself into?' Oh boy! It strongly crossed my mind, 'Old Buddy, you jack ass. I got news for you. Consider yourself as history! Jack Ass."

"I am getting rid of you. It was dark when we got home. Smiley noticed a light coming from inside the house and quickly told me to step back. Then he swung the door open and the first thing I saw was Mr. Chatman's face."

Smiley raised his voice: "What is y'all doing in my house? Y'all done scared the dickens out of me."

"Mrs. Chatman said: 'Nothin to worry bout Smiley. We thought y'all was gon be here round about supper time. That is the reason we came over here and brung some food for yo wedding. It ain't right for a woman to cook on the same day she marry. I said to my husband 'Jake', since ain't nobody here yet, and it is getting colder by the minute, we might as well be neighborly and light that fireplace and lantern for them. And by George, that's what we did. Where is yo other half?"

Mr. Chatman answered the question: "There she is. Standing rat outside the door. I will brang her in. Hello there lil woman. My name is Jake Chatman. I am pleased to meet you. I been knowing Smiley and his brothers for a number of years. He is very quiet. And he don't bother nobody. Lord, it is freezing cold out here. Come here. I ain't gon bite you. I told Smiley I was gon brang you in the house."

Before Big Mama could take a step, Mr. Chatman picked her up and carried her into the house, closed the door with his foot and said: "Smiley I done brought yo wife in just like I said I would (while still holding her). I done did yo job. I brung her over the fresh hole just for you.' (His wife, Papa and Big Mama laughed because Mr. Chatman said fresh hole instead of threshold). But Mr. Chatman ignored them and kept talking: 'I believe in being neighborly. Now you march yo-self rat over chere and git her. She ain't no bigger than a sack of taters. You gon have to fatten her up." Then he said to his wife: "Dumplin what is you waitin for? Come here and make her acquaintance."

Big Mama continued to talk: "I didn't hesitate to tell them what happened with Old Buddy and rat then they offered to trade one of their horses for that old jack ass. Mr. Chatman told Smiley that he had his eye on Old Buddy for a long time. And that he always wanted to have a jack ass of his own. At first I didn't understand why they would want a dumb jack ass. But after thinking, it came to me, I realized that they saw how displeased I was about that jack ass. And they liked Smiley so much that they were willing to give us one of their good horses. They made plans to come by early the next morning and bring their horse and take Old Buddy. I declare, them was some good neighbors. Um, um, um, as soon as they left out the door going home, the rain poured down so hard. I can close my eyes now and hear it tapping heavily on the roof along with the forceful wind ripping through the trees, carrying the rain as it splashed against the windows, causing them to rattle. I believe that was the coldest night that year. The wind found its way through every nook and crack in this house. Know what? While I'm thinking and talking about it, I realize that it was a night to treasure and remember for a lifetime. My wedding night". (Big Mama folded her hands together, sat up straight, shook her head and smiled. Then she carried on). "The horse we got from them belonged to Mrs. Chatman's sister, Mrs. Berry, who died at the age of sixteen when her daughter Martha Berry was six weeks old. At that time, Mrs. Chatman's daughter 'Maggie' was three months old. And the Chatman's are raising Martha Berry as their own child. Seems like her father washed his hands of her. I heard tell that Mrs. Berry had a shot gun wedding when she was four months in the family way. Her husband stayed with her for three months. He slept at the foot of the bed and she slept at the head. After that he ran off to stay with a gal that he met while working in Baton Rouge. He left for work one Monday morning and that was the last time she saw him. A week later, Mrs. Berry had Martha in her seventh month. Some say she gave up on life. Mr. Berry didn't even come to his wife's funeral to pay his respects. I don't know how he can sleep at night! He never tried to get in contact with Martha. I don't know what's becomin of this world!"

Papa was curious: "Mary Ellen, I didn't know you heard me talking to Old Buddy. All these years done passed by and you ain't uttered a word about it."

Big Mama replied: "Yea, well, ah, I thought about it."

Gladys was excited: "Mama, Mama, tell me some more things about you and Daddy. Please? This is fun."

Big Mama: "I guess I can tell you about the time when yo daddy decided to go in the bootlegging business."

Papa: "Mary Ellen! You going too far now! That's the one thang I don't won't Gladys to never know about me. She could lose respect for me. Keep yo mouth shut about that. I mean it."

Gladys: "I ain't gon lose respect for you Daddy. I am yo daughter! Don't you think I have a right to know about you no matter what it is? Besides the worse thing you can do is kill somebody. And I know you ain't did that Daddy. Did you?"

Papa: "No. I ain't never killed nobody. Anyhow what you wann-a know everything about me for? I declare. Girl you act like you writin a book or something."

Gladys: "Daddy one day I want to sit around my big kitchen table and tell my children about their granddaddy and grandma. And

31

who knows? I just might write a book one day about me and my Daddy and Mama. She looked at Big Mama and asked: "Mama what is the bootlegging business?"

Big Mama looked at Papa and he said: "Gone and tell her. She ain't gon be happy until she find out. And in the future, for goodness sakes watch what you say around her. A lil pig have big ears."

Big Mama began by saying: "Gladys my mouth is dry. Fix me a glass of lemonade. Smiley I don't know why you choose to keep this from Gladys. Things is changing. Nothin is like it used to be. You have to open up and tell yo daughter what done happened in yo life, whether its good or bad. If you wouldn't have went to jail you might still be doing that today."

Gladys: "When did you go to jail Daddy?"

Big Mama: "Stop butin in and let me finish my story gal. Shot Williams is dead now. He was shot down by Bueford Hanks. For years there had been rumors circulating around about Bueford's wife 'Smootie Joe' and Shot.

Bueford told Shot that he couldn't act on a rumor but if he ever caught him with his wife he would kill him on the spot. By George that is exactly what happened. Shot was a farmer with the only bootlegging business within sixty miles from any direction. That mean he made corn liquor illegally. After his death, his wife Anna and his mother Star Williams, (Ah, Star was a mighty mean Indian woman. Anna was a plain homely woman. Her looks wasn't anything to write home about).

"Anyhow, soon after Shot's death, Anna and Star came by pestering us to buy Shot's distillery along with the six male 100% bull dogs, (brothers from the same litter). Their three dog houses and their twelve feet jumping bar. The dogs were dedicated and trained to guard and protect the distillery. Star made it known that her and Anna loved those dogs real bad but they had a big problem. They needed to find a new home for them. Due to the fact that her and Anna were moving to New Orleans with her other son (Shot's brother) 'Tat Ran.' He lived in the city with a yard that wasn't big enough to accommodate the dogs. Star told us that Shot liked Smiley a lot and would've wanted him to have his dogs. She agreed that if we bought the package, they would not sell their house and move until Smiley was fully trained in both aspects. She promised to teach Smiley how to make that corn liquor, how to approach the dogs and win them over so he could control and command them. Star wanted us to promise that we would never hit or separate the dogs.

Everything was settled the following week. Star and Anna worked diligently. They brought the distillery over and hid it in the middle of some thick grapevines about twenty feet from the creek. Upon their completion of hiding the distillery, they wrapped some grapevines around it and returned to their house to bring some more things back. When they returned, Star darn near had a blame heart attack. Well, they hadn't paid attention to the exact land mark where they left the distillery. What made it so bad was the grapevines were loaded with big juicy grapes and all of them looked the same. Therefore Star and Anna were dumbfounded and flustered. Oh! They cursed and ran around searching those vines only to find nothin. Star cursed at Anna and blamed her for the mishap. Well yo daddy had a good idea and said "Mary Ellen, Im-ma try something. Watch."

He called: 'Shot IV and Shot VII.' They came straight to him and he directed them to find the distillery. They went straight to it. My mouth flew wide open! I couldn't believe what I had just saw. Star was jealous because she hadn't thought of that idea. Said she was saving that as a last resort. Anyhow, me and Smiley were impressed with those incredibly smart dogs. They were like well behaved children. All you had to do was tell them to do something one time and they were on it. From the beginning there was one thing that Smiley didn't like about the dogs. He said he wasn't about to clean up dog shit from sun up to sun down. Of course he was tied of steppin in it too. Yo neat, clean, and particular daddy thought on that matter long and hard, he came up with a plan that worked. Gladys he built an outhouse for those dogs. They stood around watching him and listening to him as he talked to them everyday while he worked on that thing. He'd tell them ten times what that outhouse was for. And they understood him quite well. But Smiley didn't know the dogs knew what he was talking about until he finished with that outhouse. I'm tellin you that those dogs were unbelievable. Smart and obedient. They started to use that toilet in order, from Shot II to Shot VII. From that day on that's where they went to do their business. Smiley was happy cause he didn't have to worry about steppin in dog shit anymore. Sometimes they would be standing in line waiting to use that outhouse.

In the meanwhile, Star, Anna and Smiley gathered the corn and all the ingredients required and put them in the distillery to start making the corn liquor, they checked on it periodically. Star committed herself to teaching Smiley everything she knew about those precious bull dogs and the new adventure he was about to embark upon. Shot was good at building things. He had built three nice dog houses. Two dogs shared each dog house. The floor was lined with hay. We had the houses facing the creek. Smiley truly loved those dogs. Everyday he'd come home and tell me something different that the dogs did. Some of the things were hard to believe and I didn't bite my tongue about tellin him: "I ain't callin you a liar but I got to see it before I believe it." Smiley would say: "Hey hey now." And the dogs would sit. He'd call out 'attention' and the dogs stood in a straight line in order of their name. Shot II, Shot III, Shot IV, Shot V, Shot VI, Shot VII.

"Shot I, loved his dogs so much and was equally proud of them. That's why he gave them his name. In the morning Smiley would go out on the garret and whistle and in return each one of the dogs would bark one time. That was their way of saying good morning to each other. They did the same thing to say goodnight. At the clap of Smiley's hands, the dogs would stop whatever they were doing and lay down. They would stand and form a circle around Smiley if he took his hat off. That was supposed to transpire if

34

Smiley had any trouble with his customers. The customers were instructed to go to the creek where the dogs were and in return they would notify Smiley by barking as a group. Then Smiley would go there and handle his business. As he conducted the business the dogs stood at attention in a straight row facing Smiley and whoever the customer was. If any strangers were poking around the distillery, the dogs would howl. Solo barking meant trouble.

Big Mama continues: "Gladys, yo daddy was a rat smart man. He made some wire baskets and taught them dogs how to catch fish. They would literally go into the creek and catch fish in the baskets then, bring um out and dump um in the pail of water which Smiley always left for them, in case they wanted to go fishing and he wasn't there. The dogs were an exception. They were extraordinarily smart. I had never been one to like dogs. But somehow they grew on me. They were the kind of watch dogs which every dog owner would desire to have. Anyhow Smiley would clean the fish and take the bones out for the dogs.

Sometimes it would be twenty fish. Smiley built a brick pit by the creek. He used that big iron pot with the legs on it to fry the fish in. Gladys you know the one I'm talking about. The one that's out there on the garret with the firewood in it. You talkin bout good, that was some of the best fish I ever et. The aroma of that fish traveled for miles.

"One day some white people were traveling and stopped by the house to ask where the cafe was. They could smell the food but couldn't find the cafe. They were lost and starving. They were on their way north with their six year old grandson. I told them, "Shucks, ain't no cafe around here. My husband is cooking. That's what y'all is smelling. It ain't nothin but some fish. I done made a pan of biscuits, a pot of crowder peas and some fried taters wit onions. I can fix y'all a helpin of vittles in a pie pan. Right away the man went in his pocket and took out some money and asked if I could fix them three pie pans of vittles so they could take it with them. I fixed the biscuits, peas and taters and they followed me to the creek for the fish. Smiley was taking some fish out of the pot when we got there.

The man rushed up to Smiley, shook his hand and after introducing himself, he asked: "Can I please have a piece of that hot fish? It smell so darn good that I can't wait until we get back on the road to eat it. If y'all don't mind we'd like to sit rat chere on the ground and eat our food."

Papa leaned his chair back on the two back legs and rested his head on the wall and fell asleep as Big Mama continued to talk: "They didn't waste no time eating. That big man rolled his shirt sleeves up and went to town. He enjoyed every bit of that food. The meal was missing one thing. Lemonade. I ran to the house and made a pitcher of lemonade. Girl we didn't have a lick of ice. But that was OK. They loved it anyway.

After they got full, they stretched out on the grass and took a three hour nap. When they woke up they acted like they didn't want to leave. I don't know why I keep saying 'they' their names were Luke and Ruth and their grandson's name was Ralph. Anyhow Luke, Ruth and Ralph were very friendly people. They made themselves at home. Me and Smiley felt so comfortable with them. We talked quite a bit. They walked through the woods and picked all kinds of fruit. Smiley fried some more fish and wrapped it up for them to take. Ralph tried to pay us but we simply refused to take it. Smiley told Ralph how to get back to the main highway. And right before they drove off, Ruth told us that we would be hearing from them. Four months later which was three weeks before Christmas, a letter came in the mail from them with a five dollar bill in it. Oh. We put it in the trunk to save it for a rainy day. We appreciated that! Gladys always treat people like you want to be treated and it will come back to you! You better believe it!

Anyhow back to the dogs, it was only one thing that Smiley gave those dogs that he wouldn't put in his own body and that was the corn liquor. Star told him to put a quarter of a cup full in their drinking water once a week during the cold weather. Said it would keep them healthy. They ate plenty of fruit and vegetables. I think watermelon might have been their favorite fruit. Know what? Those bulldogs were trained to eat from me and Smiley only.

I'd say about five or six weeks passed before Star and Anna got ants in their pants and started tasting the corn liquor, making sure the recipe was right on the T. They were here every day tasting. Star didn't miss a day taking a jar full of it with her. Said she was leaving it out at night for Shot's spirit. I told Smiley that if they didn't stop tasting it, the distillery would be dry by the time the corn liquor got done.

Finally the last day of that tasting ordeal came and Star asked me to fetch her a pint size mason jar. She filled that jar up to the rim with that corn liquor, held it up facing the sun and said: "Ain't no settlements floating around in it or nothin. This stuff is as clear as water." And she drunk pert near a quarter of that jar and gave the rest of it to Anna. Then Star threw her hands up and said: "Holy smoke. I'm good! This taste better than Shot's liquor. This recipe is rat on Q. Smiley this good stuff is ready to sell. I done gave yo wife a piece of paper wit the twenty-two customers names on it. Remember this! Only sell the liquor to the people whose name is on that there piece of paper. You can trust every one of them. I done already ranged it for them to start coming round here in a week or so." Then she started to laugh and laugh and the more she laughed the bigger her eyes got. The woman was on fire. She was walking backwards so fast. She was in a big hurry to fall on her rump. Then she had the gall to set there and curse like a sailor while she kicked her feet and swung her fists as though she was in a serious fight. Eventually she laid back and put her thumb in her mouth and fell asleep. I suppose she was mighty tipsy by then. Anna began to talk after Star was sound asleep: "That there corn liquor has a mean powerful kick to it. It will knock you on your fanny before you can say one, two, three. If Mama Star's eyes wasn't bigger than her belly, this here jar would normally last me and her six to eight months."

Big Mama continues to talk: I asked Anna: "Is that liquor gon harm Star at her ripe old age?" She told me: "Nope. It ain't gon harm her. Cause that old fart done put eight raw eggs in a quart jar wit buttermilk and gulped it down this mornin. Rat after that she fixed a heapin pile of butter beans and some okra and some hot water corn bread and ete it all. Then she licked the plate clean.
I put my hands on my hips and asked her: 'Mama Star what is you eatin like that fur this early in the mornin?' She looked at me and beck for me to come closer. I did. Mary Ellen look at my ear. Yeah. That old cow did this to me. She damn near yanked my ear off. After she damn near yanked my ear off she said 'I eat like this cause I wont to. What I eat ain't none of yo business anyway.' As soon as she got up from the table she walked up and down the kitchen floor rubbin that pot belly of hers, moanin, talking bout it was hurtin. Now I done figured it out for myself, Mama Star was greedy this mornin cause she had sot her mind on drinking that there corn liquor. When she handed me this here jar wit them red crossed eyes of hers, I knew the ball was through rollin rat then. Look at her.'

Anna still complaining, "Before one hour is up she will be done pissed on herself five times. And I'm the one who got to clean her up. I'm so mad at her rat now that I could kill her. Guess what? she is wearing them brand new draws that I bought for Shot before he went and got his self killed. I bought them draws wit my hard earned money fur his special, special, special Christmas present. But after he got killed I hid them brand new draws in the back of my dresser drawer under some more stuff fur my own Christmas present. You ain't gon hardly believe what that old woman did to me. Child she went rambling through my dresser drawer wit her nosey ass and found them draws. Then she put them on and was paradin through the house laughin, talkin bout: 'Look what I found way in the back of your dresser drawer!' I told her rat off the bat, Hell, them draws ain't lost. I put um there. Them is mine. Put um back!' She didn't pay no attention to me. She kept um on. Then she had the gall to put on Shot's old black holy hat, along wit his old black holy boots. After that she sat her narrow tight ass on the front garret, smoking Shot's pipe wit them lil chicken legs of hers crossed. I need to cool off a bit. If I don't I just might put a hurtin on that old witch. I think it will be a good idea to leave her out here until I come from huntin. I got me a big taste for some rabbit. Anyway you look at it, them dogs ain't gon let nothin happen to Mama Star cause they love her. She be ninety six years old come her birthday."

Big Mama continues to talk: "I finally got a chance to look at the piece of paper Star handed me. I was surprised to see that the first two names on the paper was Sheriff Matthews and Sheriff Harmon. Sheriff Matthews was the first customer. When Smiley looked out the window and saw him comin, he just about did his business on himself. He was scared and I was too. We laid on the floor by the bed and Smiley whispered: 'What are we going to do? He ain't supposed to come to the house. Since he didn't go to the creek, we ain't gon open the door. Who do he think he is anyway? He got a lot of nerves coming to the house?' Me and Smiley was a bit nervous for a good while after Sheriff Matthews left. But you know Sheriff Matthews had a strong hankering for corn liquor. Cause he came back real late that night. Round bout 8:00. Rat after we had retired to bed. Woke us up knocking on the door. We ain't had no choice but to open the door then. Cause Smiley opened his mouth at the wrong time and asked: 'Who is out there?' We heard a loud whisper: 'Its Sheriff Matthews! Open the door.'

"Smiley stepped out on the garret. I could hear them talkin, but I couldn't quite make out what they were saying. I was as nervous as Kuter Brown! I could imagine Sheriff Matthews putting hand cuffs on my husband and then coming in the house to get me. Oh. I wondered if me and Smiley would be in the same jail house and what would happen to you Gladys. It seemed like they were out there for hours. I walked the floor and sat on the bed until the door opened and yo daddy walked in smilin like a chess cat holdin money in both hands. I jumped off the bed and asked what took him so long.

He said after they walked to the creek to get the liquor, Sheriff

Matthews wanted to taste it. Then he wanted to talk about the dogs. Said Shot would not sell him one of them dogs for nothin. Thought he could talk Smiley into selling him one of um. Well he didn't get no where wit that. Smiley told him that the only thang that he was selling was that corn liquor and the next time he come a callin to go to the creek and the dogs would bark when he got there.

Yeah. Oh. Matthews was so glad to get that liquor, that he gave Smiley a six cent tip. He was there two or three times a week. I mean he had an obsession wit them dogs. He had the nerves to try to feed them some raw stew meat one day. That was a big mistake! Ooh! I mean them dogs scared the living shit out of him. They formed a circle around Matthews and every last one of them were howling. When me and Smiley got to the creek Sheriff Matthews was shaking like a leaf on a tree, was as red as a beet and his uniform was soaking wet wit sweat. And it was a cold day in December!

One day at supper time Smiley announced that he wasn't gonna make any more liquor. Said he had been telling the customers for two weeks that when the distillery ran empty he was going to take it down and sell it. Surely none of them were happy about that. The very next day Duke Mc Clain's two sons were drivin by and their car tire blew out. It sounded like a shot gun. The car ended up in a ditch. Smiley took the horse and some rope. Him and the boys tied the rope to the fender and between the boys pushing the car and the horse pulling it, it was out of the ditch in no time. After that they hung around talking and throwing rocks in the creek. Gladys I don't know what got into yo daddy! Maybe he was bragging or showing off. Or it could have slipped out. Whichever way you look at it he let the cat out of the bag. One thing led to the next and them boys was drinkin that hard corn liquor. I was on my way to the field to get some okra, tomatoes and corn when I noticed all of the racket they were making. Curiously I went to see just what was going on. Sure enough their frisky actions told me they had been drinking. They were dancing with each other and acting silly! I asked them: 'What y'all been

40

drinking?' They said: 'Nohtin!' I was so mad at Smiley! I could have kicked him where the sun don't shine. I told Smiley that he knew darn well that those boys were getting ready to go to the Army. They didn't have no business drinking. He knew he was wrong. That's why he got smart and sassy with me: 'Hell. Them ain't no boys. They is twenty-six and twenty-eight years old. Hell. We were chit chatting and I sort of mentioned it without thinking. They wouldn't let me rest. They kept asking me to give them a taste of it. So I gave um a tat bit. Shut yo mouth woman!

It ain't enough to hurt um and besides I was fixin to ask you to fix um some vittles so they can eat and be on their way.' I fixed them some flapjacks along with some ham and eggs. They washed it down with a glass of buttermilk. When they were leaving I told them not to mention a word about what happened. They assured me that their lips were zipped.

The next day at dinnertime I was dragging my feet waiting for Smiley to come home from the field so we could eat. I set the table. Then went to the back yard to get the sheets I had washed that morning. Gladys, you were fidgety and did not want to wait for your daddy. You wanted to eat right then. Anyhow, you fell asleep while eating. Smiley finally came in and we sat down, said our blessings and I asked him to fetch the picture of ice tea. He was on his way back to the table with it when that solo barking began. Smiley dropped that picture of ice tea in the middle of the floor and ran out the door and down the steps, then he ran back to tell me to stay in the house. He ran out the door and down the steps again only to come back once more. That time he went straight to the chiffonier (cabinet from ceiling to the floor). and took out the shot gun. He started to run so fast that he tripped over his feet and almost fell. I looked out the kitchen window and watched him run with that gun. I sensed big trouble. I had a mouth full of food, but I couldn't remember if I had chewed it or not. I attempted to spit it out, but nothing happened. I was paralyzed for a moment, but I broke out of that state of mind and went to see if you were still sleep Gladys. You were. So I took off running. I wanted to be there wit my husband and find out

41

what in the world was going on. I'm telling you it was a surprise of a lifetime.

"Sheriff Matthews had Smiley kneeling on the ground in handcuffs. And what do you suppose he said to me? The man had tears in his eyes as he told me how sorry he was and that he had no choice in the matter. Because Earnest Mc Clain came to the sheriff's office that morning and filed a complaint against Smiley for giving his sons corn liquor. Apparently his sons got sick from the stuff. Course they told Mc Clain where the liquor came from. Sheriff Matthews told me: 'I put the handcuffs on Smiley because I didn't want those two new fellows to roughen him up or anything like that. It broke my heart when they broke that distillery. That liquor wasted all over the ground and it was smelling good too. I wanted to fall on my face and drink every bit of it. I want you to know that I had nothin to do wit them threatenin to shoot the dogs if Smiley didn't show them where the distillery was. Them dirty, red neck, new bastards! I declare! Them dogs had us in a circle and were on the verge of attackin us. I'm thankful that Smiley got here in the nick of time and stopped them. It was like a horrible nightmare that I never want to go through again. Whew! I can still feel their hot breath on my neck and face. We'll take Smiley in. He will most likely be in jail for thirty days. Oh, I know that's a long time. But it could be worse. The law wont Mississippi to stay a dry state. Ain't that the craziest damn thang you done ever heard of? Hell! Every now and then a man wont a drink of liquor!"

Big Mama continues: "One of the most saddest things I ever saw in my life was six big strong muscle bound bull dogs crying. I mean righteous tears flowing down their faces. When they put Smiley in that sheriff's car and drove off. Lord, Smiley going to jail and the dogs crying, literally tore me down. My legs were shaking like a leaf on a tree and I fell down to the ground. I let out a long loud cry. The dogs sat by me with their troubled, sad, wet, faces. As though they were saying, stop crying. Everything is going to be alright. It could be worse. They were like six little soldiers. Three on each side of me as we walked to the house. I fixed them something to eat. Those dogs split up before eating . Three of them took their pan of food and went to the front yard. That's the way they did it. They stayed in the front yard and the other three stayed in the back yard. Gladys, me and you ain't had nothin to worry about. We were in good hands. Yeah. Plenty of protection at the front door and plenty of protection at the back door.

Sho nough! Smiley came home in thirty days, July 16, 1922. Boy oh boy; he was a sight for sore eyes. We were sitting on the front garret. I was plattin your hair Gladys. I had made some ice cream for dinner that day. We had ate a bit of it, and I gave the dogs a bit of it too. Smiley always told me not to give the dogs nothin sweet except fruit. Girl, I was nervous and scared that he would find out that that I gave the dogs the ice cream. I asked you not to tell him.

You didn't tell him either.

The next day we were back to our usual way of doing things. We faithfully walked down the lane everyday and the dogs always went with us. As long as I live I ain't gon never forgit this date, September 12, 1922. That day we were walking down the lane and the dogs were a lil way ahead of us rippin, runnin and playin. And all of a sudden, Shot II and Shot VII fell to the ground. We hurried to them just in time to see the rattle snake leaving. Smiley went crazy. He grabbed a big piece of wood and beat that snake to death. When he finished he threw that stick as hard as he could with all his might. Then he rushed to the house and got the wagon and put Shot II and Shot VII in it. When we got back to the house wit them, I went to get Mr. Chatman. He fetched his remedy and when we got back to the house, both of the dogs were dead. Mr. Chatman went to get some of the neighbors so they could burry the dogs. Smiley broke down and cried like a hungry new born baby! I cried rat along wit him. But he took the cake. He just couldn't handle it. Told the neighbors to do what needed to be done wit the dogs. The other four dogs were dead within three weeks. They refused to eat or drink. We tried everything we knew to git them to eat, but nothin worked. They loved Shot II and Shot VII so much that they didn't want to go on without them. Every since that happened, Smiley ain't never talked about them again. Oh. I remember a time or two when he got up in the morning and forgot they were dead and went out on the garret and whistled and waited for them to respond. He was tore down by the lost of those dogs to the point that he never wanted to talk about getting any more dogs. The lost of the dogs were like losing a child.

Gladys you know once the mind starts the process of reminiscence, its like watching a picture show. Everything comes up on the screen. And talking about the dogs has reminded me of an expression that I have been hearing since I was a child. 'When it rain it pours.' You better believe it! That for sure is a true saying. Your Grandparents, my mama and daddy died three months apart from each other. First Mama died with a stroke. Then Daddy died from his mule kicking him in the stomach. My brothers was so darn mad at that mule for killing Daddy that they stabbed him in both of his eyes with the hay fork and he went blind. Yeah. He stumbled around bumping into everything until he died. (Looking at the floor with an unhappy expression on her face). Mama had been sick on and off. But Daddy was as strong as an ox. Who would've knowd that a strong healthy man would get up in the mornin and go to work in the field just to have his dumb mule kill him. You talking about a hurtin! I ain't never got over that. I don't think I ever will. Mama and Daddy's death, the dogs death.

Gladys talked: "Mama I remember when we went to both of their funerals. Everybody was crying and wearing black clothes that smell like moth balls. Mama, I believe it was a bit embarrassing for Daddy to re-live that corn liquor situation and painfully sad for him to hear about the dogs all over again. Anyhow, he is my father and I love him no matter what he did. You know, its all kind of exciting to me. I am the only one in school who's father ever owned his own business."

Big Mama continues: The three years that Smiley was affiliated with the liquor business had a good side to it. He managed to save every single penny that he earned from it. It was a rat smart thing

44

to do. Gladys you were two years old when yo daddy took up that business. Look at him. He done fell asleep leaning back on the wall like that. I hope that chair don't fall from under him. Bless his heart. Lord, it seems like I been talking for hours. The ice done melted in my lemonade. Ha. I forgot that I had it sittin here.

Four Years Later 1936:
Curley and Gladys Got Married

Curley Holmes, twenty-five years old and Gladys Stean Jackson, eighteen years old, were married on April 19, 1936 **(my parents)**.

Curley was a good looking soldier, eager to start a family with his gorgeous wife. His intentions were to build a house for his wife and children when he got out of the Army, but at that immediate time they moved into a two room flat which was next door to Papa and Big Mama's house. It was convenient. Curley shared his plans for the future with Papa and Big Mama. So Papa suggested that they put their money together and buy some land and build two houses on it. They shook hands, agreed on it and set a goal to start the project in one year. Curley was sent to France in May of 1936 for one year. When he returned to the United States, he was electrified with enthusiasm to be home with his wife and three and a ½ month old handsome son with his mother's big, pretty, eyes. Edward Jean Holmes, (June) Curley landed a job at the electric power company in Gloster, Mississippi as an electrician.

Gladys was a seamstress, therefore she sewed for people in town as they needed it. When she wasn't sewing, expecting another child didn't keep her from helping with the chores in the fields. She gave birth to their second baby, a tiny girl with blond, silky, hair and green eyes. Simply gorgeous! Big Mama named her Doll because she looked just like a little doll.

Twenty six months later, Mama gave birth to an incredibly huge son. He had curly sandy hair and green eyes. So cute! Thomas James Holmes, (T. J.) The midwife (Mrs. Whitmore), said she had been delivering babies for thirty years and had never seen or heard tell of a new born baby weighing that much. She told Gladys that she went from one extreme to another, meaning Doll was a seven month pre-mature 2 ½ pounder and T. J. was a full term 12 ½ pounder.

46

December 1940

The Jackson And Holmes Family Moved To Their New Homes In Gloster, Mississippi:

The family had breakfast at Papa and Big Mama's house. It was their last day at Broomfield's place. Before they ate they joined hands and thanked God for His presence, guidance and for their new blessed homes. As they ate, Big Mama talked about the two things which she was feeling deep down inside, happiness and sadness. Happiness because they were leaving directly after breakfast and sadness because they were leaving all of their friends and neighbors behind. Big Mama and Mama were in their kitchen packing dishes when Mr. and Mrs. Chatman walked in along with Martha, Maggie and their families.

They were ready to help load the wagon and truck. Although they had said their good-byes the day before, Big Mama and Mama's eyes lit up with joy. It was obvious they had friends for a lifetime and a few miles apart would only make them appreciate each other more and value their time spent together.

Papa and Daddy had put their money together and purchased forty-two acres of land, very nice acreage with a creek stocked with a variety of fish. (Occasionally you would get a glimpse of the bold, ashy brown, lazy, water moccasin indulging in the sun, bathing where the water was very shallow). There was a pond with ducks floating in it. Fruit trees were plentiful and distributed throughout the land.

Just beyond the creek were large black walnut and pecan trees that produced awesome tasting walnuts and pecans. The trees also served as shade trees for breaking after a hot day's work in the field. Everybody was known for going there to kick back, keep cool and stuff themselves with black walnuts and pecans. It was a beautiful, peaceful, place!

Behind the barn leading down the lane, you would find patches of blackberries, maypops, musca dimes (concord grapes), etc. It took Papa and Daddy nine months of all kinds of weather and extremely hard work to successfully build their two homes. They praised God and gave thanks to Papa's brothers, Curley's brothers and their friends and neighbors for their tremendous help in building their homes.

Papa and Big Mama's home was situated on a hill and one mile from their closest neighbor, widower Zig Evans and his two sons, Bill and Huey. The home was simple. It consisted of two bedrooms each with a fireplace. The kitchen was roomy and comfortable. A front and back porch was a must. It was built on a hill overlooking an unpaved road with a bridge crossing over the creek. The bridge was situated on a winding unpaved road, a most glorious place where one could go and sit on the edge of that wooden bridge which crossed over the creek and swing their feet over the water and meditate for hours. Or throw rocks in the water and watch the circles expand and disappear.
The country scenery was breathtaking and pleasurable in all four seasons. The air was pure, refreshing and healthy for the body, mind, and soul. The entire front yard consisted of Big Mama's beautifully arranged flower garden. It was a perfect picture to behold. The fragrances was astounding! It was something that you would want to capture in a bottle, keep it with you and only remove the cover to refresh your senses with those sweet precious unforgettable lasting scents. Surely, It was something to write home about. They had the necessary equipment needed to continue on farming at their new home. Papa loved birds and was fascinated by them so much, that he made a big red bird house and put it in the front yard where he could appreciate watching the birds and their wondrous activities. They flew there for the summers and flew to a warmer climate in the winter months.

During the summers, Papa and Big Mama took pleasure in sitting on the front porch after a hard day's work in the field. Just to acknowledge the beautiful work of mother nature was comforting and relaxing. Occasionally they would see a cloud of dust in the road. They knew that in the mist of that dust was a car. There was a good chance that company was coming. Patiently, they would stand on the edge of the porch watching the driveway.

If the car turned into the driveway, Big Mama would rush into the kitchen and start up a fire in the stove and start preparing some tasty food for their company. They were plain, honest, country, sincere, warm, hospitable, people. They loved to have people visit them and make themselves comfortable and feel at home anytime.

Daddy and Mama's house was built one fourth mile from the road and a half mile from Papa's and Big Mama's house. They were close enough to communicate by opening a window or going out in the yard and hollering from house to house. Their closest neighbor, Mr. and Mrs. Sears, (friendly people), lived one mile up the road. Across the road from them lived the Eubin family, (not friendly). Daddy and Mama's home was roomy and comfortable. Three bedrooms, a big kitchen and a big living room with a fireplace. There was a front and back porch, plus an out-house situated in the far corner of the back yard. June, Doll and T. J. roamed that spacious countryside as they grew. Daddy was the toy maker. He made a swing in the big cedar tree that was in the front yard, twenty feet from that was a see-saw, twenty feet from that was a hammock. Mama told Daddy that those toys were a bit too big for June, Doll and T. J.. Daddy told her that those three youngsters were growing fast and before she knew it they would be running around and playing with them.

There was a rather large tree trunk in the back yard which was mainly used for cutting firewood. There was an array of deep green beautiful trees which outlined the back yard. In one corner of the yard was a chicken coop. There was a car shed on the side of the house, and next to that was maypop vines with exceptionally sweet maypops.

From 1943 To 1969:

Mama gave birth to a stillborn girl. It was devastating and painful for her; she was down and out for weeks. One day she said; 'I have three lovely children. I am blessed and thankful to have them. I must go on with my life.'

Mama's friend Maggie Chatman, her husband and children moved

49

up the road from them. Mama, June, Doll and T. J. walked to Maggie's house to visit her and her children all the time. And on their way back home, Maggie and her children would walk Mama, June, Doll and T. J. to the graveyard, which was half way home. Mama enjoyed stopping on the side of the road and helping herself to the red clay to take home and eat.

About a year later, she gave birth to Curley, an attractive chubby boy with big beautiful hazel brown eyes, and brown straight hair. Curley only lived for six weeks. That was another traumatic experience to befall her and the family as well. Reverend Clinton, Maggie, some of the neighbors and members from church, would take turns coming by to check on Mama, encourage her and have prayer. Some of the ladies from church came up with a splendid idea to keep Mama occupied as much as time would allow by quilting. They set the frame for quilting in the ceiling. Every other day three people would come and work on the quilt with Big Mama and Mama. Big Mama made tea cakes and coffee to snack on while they were quilting. Usually they worked on the quilt three to four hours each time they came. While quilting and snacking, they had fun gossiping about all sorts of amusing things. Their topics were on: how Mrs. Hanks strutted up and down the isles in church every Sunday with her slip hanging, and about Sister Wilson wearing the same old dirty dress to church every Sunday.

Nora talked about Deacon Howard: "That man would sit on the front seat, and in the middle of the sermon, stand up just enough to pass gas and stink up the whole church. He didn't want that gas bubbling around in his draws. Anyhow, after that he would shake his head, hold his nose and look back to see if anyone suspected he was the one who did it. The man was in trouble! He couldn't stand his own poot. He had no shame, and the first thang he wanted to do after church was shake all the women hands and try like heck to kiss um."

The last time he brought his mean fart to church and dumped it he was in for a big surprise. After Deacon Howard came in and took his seat, the whole congregation moved to the opposite side of the pew. He hadn't realized that until that gas of his began to ride the air and the preacher, as well as the congregation roared with laughter.

The preacher paused long enough to say: "Quit that! Y'all ain't right." That must have been a joke because before he could finish saying that, spit was running down the sides of his mouth, I am telling you that the preacher had a g-o-o-o-o-d laugh.
Anyhow, I politely whispered: 'you can stand in front of the whole congregation and shout, clap yo hands, stomp yo feet, and laugh at Deacon Howard, and you are saying it ain't right for us to do it. Wait just a cotton pickin minute preacher, you need to shit or git off the pot!'

That happened about two years ago, and ain't nobody seen Deacon Howard since then."

They also engaged in telling hilarious jokes that would cause one to forget their problems and have endless gut busting laughter. With God's help, along with her friends and neighbors, Mama's case of blues diminished. Her face became possessed with a glow of peace and harmony. Somehow she developed a positive spirit that was stronger than ever before. She and Daddy set more goals and commenced to reach them.

Three years later, in the middle of a furious stormy night in January, Daddy was forced to get out of their warn bed, and go to town in that frightful weather to bring back Mrs. Duck, the midwife. While on their way back home, Daddy discovered that the bridge had washed away. He drove back up the hill and parked the car next to the graveyard. He and Mrs. Duck walked down that dark, slippery, muddy, road and proceeded to walk across the creek. Unfortunately, the freezing cold water was way over Mrs. Duck's head. So Daddy had to carry her through the water to safety. He immediately went back through the water to retrieve her black bag. Fifteen minutes later they arrived home soaking wet. Daddy was rewarded dearly. Bare foot, cold and soaking

wet, Mrs. Duck delivered a gorgeous, sweet, lovable baby girl with dimples, freckles, and curly brown hair (Me), Mama said; "I'll name her Rosetta. That's such a beautiful name."
Daddy said: "No!! You and Big Mama named June, Doll and T. J.. If you don't mind, I am going to name her. President Truman's air plane was named Bettye Joe. I always thought to myself, If I have another daughter, I will name her Bettye Joe. I like that name! Well? What do y'all think? Bettye Joe, how do it sound?"
Everybody thought it was a nice name. It was final.

Big Mama gave Mrs. Duck dry clothing to put on. She dressed and waited by the fireplace for her boots to dry. She ended up staying over night due to the storm. The commotion woke June, Doll and T. J.. Therefore, the whole household was up for the remaining of the night. Everyone was sitting and laying around the blazing fire in the fireplace, eating popcorn, homemade peanut brittle and boiled peanuts while the storm continued to whip and roar vigorously outside. After the first peek of daylight the next morning, while it was still raining, Papa went to the creek and gathered a bucket of fish, frogs and crayfish which had been washed upon the land from the flood. Big Mama's variety of fried fish, frog legs and steamed crayfish was enjoyed by everyone.
I was the baby for one year and ten months. Then along came another boy, Richard Noble. He was uch a cute baby, with gorgeous, big, dark, brown eyes, accompanied with long eye lashes and the prettiest straight blue black hair. Surely he would grow up to be a tall handsome man.

Nine Months Later: June 1949

Papa and Big Mama left early that Friday morning, taking Doll with them to New Orleans, Louisiana. They were to be gone for the weekend, visiting with Papa's brother, his wife and children. Daddy was at work. He promised June and T. J. that after they were done with their chores, they could accompany Bill and Huey to Roy Roger's Creek and take their B-B guns along with them.

June: "Mama, everything is finished. We done milked the cows, slopped the hogs, filled the troughs, gathered the eggs and fed the chickens. I did most of the work. T. J., that chump was goofin off again. He was chasin a baby rabbit and throwin rocks at him."

T. J.: Mama, I was trying to catch the rabbit so you could cook him for supper. I was trying to save Daddy a huntin trip.

T. J., what am I going to do with you? Do you want to miss out on your venture and stay home with me today?" Mama asked.

T. J.: "No Mam! Mama, please let me go. I don't want to stay home. I'll do all the chores tomorrow by myself."

Mama: "Yep! I know you will! Im-ma see to that. Is that clear?"

T. J.: "Yes Mam. "

Mama: I packed some ham and biscuit sandwiches, a dozen boiled eggs, four pint jars of those peaches that I canned last week, some baked peanut and four quart jars of orange soft drink. Its enough food for all of you boys. I doubt if you will eat all of it. Look at y'all! Lord my boys are growing up fast. This is the first time y'all ever been ten miles away from home by yourselves. I want y'all to watch for cars. Y'all know how some people high tail it up and down the road like they own it. T. J., this ain't no time to play jokes on nobody, so leave your pranks at home!

T. J.: (giggling with his head down.) Yes Mam. I'll leave them home. Mama, June done called me a bad word ten times today.

Mama: What did he call you?

T. J. : He called me a hum dinger!

Mama smiled and shook her head saying: That ain't no bad word.

T. J: It sound like a bad word.

June: Mama, Im-ma watch T. J. like a hawk watch a chicken and if he step out of line, I'll slug him good.

June and T. J.; Thank you for the lunch Mama. We'll be very careful.

June: I know that Bill and Huey will like the food. They ain't got no Mama to cook for them. She died five years ago.

T. J.: They out there whistlin for us. Come on June. Let's go.

Mama: Y'all give me a hug and kiss before you climb upon those horses. Remember! I want y'all back home before dark! OK? Oh! I hear Richard crying, I better get back in the house and tend to him. (waving as she headed for the door). Bye Bye. Don't forget! Be home before dark!

The four boys were slowly walking their horses down the driveway towards the road when they heard Mama's urgent screaming voice calling, "June come here quick."
June turned his horse around and raced back to the house. He shouted: "Mama what is it? What's wrong?"
Mama answered him: "Richard is sick! Go quickly and get Mrs. Sears. Tell her to come right away."
June ran and jumped on his horse and took off to Mrs. Sears' house with T. J., Bill and Huey following him. While racing down Mrs. Sears driveway, they spotted her in the back yard. She was picking pecans off the ground. They approached her.

Mrs. Sears spoke: "Good morning ! Let me ask y'all this. What brings you boys here so early in the day riding those horses like a bat out of hell?"

June: (out of breath). Mrs. Sears! (Then he paused breathing hard). Mrs. Sears: Wait a minute June. Catch your breath. Now, let me ask you this. What is it that you're trying to say?

June: Mama say come quick! Richard is sick.

Mrs. Sears : What's the matter wit him?

June: I don't know. His tongue is hanging out of his mouth and his eyes is rolling around in his head and his body is shakin.

Mrs. Sears: Help me upon this horse and let's go. T. J. run back there and shut my back door. I stepped out here to get some pecans and left the door open.

"When they got back to the house Mrs. Sears immediately took Richard from Mama's arms and sat in the rocking chair with him. She instructed Mama to give her a cold wet cloth and a pan of warm water. She put the cloth on Richard's forehead and in the meanwhile Mama kneeled on the floor holding the pan of warm water for Mrs. Sears to bathe his feet.

She assured Mama: "Let me tell you this. Gladys, you did the right thing by calling me. As a child I saw this condition take place a many times. My baby sister, August, had the same thing. They call it spasms. Richard just had a spasm attack. My mother taught me and my brothers what to do if-fin August had an attack while her and my father wasn't around. Don't rightly know what causes them, but I do know that he will grow out of it just like August did.

Gladys, I want you to remember this here remedy, put a cold wet cloth on his forehead and put his feet in a pan of warm water. That will bring him out of those spasms every time. Look at him wit those big, pretty eyes and them long eyelashes. He's looking at me like he's thinking, 'what in the hell is this white woman doing holding me?' Gladys you can rest now. Richard is out of danger and feeling fine."

Mama nursed Richard and he fell asleep.

June told Mama that they decided not to go on their venture as planned. They wanted to stick around the house in case Richard got sick again.

Mrs. Sears heard the conversation and said: "let me tell y'all this. Staying home is nonsense. Y'all keep the plans you had and go, besides you might not get a chance like this again. Don't worry about Richard. he's just fine now. Besides, Im-ma stay here wit yo mama for a while and keep an eye on Richard. Lord knows, I ain't got nothing else to do."

The four boys took her advice and left for their venture at Roy Roger's Creek. Mama overwhelmingly and wholehearted expressed her gratitude to Mrs. Sears and offered to repay her. She also let Mrs. Sears know how frightened she was;

"I was so scared. I thought Richard was going to die. You remember before I had Bettye Joe, I had a stillborn and after that Curley died when he was six weeks old. Mrs. Sears, I thank God for the blessing of having you here with me today."

Mrs. Sears shared a secret with Mama: "Gladys, this is the first time that I felt needed, for such a very long time. And damet, it felt good. Holding a baby in my arms was a sweet pleasure that I ain't likely to never forget. It made me feel worthy and alive. That alone is all the pay that I will ever need."

She walked to the stove while Mama was taking a skillet of cornbread from the oven and kept on talking: "Let me tell you this. I ain't trying to be nosey or nothin like that. Let me ask you this. How you gon feed yo husband and children wit that lil biddy skillet of cornbread? That's just enough to feed two people."

Mama blushed and answered her: "Oh I made this for me. After skimming the milk this morning and getting more cream than I normally get, I decided that I wanted me some milk and bread wit some of that fresh cream in it."

Mrs. Sears responded: "I ain't had me no milk and bread since I got married. Know what? That cornbread is smelling pretty darn good. Do you suppose its enough for me? Tell me yeah. If I don't get some of that milk, bread and cream today, I just might kick the bucket!"

Mama told her: "It certainly is enough for you. I'll fix a bowl for you right now while the bread is still piping hot. Boy, that's when it taste the best. I done fixed it for you. Let's eat."

Mrs. Sears talked while she ate: "Oou wee. This is good. Its a long overdue favorite of mine. I can't help but notice them fine looking peaches over there in the cupboard! Did your mother can them for you?"

"No. I canned them." Mama replied.

Mrs. Sears shared things about herself to Mama: "You know, I have two peach trees in the yard, but I don't know a darn thing about canning peaches or anything like that. I take a box of salt and go sit under the tree that has the most peaches on the ground. I cross my legs and lean back on the tree trunk. I like being betwix the peaches. Then I load them up wit salt, I love salt. I can't get enough of it. Anyhow, I eat until my stomach can't hold no mo. Then, I sit there noddin until I fall asleep. That is the bestest sleep in the whole world. But there's one thing that I haven't been able to figure out yet; why do I always wake up with a lowdown mean headache after eatin them salty peaches?"

"Mrs. Sears, I will can your peaches for you. But it will have to be within the next three weeks, that-a-way they won't have a chance to get too ripe and spoil." Mama said.
Mrs. Sears was touched by Mama's suggestion and thanked her in advance. She immediately became enthusiastic and started contemplating on enjoying canned peaches from her own back yard throughout the winter."
After eating, they checked on Richard. He was enjoying a restful sleep. Mrs. Sears led the way back to the kitchen. She gazed out the window as she told Mama that her and Mr. Sears

came by frequently to see how Papa and Daddy were building their houses, and that they wondered what kind of people the Jackson's and Holmes's were. She confessed that they went horse back riding four or five times a week and almost every time they would end up in front of our house. They'd stay there momentarily, just to see what was going on from Papa's and Big Mama's house to our house as far as the children were concerned. Mrs. Sears was in a mood for talking:

"Let me tell you this. Sometimes Curley and the boys would be in the yard wrestling on the ground, or they'd be playing baseball, sometimes he'd be pushing them in the swing, they were having so much fun. One day Curley was relaxing in the hammock and the boys kept playing around him and jumping on the hammock, he was telling them to stop jumping on the hammock and all of a sudden the limb on the tree that the head part of the hammock was tied to broke and Curley's head went back. He was hanging up-side-down. That scared June and T. J., so they ran straight to your mother's house. It always gave me a sense of joy and peace to see those children laughin and playin all the time. So I did the only thing I could do. I closed my eyed real tight and pretended that I had children too. Three girls and three boys. I'd dress my girls dainty and make a big fuss over them. I daydream an awful lot when I'm in the kitchen cookin; 'I'm waiting for my daughters to come in from playin so they can sit the table for me. I'd tell them a story before they went to bed.'
So many things go on in my head at times that my thoughts get so real and heavy til I break down and cry hard for a long time and my eyes become red and swollen. I don't feel like a whole woman. I feel empty inside, like somethin important is missin. Why can't I have children like you, Gladys? I love children, I would make a dam good mother! Gladys I don't expect you to understand what I'm tellin you, cause you got children."

Mama made a pot of sarsaparilla tea, they sipped it as their conversation led from one thing to another and grew deeper and deeper. Mrs. Sears indicated that she was forty years old and that she had been married for twenty-three years to a man twenty years her senior, who complained every day about her cooking being salty. She was lonely, miserable, and unhappy most of the time. She continued the discussion about her long desire to have children from the day she were married. But unfortunately, Mr. Sears' accident in the Army prevented him from having the experience and pleasure of becoming a natural father due to the fact that a portion of his male productive system were shattered by a gun shot. The bullet twisted, turned and ripped causing damage to his organ leaving him sterile.

Mrs. Sears was loquacious: "That old mean fart can't do nothin but shoot blanks and give me worms. I don't care if that big funky bear do have money. All I know is that he has deprived me of the things I wanted most, 'children!'

Gladys, let me tell you this. Forgive me for spillin my guts, but I need to talk to somebody before I go crazy. I been keeping this stuff bottled up in me for twenty-three years. Ah, I spend about four hours a day taking care of the horses. That kind of keep my concentration strictly on them and off of myself. But when I'm walkin back to the house from the stable, it hit me like a pile of bricks that I'm going to a quiet childless house. No children to tire me out from runnin after them all day. No children to teach things like my mama taught me. I'm going damn crazy. Sometimes I feel like pulling my hair out. And to top it off, I get a headache rat before Sears get home from work everyday. Its been like that for years. I need help! What do you think I should do Gladys?"

Mama asked her if she had shared her feelings with Mr. Sears about wanting children so badly.
She replied: "Yes. You know having children and his money were the reasons I got married. I used to mention it quite a bit when we first got married, he always said he wanted to wait for a while. I found out the truth about his condition by pure accident. He doesn't know that I know. I wish I could find the right words to bring it up. It has been pure torture to keep my lips sealed about this thing. Sometimes, I feel sorry for him when we're gettin along good or he do something nice for me. I wish he would have

been a man and told me about this thing before he married me."

Mama suggested that she tell him exactly how she felt and perhaps they could help her relatives by raising some of their children. Mrs. Sears thought that was a great idea and it gave her a boost of enthusiasm and determination to approach her husband, her anticipation was to discuss it with him as soon as he returned home from work.

She wanted to know how Mama seasoned her food: " Do you like salt?" She asked. "Do you cook with salt?"

Mama answered her: "Yeah. Yeah I like salt. I season my food with it every day. Why you ask?"

Mrs. Sears responded: "You know what? I love salt so much that I put it on damn near everything I eat. Sears is on my back about me using too much salt. He been coming home lately and going straight to the stove to taste the food. Then he git mad and spit the food back in the pot and take it outside to the dogs. You know that's a damn shame. Yesterday he told me not to cook anything else for him. It hurt my feelings real bad. (pausing) I think I hear Richard crying. Let me check on him!"
He was still asleep.
She told Mama that she was leaving and to send for her if anything happened. Mama walked her to the driveway and watched her as she walked up the road and disappeared over the hill.

That evening, June and T. J. arrived a bit before dark. They were totally worn out from their exciting adventure. They raved about the astounding day, they encountered. T. J. surprised Daddy and Mama. He made them proud that evening! Somehow, he acquired an energy boost and did his chores diligently. After it was dark, he retrieved the flashlight and went to the henhouse and gathered the eggs and kept a positive attitude about doing it. After finishing everything, he went to June and apologized for not helping out with the chores that morning. He also promised to hang in there with him and share all the shores equally in the future. T. J.'s apologizing to June and making things right was good and relaxing for Daddy and Mama. T. J. was blessed with some kind of sense of humor. 'Funny, fun-filled, always laughing and joking around, no matter what.'

Later that evening the household was kicked back, cooperating, counting their blessings and talking about the stresses of that day. As the lovely sound of the heavy rain began to overflow the roof and windows, the conversation changed. Ghost tales started to circulate the room and things were getting a little frightful. Everyone was on the edge of their seat taking everything in as Mama told Daddy about Maggie Chatman's encounter and experience with ghosts when her husband went to Natchez, Mississippi to attend his grandmother's funeral.

Mama talking: "On the evening of the funeral, Maggie and some of her family had dinner and left the kitchen table without clearing it. They resumed to the front room to engage in drinking coffee, smoking cigars, cigarettes, pipes, and having a general conversation. But their conversation was interrupted abruptly. The kitchen door opened and something walked in and closed it back. Then it walked to the table, pulled a chair back and sat down and scooted the chair closer to the table. It picked up a fork and commenced to eat leftovers from Maggie's plate. (Maggie's intentions were to eat her leftovers later). Anyway, while the thing ate, the people in the front room could hear the fork touching the plate. They glanced over the room and took a roll call. Everyone was there.

Then they whispered: "Maggie, who else you done invited here? You must know them real good. They done went straight to yo kitchen and put they foots under yo table befo speakin to us."

Maggie told them: "Y'all is the only one I told to come here. Why don't y'all go see who it is?"
Everybody shook their heads. Therefore, she asked in a low nervous voice:

"Who is in the kitchen?" There was no answer. She looked around the room and everybody's faces were grey, and they were uptight and apprehensive about going to the kitchen to see who was in there eating. Maggie finally went to the kitchen and was in for a rude awakening. She saw the fork moving up and down as if someone was feeding their self, but nobody was there. The full glass of tea went up and when it came down it was empty. The thing burped several times. The empty chair scooted back. The footsteps approached her. She felt very warm air as it moved past her scared, motionless body. The next thing she remembered was laying in the bed as her mother held smelling salt under her nose.

Mama's story was cut short in the rainy darkness of that spooky night, as something hit our back door with a force so hard and heavy that it brought us to a halt. Within the next minute four more bangs came. The loud noise was so penetrating, that it caused everyone of us to jump to our feet. The room was filled with absolute quietness. Daddy whispered: "Don't nobody move. Stay where you are. I'm going out side to see who in the hell is behind that noise!"

Who ever was on the other side of the door was desperate to get inside. They were shaking the door knob and kicking the door frantically trying to get in the house. Daddy finished loading the shot gun. Then he stood in front of the door and said: "I got my shot gun loaded and cocked. When I count to three, I'm coming out shooting. Im'ma blow you into smithereens."

At the point of counting 'one' he heard a familiar clamor voice coming from the other side of the door:

"Daddy! Daddy! This is T. J.! Yo son! Don't blow me into smithereens! Don't shoot me! Don't shot me! Daddy! Please! Put the gun down! I was just out here having some fun. Playing a little trick on y'all! That's all! Shucks! It ain't nothing for y'all to get scared and bent out of shape about! I'm sorry! Please! If I knowed y'all was gon git scared, I wouldn't have did it."

Daddy opened the door and there stood T. J. with his dripping

62

wet hair covering his eye brows. He held his head down and put his finger in his mouth. His body language was an indication that he was surely sorry for that silly inappropriate prank of his. Daddy told him that he wasn't going to whoop him right then, because as mad as he was at that present time, if he hit him he would kill him. He just turned and walked away angrily. Mama had T. J. come in the house and get out of his wet clothing. She asked him what possessed him to do a foolish thing like that?

Smiling proudly, he said the ghost story about Miss Maggie gave him the idea. Mama gave him the damnet to hell look and slapped him in the mouth. He in return apologized again for what he did. He was aware of the uneasy position his foolishness put the family in and suggested making some peanut brittle to makeup for it. Just when he thought he was out of hot water and everything was back to normal he went back to his original self, laughing and teasing about the frightful event. Daddy overheard him and gave him a surprise that he would have never suspected in his wildest dreams. Daddy put a chair in the middle of the floor, sat in it and motioned for T. J. to lay across his lap. He gave June his belt and told him to give T. J. the licking that he so well deserved. T. J. got a really good licking, while we stood around watching. After that, he stood leaning on the front door with his mouth stuck out and mad with the whole household because he got a good licking. While he listened to what Daddy said.

Daddy told us a story about what happened ten years prior that night. About how the actions of a foolish man and his jokes caused an innocent man to spend seven precious days away from his lovely wife and children in jail. The story was mainly directed to T. J.. Daddy was on his lunch break at work. He had just sat down to eat his lunch and read the newspaper, when his co-worker, Mo Hicks, (a practical joker who was always horsing around on the job), walked up to him holding a black rattle snake. As he stood over Daddy, the snake was wiggling.

Mo Hicks said: "Look at this Curley. I done found me a rattle snake. Hey, you know something? I ain't never gave you nothin. But Im-ma give you somethin today. Here you can have this

63

snake. I hope he don't kill ya."

He threw the snake at Daddy and it landed around Daddy's neck. Naturally, Daddy was afraid of rattle snakes. He stumbled and chocked on the food he was chewing while he was getting up from his comfortable seat on the bench. He was scared to touch the snake for fear of getting bit. He jumped around trying to shake that beast off of him. His co-workers was no help. They scattered to safety. Finally the snake fell to the ground, Daddy grabbed his thermos bottle and poured his hot coffee on the snake, before he stomped his head until it was beneath the soil.

Yeah! Well, that freaking Mo Hicks was just getting started. He thought that was the funniest thing he ever saw. He ran around and clapped his hands like a five year old child, saying: "I got Curley good. Ha, ha, ha. Did y'all see how he was running scared, jumping and kicking? Ha, ha, ha, ha. When the snake fell to the ground, ha, ha, ha, Curley poured his good smellin, delicious, hot, coffee on that snake and stomped him til he gived out of breath. That was so funny! Curley, I forgot to tell you one thang. Ha, ha, ha, ha, the snake was already dead. Ha, ha, ha aah. Did y'all take notice to how Curley was tap dancing on that lil oh snake's head? Ha, ha, ha, ooh. I mean his face was bout red as a pickled beet. Oh man! Ha, ha, ha. Now, that's the kind of stuff to write home about. Ha, ha ha."

Daddy was some kind of pissed off. As he stood there biting his tongue, with both hands in a fist (That's what he'd do whenever he got really angry).

So he walked up to Mo Hicks while he was still laughing and very comely said: "Hicks! How many times have I told you not to play with me?"
Then he hit him one time. It was a mighty powerful blow! Daddy knocked Hicks into a state of unconsciousness plus he knocked out seven of his teeth. The ambulance came and took Hicks to the hospital. The police came and took Daddy to jail. The police informed Daddy that if Mo Hicks died, he would be in jail forever.

Seven days later Mo Hicks came out of his unconsciousness. The police released Daddy from jail immediately after questioning Mo Hicks.

Six months later, Hicks came to visit Daddy and Mama. He apologized for being a silly old grown man. He told them that if it was anything that he could have done to change that devastating day, he would give his right hand to do it and make things right. He gave Daddy an envelope with money, that he figured Daddy lost from work while he was in jail. He told Daddy that he wouldn't be returning to work because none of their co-workers liked him or spoke to him since he played that sick distasteful snake joke on him. He said he was going crazy because he couldn't stand the quiet treatment from the coworkers. He indicated that his joking days were done and over with. Years later, T. J. thanked Daddy for that valuable lesson. He realized that it was alright to joke around and have fun, but not to the extreme.

The Family Continues To Grow And Enrich:

Mama gave birth to 'Charlie Bruce', another beautiful boy with simply big gorgeous brown eyes, long eye lashes, thick eye-brawls black hair and deep dimples that highlighted his round face. Although everyone was hoping for another girl, Charlie was absolutely a welcome little bundle of joy One year and nine months passed, Mama got sick again, and Miss Dick came with her black bag again. That time she told Richard, Charlie and me to play in the front yard and be very quiet. If we did that, she would kill two birds with one stone, make Mama feel better and give us the baby which she had in her black bag.

She looked at us one last time before walking away and added as she pointed to her black bag: "If y'all ain't quiet, I will take this baby and give it to somebody else."

We followed her instructions. I was so happy that I couldn't stand it. Richard said: "When I grow up, I will be just like Miss Duck. I will kill two birds with one stone."

Big Mama, Papa and Daddy were in the house. June, Doll, T. J., Richard, Charlie and I were outside.

Big Mama came out and said: "Lord, I was hoping that it would be a girl. They already had four boys. Y'all got another brother. He's the prettiest little thang you ever wanna see. He got curly blond hair, big pretty green eyes, long fingers and long feet. Doll, he look like you and T. J. from head to toe."

We were all pleased to have another brother. 'Robert Earl'. Richard and I loved Miss Duck with a passion.

Mama got sick again two years later, and Miss Duck came to the house again with her black bag hanging off her arm. Again, we followed her instructions to be quiet. That time was different, Miss Duck accompanied Daddy and Mama to the hospital in Centerville, Mississippi. Five days later she returned home with 'Emerson' an adorable boy with big lovely brown eyes, straight long brown hair. (Six boys).

Daddy, Mama, Papa and Big Mama had a pleasurable time growing with us as they taught and disciplined us. When June, Doll and T. J. began school, they had to walk three miles to get there. Daddy was uncomfortable with that and mentioned to the principal about having a bus pick them up at our home. The principal suggested that they continue to walk because it was only two other students in that vicinity and they hardly ever came to school and when they did come they didn't complain about the walk. He concluded that it was senseless to have a big bus come our way just to pick up a handfull of children. Daddy disagreed and refused to accept the principal's answer. He went to the court house in Liberty, Mississippi and the results were immediate and astounding. Within a week a bus arrived at our driveway bright and early. The bus turned around in our driveway. As the word of the bus coming to our driveway circulated, children that lived further down the road was there waiting for the bus too. It was a blessing to have a ride to and from school especially in the harsh winter months.

Christmas Holidays:

Mama always baked two fruitcakes the day after Thanksgiving. And the week before Christmas, she'd bake seven cakes, a chocolate cake, two coconut cakes, a plain pound cake, a lemon pound cake, a buttermilk pound cake and a vanilla cake with apple jelly between each layer and chocolate icing. On Christmas day she'd bake roasting hens, make dressing and all the trimmings, to make a hearty delightful Christmas dinner.

It was Daddy's tradition to take us with him to the woods and let us pick a Christmas tree. After picking it, he would cut it down and carry it home. Together, we decorated the tree with popcorn strung on thread, red berries on a string of thread, red, blue and green crepe paper. And to kick it off, simply beautiful multicolor Christmas lights with a star on the top of the tree. I loved Mississippi Christmases. It's one of my fondest childhood memories. We were treated with silver bells, gigantic peppermint sticks that would last a week. We would take an orange and squeeze it, then make a opening on one end and stuff a piece of peppermint candy in the orange and once all the juice was gone, we'd get another orange.

Christmas Eve was a day that we looked forward to. I loved to see it coming but hated to see it go. Gloster, Mississippians would congregate on Christmas Eve and do fireworks. Our neighbors, friends and family joined us for the event. We had a fire blazing in the back yard for light and warmth as well. We huddled around the fire and sang Christmas carols, while waiting for Papa and Daddy to start the fireworks. Finally, they captured our full attention by throwing several flairs in the air. It seemed to have lit the entire sky. For forty-five minutes or so, the amazing different colors of the fireworks beautified the sky, as they lit it up. The firecrackers were awesome, as they sounded off with thunder of bliss. With eagerness and excitement, we enjoyed our entertainment tremendously, well into the splendid, cold, crisp, darkness of the night.

We always left a cup of coffee, for Santa Claus, on the shelf, over the fireplace in the living room, on Christmas Eve. That was Daddy's idea. He told us that Santa Claus loved coffee. Santa Claus brought us clothes, toys and the wool scarves that were identical to the ones which Daddy made for some people that lived in town, but before we could say anything,
Daddy would takeover: "Get a load of this! These scarves look just like the ones I made for the people in town. How can that be?"

It was a puzzle to us.

Reverend Clinton made it his business to be at our home on Christmas Day. He was certain to bring a pretty wrapped box with bubble gum in it for us. He would carry it tucked under his arm. It was something that we liked and looked forward to having, because in the country bubble gum or any kind of gum was a rare thing to have.

I can remember the times when we'd have company for dinner and when they sat down to the table, they would stick their gum underneath the table before eating and nine times out of ten they would always forget their gum. But Richard, Charlie and I didn't forget. We'd take that gum and chew it for days and when we got tired of it, we'd stick it back underneath the table.

Anyhow on this one particular Christmas Day, dinner wasn't quite ready when Reverend Clinton arrived. So Mama had Richard and Charlie entertain him in the living room while her and Doll finished cooking. Reverend Clinton was accustomed to visiting with us so he made himself quite at home. He took his shoes off, crossed his legs exposing his smelly, air conditioned socks. He took his red and white handkerchief and blew his nose on it, then he folded it on his lap and put it in his back pant pocket. Then he rubbed his hands together to ensure dryness.

Richard and Charlie inspected him from head to toe.

They were very inquisitive: "Why do you come to our house and eat all the time? Do you have a wife? You got a lot of holes in your socks. How come yo wife don't sew yo socks? Them is the same socks you had on the last time you came over here. Papa said when you take off your socks, they will stand in a corner by they self. Do you want to go to the creek and wash yo stinking feet?"

Richard said: "I know something about you, Reverend Clinton. You long winded. That's why Daddy is gon to say the blessings today. He said, if you say them, the food will be good and cold by the time you finish."

Charlie was the gabbiest: "Do you want to know what happened to me the other day? Ok. Mama was in the kitchen snapping beans and the Watkins man knocked on the door. June told Mama that the Watkins man wanted to sell her some pots and pans. Mama got real mad and said: 'You tell that white cracker that I ain't here. I don't feel like being bothered wit him. I ain't buying shit from him! He done sold them same pots and pans to Mrs. Sears for eight dollars. And he want to charge me eight dollars and twenty cents. We can use some new pots and pans, but I ain't buying his. He ain't gon git rich off of us. I told him that I didn't want um the last time he was here. Tell him to take his high price ass on from around here.'
"Guess what June told that Watkins man?

All he said was: 'Mama ain't home.'
But I told him everything Mama said. I told him: 'Mr. Watkins man, Mama is home! She is in the kitchen snapping beans and she told June to 'tell that white cracker that I ain't buying shit from him.
You want her to pay twenty cents more than Mrs. Sears paid you

69

for them.
Mama said take your high price ass on from around here.'
What chew waitin fo? Shoo! Go on! Take yo high price ass on
from around here like Mama said."

June and Charlie stood on the porch until the Watkins man
walked to his car and drove off. Charlie looked up at June with a
big smile.   He was so proud of himself for letting the Watkins
man know what Mama said behind his back! But June wiped that
smile off his face real quick with a slap across his mouth, 'pow.'

Charlie ran straight to Mama crying: 'June punched me in the
mouth.'

Mama responded: "Um huh! I heard everything that went on.
Come here."
He rushed to Mama thinking she was going to sympathize with
him. She slapped him on the back of his head instead, 'pow' and
reached for him because she wasn't finished with him. He stepped
out of her reach and she lost the grip of the pan of snap beans and
dropped them on the floor.

Therefore, Charlie ran straight to Big Mama and told her what
happened.
She responded; "Um huh! Charlie Bruce, Go out there in the
garden and bring me a switch from the plum tree".

With excitement, Charlie took her a branch from the plum tree.
(He was probably thinking Big Mama was on his side and was
going to whip Mama with that big branch, but that's not what
happened.)

Big Mama complained: "I didn't want you to bring half of the
tree. I declare. If you want something done right you gotta do it
yourself!"
She took a little switch from the branch and said: "Come here."
Big Mama whipped Charlie with that switch something terrible.
With anger he told Big Mama: "I'm mad at you, June and Mama!

I'm going to the creek and tell Papa that y'all whooped me cause I told the Watkins man what Mama said."

He told Papa alright! And Papa lost the grip on the big fish that he had just took off the hook freeing him to flop back into the water.

As Papa glanced into the water he came out of his quiet shell: "Say what? You told the Watkins man what? Boy, I done told you a hundred times, to stay out of grown peoples faces, taking in what they say and repeating it. I ain't never saw fit to whoop my grand chillens. But boy! You done struck out and took the cake! Im-ma whoop yo ass today!" He did.

And Charlie said: "I'm mad at everybody. I'm-ma tell Daddy on all of y'all."

He waited by the mail box for Daddy to come home from work. When he told Daddy what happened, Daddy whipped Charlie and had a talk with him about talking too much and repeating what he hears grown-ups say. Reverend Clinton thought Charlie's story was amusing.

Dinner was almost ready when Mama called Charlie to the kitchen and gave him a glass of red punch to take to Reverend Clinton. Charlie took the punch and as soon as he reached the living room, he drunk two thirds of the punch, before giving it to Reverend Clinton. Reverend Clinton was stunned, even-though he took the almost empty glass of punch and swallowed it in one gulp. Charlie had no idea that Daddy and Mama saw him drinking the punch. He took the glass back to Mama.

And Daddy asked Charlie: "What is that red stuff on your mouth and new white shirt?"

Charlie answered: "I don't know."

"No doubt about it. That's red punch. I can smell it." Daddy voiced his opinion.

Charlie's eyes got big as he talked and shook his head. " Daddy I don't know how this red punch got on my mouth and shirt."

Mama and Daddy thought that was the funniest thing. Daddy kept probing: "Me and yo Mama saw you drink that punch. I just want to know what made you do it."

Charlie stuck his index finger in his nose and said: "Daddy, the devil made me do that."

Daddy asked: "How did he make you do it?

Charlie thought before answering: "The, devil, said, 'Charlie, drink, that, red, punch.' That's why I drunk it."

By that time the whole family had gathered in the kitchen and giggled while Daddy continued to probe Charlie:

"How do you know it was the devil that told you to drink the punch?" Charlie was silent.

"Did you see him?" Daddy asked.

Charlie said: "Yes sir." Then he immediately changed his mind: "No sir." Then he said: "Daddy, I got to pee!"

He ran out the door and headed straight for Papa and Big Mama's house. He'd run a few steps, stop and look back. When he reached their house he ran to their bedroom and looked out the window towards our house. Big Mama asked him to carry a pan of biscuits to our house for dinner because her and Papa's hands were full. Charlie refused to do it: "I don't wanna go back to the house right now, cause Daddy gon whoop me for drinking Reverend Clinton's red punch."
He carried the biscuits because Big Mama insisted. Our Christmas dinner was superb as usual. Daddy said the blessings.

Charlie did not get a whooping for drinking Reverend Clinton's red punch. But he learned a good lesson. What goes around, comes around. Reverend Clinton drank Charlie's red punch and offered to give him a glass of water. Charlie didn't think that was funny. He was so mad that he wanted to fight the reverend: "In two years I will be a man like my daddy. And I will slap you so hard that it will knock your socks off. You better believe, I ain't playin."

June Busted For Smoking:

It had turned out to be a wonderfully beautiful sunny Friday afternoon in April, after the heavy rainfall that morning. We also had an especially nice surprise earlier that morning: the bus didn't come to pick us up for school. Doll suggested that we save our lunches and wait for the twelve O clock whistle in town to blow and have a picnic in the front yard. The rain prevented us from having our picnic as planned, so we had a lovely picnic on the front porch.

Later that afternoon, June was sitting on the back porch enjoying his singing. He paused long enough to ask me to find some dried leaves and bring them to him. I followed his instructions. He was tearing a brown paper bag into small pieces.

Me: June, what is you doing that for?

June: Cause Im-ma make me some cigarettes and smoke um.

Me: You gon git a whoopin.

June: No I ain't either. Who gon whoop me? Mama is at Papa and Big Mama's house sewing that can-can slip and dress that she cut out for you this morning. Daddy is at work. He ain't gon be home until six O clock this evening. Besides I am much too big and too old to git a whoopin. Hey, Bettye Joe, my whoopin days are over. I'll be fifteen years old in seven months. That's just around the corner. Hey, I got me a tall pretty girl friend in the twelfth grade . And she live in Crosby, Mississippi.

Me: What's her name June?

June: Brenda. Her father and mother are bringing her over here to see me Sunday after we git out of church. Mama said her and Big Mama is gon cook dinner for them. She buy me a Coco-Cola and peanuts every time we take our afternoon recess. I think she love me. She told me that I am a very handsome fellow, but I already

74

knew that.

Me: Do she smoke cigarettes, June?

June: No, but my partners Huey and Billy, sneak a cigarette from their father everyday after they eat supper, then they go to the barn and smoke it together.

I was running up and down the steps and clapping my hands as June continued to sit on the back porch, smoking and talking with me. With his back turned to the door, he stood up and began to sing his favorite song. (He would always sing this song early in the morning before he got out of bed. Waking up to his singing and Mama good smelling cooking was awesome.) "Lordy Miss Clody I'm gonna Tell My Mama What You Been Doing To Me."

He was in a good mood and having a wonderful time. His singing sounded pretty good to me. So I really started to clap my hands as I ran up and down the steps.

All of a sudden, a party pooper stormed out of the door with a belt in his hands. (Daddy) saying "Come here boy. I got a surprise for you today. You gon git a whooping like you ain't never got before. When I finish with you, you ain't gon be able to sit down for a month."

That just about scared the daylights out of June and me too. June was in a state of shock. His legs were shaking terribly. His mouth and eyes were wide open.
I suppose he was thinking: 'Daddy what are you doing home from work four hours early?' Daddy's walking towards June caused an interruption in his thoughts. He threw his homemade cigarette on the ground, Daddy put it out and asked June if he was trying to start a fire. June ran from Daddy. Daddy was on June's heels, close enough that he grabbed his shirt collar. But June's fear of a good whooping and determination along with his adrenaline, empowered him to escape Daddy's grasp. One minute he was on his knees staring up at Daddy and the next minute he was ten feet

away opening the car door as he glanced over his shoulder at Daddy. He jumped in the car and locked the doors.

Every time Daddy unlocked the door with his key, June would lock it back. Neither one of them realized that I was behind June. And when he attempted to close the car door, it hit me over my right eye and caused a cut. When Daddy saw the blood running down my face, he took me in the house and administered first aid on my eye. Daddy was angry with June, but it didn't last very long. By supper time he was joking about how scared June was when he saw him at the back door and how fast he ran from him. He said it taught him a lesson about being a father and he was going to take a different approach to discipline June on that smoking thing. I kept running back and forth to the car telling June what was going on in the house. He rolled the car window down, gave me a nickel, apologized for the accident and promised to take me to the store and buy me some candy. He was hungry and wanted to know what Mama cooked for supper.

I told him: "Some chicken, some fried potatoes, some squash and some can biscuits."

He said: "You fooling me. It ain't no such thing as can biscuits. Where did you get a tall tell like that from?"

I replied: "I ain't tellin no tall talel. Daddy brought a bag full of can biscuits from the store in Mc Comb.

He said: 'thangs is gettin modern and a lot of people won't be makin biscuits no mo. They gon buy um from the store and save time.' He took some of um to Papa and Big Mama."

Guess what? They were in a round can and Daddy took the blue paper off the can and beat the can on the table. Guess what happened then? It blew up and sounded just like a firecracker; boom! Then Mama took them biscuits out and put um on the biscuit pan and cooked um. Mama say they don't smell like her biscuits, they don't look like her biscuits and they don't taste like her biscuits. June was curious and asked me to bring him two or three of those can biscuits and not to mention it to Daddy and Mama. I took him three biscuits and they were gone in no time. I asked him if they tasted like Mama's biscuits. He told me that they were gone before he could decide and he needed more.

"Hey little sister, fix me a plate and take the onions out of the potatoes and bring me six more of them lil can biscuits. Oh, bring me some jelly too."

I fixed his plate and before I could dash out of the kitchen, Mama walked in and asked: "Are you still hungry? Girl give me that plate. I declare yo eyes are bigger than yo belly. You can't eat all of this food."

She left a teaspoon of everything on the plate and broke a biscuit in half and broke a piece of that for herself. June didn't complain. He gobbled it up and licked the plate.

Five minutes later Mama was concerned about June: "I know June is hungry about now. Im-ma fix him a bite to eat. I want you to take it to him and don't mention it to yo daddy."

I took June the plate for Mama. He was delighted to get it and enjoyed every bit of it.

Five minutes after that, Daddy was concerned about June eating: "Hey baby girl, you wanna take June a plate? I know he's hungry. That boy love to eat. Don't mention this to yo mama."

I took the plate to June for Daddy, and he ate all of it and was thankful. Ten minutes after that, Doll fixed June a plate and asked me to take it to him and she promised: "If you don't mention this to Daddy and Mama I will bring you some candy from town tomorrow."

I took the plate to June for Doll. He ate it and was appreciative.

Not long after that, T. J. had a shoe box with some of Papa and Big Mama's supper in it. He showed me a whistle that he had made from a sugar cane stalk and told me: "You can have this whistle if you take this food to June and don't mention it to Daddy and Mama."

I took June T. J.'s food and he was overwhelmed as he ate. He also shared it with me. I asked him if he was coming in the house before it got dark.

He answered: "No. Im-ma sleep in the car all night long and give Daddy a chance to cool off and forget about what happened. Daddy cannot stay mad long. Me, him and T. J. is going huntin in the mornin."

By 8: p.m. the lights were out and everyone were fast asleep. The outdoor surroundings were motionless and pitch black. It was certainly not a place where one would want to be by himself. June was awake and his heart sounded like a drum; he was in desperate need to use the toilet. He opened the car door on the passenger's side and proceeded to put his bare feet on the cool ground. Instead of the cool ground, his feet landed on something warm and furry. That scared him tremendously and he screamed like a girl and jerked his feet back and closed the car doorn with such force that the window shattered. He realized at that very moment that he had three big problems. He began to pray for his three problems to be rectified in a friendly manner.

He had a serious thought; 'either I'm gonna use the bathroom in my dungarees and have the car smelling for weeks or I'm gonna call Daddy or T. J. and ask one of them to accompany me to the toilet, cause I have to go real bad. Oooh, my stomach is bloated, swollen, too full and ready to explode. I can't stand it. Help! Help me! Why did everybody give me all of that food? My stomach can only hold so much. He started out calling T. J. in a low voice and ended up calling Daddy as loud as he possibly could. He woke the entire household. There was a chronic chilling urgency in his voice. We wanted to rescue him but Daddy told us to be quiet and let June stew in his own juice for a while. Then he would go out there and see what he was hooping and hollering about.

Minutes later Daddy went to the back yard with a flashlight and told the rest of us to stay in the house. June got out of the car and asked Daddy to walk to the toilet with him.

Daddy laughed and teased him; "On one hand you are old enough to smoke, but on the other hand you are too scared to go to the toilet after dark."
Daddy awaited June outside of the toilet. (By then Mama and the rest of the family was there too.) Assuming it was only him and Daddy out there. June took advantage of the situation and explained the details on how the car window happened to get broken. We laughed. Daddy told June that the warm, furry, thing under his feet was Marble. our dog.

June asked: "What's everybody doing outside of the toilet this time of night? Y'all should be in the bed. I don't see nothing funny. Marble? Daddy are you sure it was her? Cause she didn't say anything."

T. J. answered that one: "yup. That was her June. She's a dog. What did you expect her to say? 'June git yo feet off my back?' Boy! I can't wait for school Monday, (laughing) Im-ma tell all of our partners about this."

June was angry: "Daddy tell Doll and T. J. not to go blabbing about this in school. They could ruin my image for life." He told Daddy that he would get a job working for Mr. Sears after school and use the money to pay to have the car window replaced. Daddy accepted June's offer and told him that he was going to the store the next morning before they went hunting and he wanted him to go along.

The next day, they were in the store and Daddy gave June some money: "Here's two bits, buy yourself a pack of cigarettes."

June was overjoyed: "For real Daddy? Is you fooling me? You

mean it for real? (smiling) I can buy me a pack of cigarettes? Wow! Wow! Wow!"

He bought a pack of cigarettes and put them in his shirt pocket. Nobody could've told him that he wasn't a man the way he walked out of the store bobbing his head and snapping his fingers. After having breakfast, it was a bit too late to go hunting. The sun was up and Daddy was accustomed to going hunting at the break of dawn. Therefore he suggested that the three of them leave their guns at home and take off for the woods. T. J. wanted to know:

"What we gon do without a gun?"

Daddy answered him: "Wait and be patient, you'll find out when the time is right."

They walked uphill along the creek's border to a site that wasn't familiar to them. The trees seemed taller and greener. The air was a sweet fragrance of fruit and flowers. It was simply gorgeous. Mother Earth had it going on. The warm sun shone through the trees and shrubs brighter than ever before due to the fact that they were on elevated land perhaps a mountain. They stumbled upon a glorious garden of blackberry bushes that was loaded with the biggest, plump, blackberries they had ever seen. They were mesmerized as they stood in the midst of that awesome place.

"Look at all of these sweet, juicy blackberries. How come we ain't never been here before? Daddy, can we come back here next week and bring our friends with us? We can take a whole heap of these blackberries home with us. Mama can make a blackberry cobbler for supper." June and T. J. excitedly spit out.

They pigged out on the blackberries and followed Daddy uphill until they came to another site on the hill's edge, where they stood and watched the flowing creek sixty feet below which had a frightening rhythmic tune of its own. It was a scary predicament being that high up and seeing all the rocky hill between them and the water. All three of them got dizzy and almost lost their equilibrium. The time they spent there was minimal. They traveled back through the blackberry garden and picked enough blackberries for Mama to make a cobbler. Tracing their way back to an area of the creek where they usually went fishing, put them at ease. Daddy relaxed on the rich green soft carpet-like grass, took a deep breath and laid back.

T. J. asked Daddy: "Hey Daddy do you want to try out my new nigger shooter? (Slingshot) I made this one yesterday."

"Daddy got up, took the nigger shooter, lit a cigarette and told June: "Hey June; its cigarette time. Light one up."

June didn't waste any time. He lit a cigarette and smoked it while watching Daddy try out T. J.'s nigger shooter. Ten minutes later Daddy told him it was time to smoke again. He fired up another cigarette and smoked it.

Glancing at T. J., he said; "Be patient and don't worry little brother. In a couple of years you will be in my shoes. (smiling) See I'm old enough to be Daddy's 'ace spoon coon.' I'll be going to town wit him on Saturdays and smoking. One day you will follow in my footsteps."

Daddy sat on the grass. June and T. J. followed suit. They were chilling out as June's curious mind prompted him to ask all kind of questions about the birds and the bees. June thought he was on cloud nine as he resumed to chill out and smoke in Daddy's presence and find out the answers to his intimate questions. He smoked six cigarettes in fifty minutes. Surprise, surprise, surprise. Smoking those six cigarettes within fifty minutes completely changed June's mind about smoking and left him in a total mess! He couldn't even stand up and walk straight. He said the smell of cigarettes on his hands and clothing were sickening. That was about the time when he began to vomit the blackberries that he pigged out on earlier. He panicked and darn near had a heart attack. Naturally, he assumed the worst:

"(Crying), I'm throwing up blood. I'm sick cause I smoked all of them dang stinking cigarettes. I got me a ree-eel bad headache. Help me! Please help me! I hate cigarettes! I ain't gon never smoke another cigarette."
He glanced over his shoulder at Daddy and commented: "That look like a smile on your face. Daddy, is you smiling? I'm throwing up blood and you ain't saying nothing. Daddy, why did you buy these cigarettes for me anyway? I'm too young to smoke. I'm mad at you. You got some TALL explaining to do. T. J., run and tell Mama that I'm ree-eel sick. (still crying) Help me! I'm up the paddle without a creek. I, I mean I'm up the creek without a battle. Ah, a paddle."

Daddy told June: "Have another cigarette. That's all you need."

That episode frightened T. J. to the point that he was trembling. His conscious was giving him heck. In his sock was a cigarette that he had stole from Daddy several days before that incident. He carried it around and showed it to his school mates in the classroom. He beat it to the creek as fast as his legs could carry him and squatted. His unsteady hands took the badly crumbled cigarette (most of the tobacco was left in his sock), out of his sock and threw it in the creek.

Then he mumbled: "Man, oh man! I'm so glad that wasn't me! Better June than me." He observed the empty cigarette paper as it floated on the water. A guilt feeling grabbed his conscious and would not let go. It was concerning something that occurred two days prior, in his classroom; he talked with his classmates: "I have a secret show and tell, but I ain't showing y'all nothin until old lady Hobb start writing the lesson on the blackboard." (Old lady Hobb was the teacher).

As soon as Old Lady Hobb turned her back to the class and picked up the chalk, T. J. 'The Comedian' took over. He was stationed at his desk which was conveniently located in the back of the room. He had the full attention of the entire class. He crossed his leg and took the cigarette and match out of his sock.

He put the cigarette in his mouth and took the match and pretended he was trying to strike it on the bottom of his shoe. Some of the students were whispering: "I dare you. I double dare you to strike that match and smoke that cigarette."
Thirteen of them had a nickel in their hands, whispering: "Here's a nickel saying you wont do it."

Old lady Hobb whirled around:
"What's this noise about? Why is my class facing the back of the room? The only one that's facing the front of the classroom and paying attention to me is T. J.." She walked to the back of the classroom, looked out the window and observed nothing unusual.

She talked calmly: "After recess I will have a questionnaire! There will be ten questions concerning the lesson I just wrote on the blackboard and explained. Anyone failing this test will remain after school for one hour for the remainder of this week. This is the third time this week I found you all facing the back of this classroom. I refuse to put up with it any longer." Oh!: "Thank you T. J.. I'm proud of you. Most of all, I appreciate your full attention. I know you will get 100% on the test, as you always do. The next time I see your parents in town, I will give them a good report on you. Friday, I will bring you a Baby Ruth for being a good attentive student. You are a well behaved boy."

T. J. was all smiles and extremely courteous: "Thank you Mrs. Hobb, Yes Mam., No Mam. You are a splendid teacher. You're the best teacher I ever had. Mrs. Hobb, may I stay after school and clean the blackboard for you?" His class mates wasn't upset with him for getting them in trouble. For some reason they loved him unconditionally and those thirteen students still gave him their nickels.

As he continued to think, he recalled a conversation he had with June previously:

"June, my partner Mile Simmons said that any boy who go home from school and read and do their homework, is a sissy. He said

83

that boys is supposed to go fishing, swimming, hunting, and courting after school. What do you have to say about that, June?"

June answered him: "That ain't nothing but a lot of nonsense! Ain't you heard about what your partner's daddy and mama did when he was a baby? Well im-ma tell you what happened rat now. One Friday morning they took Mile to his grandmother's house and told her to watch him while they went to the Piggly Wiggly to buy some milk. They was supposed to come rat back. They went to town and hopped the train going north. His grandmother haven't seen hide nor hair of them since then. She never went to school a day in her life. Now she's senile. Therefore, Mile Simmons doesn't have anyone to help him with his lessons at home. You better believe that if things were different he's do his lessons at home just like you do. I think your partner is a bit jealous because you git excellent grades. And another thing, stop fibbing by telling your classmates that you get 100 's and A's because you take lucky guesses on your tests. Hold your head up and don't be ashamed of something you're doing good. Little brother, I'm proud of you for making it your business to read and study your lessons every day without Daddy or Mama telling you to do it."

T. J. spoke to himself: "Gee! All of this thinking is giving me a headache! Its time for me to straighten up and fly right! I'll have to give my hard earned $.65 back to my classmates. I won't accept the Baby Ruth from Mrs. Hobb. I'll tell her that I don't deserve it, but I ain't telling her why." He anticipated on asking Daddy and Mama if Mile Simmons could spend the night at our home once a week so he could help him get ahead in his lessons. In return, Mile could do his chores. A fair trade.

Daddy interrupted T. J.' s thoughts by splashing the cool, crisp, creek water on June's face in hope of making him feel better. In the meanwhile, Daddy told them a story about how he was introduced to smoking and regretted it up until that particular time:

"When I was in the Army, most of the fellows were smokers. One

84

night I was in my bunk reading, and the fellow in the bunk nest to me asked if I had any matches; I nodded my head and he threw his cigarette to me and asked me to light it for him. I lit it and threw it back to him. Shortly after that, he threw two cigarettes my way and said 'light one for me and keep the other one for yourself. Man, git yo head out of that book. You read too much for me. Do something different. Smoke a cigarette.'

I put the cigarette in the book that I was reading. It was the tragic death of my best friend that started me to smoking. We knew each other from childhood, but we became good friends when we were put together in the Army. I broke down when I heard of his death and everybody was pushing cigarettes in my face. 'Here Curley smoke this cigarette. It'll calm you down.' I don't know if it settled my nerves or not. Within a year, I was smoking on the regular basis. That was one of the worst mistakes I ever made."

Daddy and T. J. walked by June's side on the way home and assisted him when he needed it.

Daddy asked: "Y'all understand why I didn't want to bring the guns now?"

When they arrived home, dinner was ready. Everyone but June sat down to eat. He was still gagging and puking. The smell of food made it worse. It took him the rest of the day to rejuvenate. The next day he was happy and rocking and rolling. He said the blessings and thanked God for the outcome of his pertinent smoking experience which turned out to be a well taught lesson that he wasn't likely to forget.

He also thanked Him for the four plates of food which he received while hiding out in the car. (Everyone gave me a strange look. I was very cool! I smiled and kept my lips zipped). June indulged in a big breakfast.

That afternoon, directly after church, June's girlfriend, Brenda Howard and her parents paid us a visit. Papa and Big Mama also joined us. We had a good wholesome country dinner, a pleasant interesting conversation and a delicious blackberry cobbler for dessert, which brought everybody back for a second and third helping. June barely ate, he was extremely quiet. Perhaps he was busy praying that Doll or T. J. wouldn't tell his girlfriend what happened to him that Friday. They didn't ruin his image.

When Curley Holmes Bought His 1952 Green Chevrolet:

Early that Saturday morning, while they were discussing their plans for that afternoon, Daddy and Mama consumed the lovely breakfast she prepared. (Coffee, fried ham, over easy egg, grits, hot buttered biscuits and fresh pears with cream, sugar and a pinch of nutmeg.) Daddy was a very affectionate and appreciative person:

"Aa hhh! Honey, the breakfast was magnificent. You are a good wife and I love you with a passion. I thank God every day for you. Marrying you was the best thing that ever happened to me. I wouldn't trade you for nothing in this world. Sit on my lap, baby, so we can finish talking about what we're going to do after I pick up our brand spanking new car. Have the kids ready and tell Mama and Papa to be ready also. By the way, starting Friday after I get off work, Im-ma start teaching you how to drive. Yeah! We'll go out every day until you learn."

Mama jumped for joy and said: "In a month I will be driving. Baby, you better believe I am a fast learner."

Daddy anticipated that he would be home no later than one p.m.. Papa and Big Mama would be home from town by then. They made plans to drive to Centerville, Mississippi and visit with Big Mama's' niece (Trudy Louella), for a minute or two. From there they would go to 'Le Blanc's Come Back' for dinner. Daddy's cousin recommended it and she raved about it. Le Blanc's Come Back's Restaurant had quite a reputation for having the best tasting sea food, soul food and Creole food in that part of Mississippi. His motto was 'Once you eat at my restaurant, you will come back.' The restaurant accommodated fifty people and it was equipped with a juke box that contained all the latest records. It was a place where you could go and enjoy a wonderfully prepared delicious meal that was just perfect for a king and participate in other activities such as shooting pool, playing cards, listen to live music and dance. Mama was due to have June, Doll, T. J., Richard, Charlie and me dressed in our Sunday clothes. Daddy picked out the outfit that he wanted Mama to wear, which was her charcoal grey tunic suit with her lace trimmed white blouse and her grey high hill shoes with the straps that wrapped around her ankles. He winked his eye at her and smiled as she walked him to the car. They kissed passionately before he drove off.

Six feet, two inches tall, with his Stetson hat positioned on the right side of his head matching his navy blue pin-stripped suit and Stacey Adams Shoes, He was a proud man. Curley Holmes was ready! He opened the door to his brand spanking new 1952 green Chevrolet. He stood there for a while shaking his head and taking it all in. He leaned over and put his head in the car, looking from the front to the back with a smile that wouldn't wait. He closed the door admiring the car as he took five steps backwards. Before getting in the car, he walked around it one more time, noticing every detail.

Finally he got in the car and as he sat there he recalled a conversation that he had with Mama on the day that he met her. Im-ma build you and our children a house from the ground and I'm-ma put you in a brand new car! Chills came over him while a joyous smile occupied his good looking face. He threw his hands up and thanked God. Then he shook his head with delight. He started the motor and slowly drove off the Chevrolet dealership lot. Driving down the main street, headed for the highway to take him home, he switched the radio station until he found a record playing by Fats Domino. He turned the volume up and jammed, moving his shoulders and bobbing his head in a quaint way. He pulled off the road into our drive way and waited for the record to finish playing before he retrieved the mail from our mail box.

Mr. Sears was driving down the road and spotted Daddy sitting in the car. Mr. Sears lost control of his car. He drove to the wrong side of the road and knocked our mail box down.

Anxiously he jumped out of his car and walked towards Daddy saying: "Curley don't you be mad at me now."

Daddy interrupted him: "Watch out Mr. Sears. Your car is still moving."

Mr. Sears rushed back to his car, opened the door and put his foot on the breaks while he was standing. Although in an awkward position he fought and finally shifted the gears into park.

Embarrassed, he slammed the door shut and hurried to Daddy with an apology: "Now Curley, I am sorry about that mail box. Let me tell you this. Hold your top and don't git mad. I'll have that mail box back in the upright position and fixed like new before the day is over. I stand on my word."

Daddy: "Mr. Sears, your face is blood red and you don't look well. Are you alright? You had me worried. Is something wrong with Mrs. Sears? Looks to me like your mind is a hundred miles away. Come on. Talk to me!"

Mr. Sears answered in a low dry voice: "Other than my ass hurting like the dickens and its black and blue, I'm fine and dandy. Don't ask me why it's like that, cause I can't rightly tell you. My wife told me the other day that she is planning on dying in the middle of next month. Oh, course I love that little woman. I admit, I boss her around and I'm pretty darn mean to her and I'll admit that I'm pretty dang jealous of her too. That's why I don't allow her to go anywhere without me. I know that if she go out by herself she'll meet a young man and leave me for him. I'm twenty-five years older than her. I cant give her no children. And I done kept the truth from her all these years. If she die, ah, ah, well, I just don't know. I aint got no choice but to um maybe I'll find somebody else and marry them. I'll do it rat after I leave the graveyard from burying her cause I ain't about to stay in that big house by myself. Its spooky! S-t-r-a-n-g-e thangs happen there at night. I need somebody to take care of me like my wife did before she got sick. Im-ma miss her a heap. I'll give my right hand to have my wife well again. I feel responsible cause she is in that shape. I'm sorry for the mean, nasty things I did to her. I would be a different man if I had the chance to do it all over again."

After a long silence and staring at each other, Mr. Sears began to talk again: "I might as well. Curley, let me tell you this. Two nights ago, I was sleeping fairly good and something awful powerful kicked me on the left side of my ass. And I mean it woke me up. I jumped out of that bed and turned the light on. I looked everywhere and didn't see a damn thang. My wife was sleeping like a baby with the covers over her head. I didn't bother to wake her. My mind kept telling me that she was the one that kicked me.

Curley I had to laugh about that one. Them dead legs of hers stopped working when she had that stroke. I know she wish she could lift her foot to my ass. Yeah. That will never happen! The next morning I had her inspect my sore ass and she said it was red, black and blue. She laughed at me when I told her how it got there. I suppose if I went to the doctor with this story he'd laugh at me too. I imagine he would tell me that I need to be put in the crazy house.

Curley let me ask you this. Now don't git me wrong, I ain't trying to git in your business or nothin like that. Who's brand new green Chevrolet is that? And why are you driving it?"

Daddy gave Mr. Sears his best smile before he spoke: "Its mine! Ain't she a beauty?"

That knocked Mr. Sears off balance and broke heart: "what? Its yo- yo- your yours? How can that be? Curley you know I don't believe that for a minute. You and yo father-n-law (Smiley) still have to pay for y'all's land. You got a wife and a house full of crumb-snatchers and from the looks of thangs they is still coming.

How you gon pay for all of that plus a brand spanking new 1952 green Chevrolet?" (Sears crossed his arms and made a comment to himself; 'you better make this a good story).

"Look-a-here Sears. You done went too damn far." Replied Daddy.

Sears broke in: "Now wait a minute Curley, I aint through talkin yet. You gon git your chance. What was wrong with that 1929 Chevrolet y'all had? That was a pretty good car. wasn't it? I am concerned about you like a father is concerned about his son. That's all. Curley, I thank you done bit off more than you can chew. It ain't no way possible on this earth you gon be able to pay for that there fine au-to-mo-bile."

Angered, Daddy threw his freshly lit cigarette on the ground and stomped it. His fists were formed as he bit his tongue and moved so close to Sears that their shoes were kissing. They were face to face as he put Mr. Sears in his place:

"Just a damn minute! Who in the hell do you think you're talking to? Shit! I don't have to answer to you for a dam thing. You can rest assured, I ain't yo boy, I am not looking for a father. I've been on my own since I was a boy. I was in the Army for ten years. I have traveled the world. I've worked hard to get where I am. Let me tell you this Sears! I can chew any damn thing I bite! What goes on in my house ain't none of your damn business. Respect me for being a man! Oh. Let me tell you this! This land was paid for before me and my father-n-law built our houses on it. Let me give you some advice Sears. Clean your house and stay the hell out of mine. How would you feel if I came to your house and asked all kind of questions about your personal business? We've been pretty good neighbors for each other. Both of us have had crisis and helped the other one out. We go hunting together sometimes. Sometimes you go hunting and bring us a rabbit and vice versa. But listen to me Sears and get this straight! You better hurry up and believe that I ain't gon kiss your ass. And I'm not about to take any shit off of you either."

90

Mr. Sears: "Curley you got yourself some kind of temper. I didn't know that. I guess I did open my mouth and put my foot in it. I didn't mean no harm. You bet we gon still be good neighbors to each others. Who else do we have? Well, I see yo wife and children are waitin for you. Look like everybody is all dressed up and what not. I see y'all is going somewhere. I aint never drove me a brand new Chevrolet before. Curley, do you mind if I take a spin in yo new car before y'all leave?"

Daddy: "I made plans for the family. I'm pretty sure they are ready to get started. They are sitting on the garret waiting patiently. Hey, we have been talking for fifteen or twenty minutes."

Mr. Sears opened the car door on the driver's side and sat in the car. Mama, June Doll and T. J. walked down the driveway to the car and raved.

Daddy pulled Mama to the side and they talked: "Git rid of Sears so we can go. Mama and Daddy been ready since they got home from town this morning and the children has been ready since this morning. They are excited and ready to go."

Daddy shook his head and bit his bottom lip as he told Mama: "Yeah! That old bastard had the nerve to ask me if he could take a spin in the car before we leave."

Mama didn't give him a chance to finish talking: "No! No! No! Hell no! That cracker ain't riding in that car before me! What kind of problem do he have? He done ran over our mailbox and made it as flat as a pancake. Now he want to drive our brand new car. What is next? Curley, you know as well as I do, that man is jealous cause we got that car. I wouldn't be surprised if he drove it in the creek."

Daddy agreed: "Yeah! I know he is. Its obvious in his face and his unsteady fake voice. 'Curley, let me tell you this. I'm happy for you, but I just don't thank you can handle the car note.' (laughing) It's not my fault that he can't handle it because we're

91

shitin in high cotton. He made me so mad that I had to curse. I don't like the way he think in the least. Its alright, fine and dandy for us to go to work everyday, but its not alright fine and dandy for us to buy a new car. He cannot put me under his foot.

Honey, you know although Sears disrespected and upset me today I'm feeling a sense of sadness for him. Gladys Sears thinks his wife is dying in the middle of next month. I don't know where he got a far-fetched cock-a-mine idea like that from."

Mama questioned him: "Huh? Why would he think a fool thing like that?"
Daddy assumed: "Remember when you told me that she gave him notice that she was leaving him next month; That dummy thought she was telling him that she was dying. He's really torn up about it. Tell Mrs. Sears not to kick that big man any more. She got away with it the other day. Its time for her to leave well enough alone. Next time he might not be sleep. I hate to think what he would do to her if he found out. Has she made up her mind about how many horses she's leaving behind? Perhaps we can buy the ones that she leave."

Mama responded: "Yes. She changed her mind again. Says she's taking all nine of them, because she feel like they are her children. I doubt if she will kick Sears again. She was shaking like a leaf on a tree when she told me and Mama about it. She told us that he had a strange outrageous behavior. He took his gun and walked around the house cursing just waiting for something to move so he could shoot it. Then, he sat in the chair that's in their bedroom talking to himself. He peed in the middle of the floor three times. He carried on for the rest of the night terribly. That grown man had every light in the house on. He was too scared to go back to sleep. That frightened her. She didn't sleep a wink either. She was too scared to take the covers from over her head and look at him. Finally it happened. The wind blew the curtain and Sears shot the curtain and the window broke. He sat there for an hour before taking a step to see if anything was outside the window."

Daddy said: "The time is not standing still, I'm ready to get on the road. What? What in the hell is Sears doing with his big ass head under the hood? Does he think that by having half of a wee-wee and two crushed balls give him the right to poke around the car like that? Dammit. What is he looking for? Hey Richard, bring me a rock. Im-ma throw it and hit Sears in his big ass. That bastard! I hate his damn ways."

Mama said: "Settle down Curley! Don't allow yourself to get angry again. The day is going to end the same way it started, absolutely beautiful and nothing less. Give me that rock. What if you miss Sears's big ass and hit the car? We will not let Sears spoil it for us. I'm going to get Mama and Daddy so we can get started."

All of us were approaching the car when Mr. Sears blurted out: "Hey. Can we please swap cars long enough to drive to my house and back? That's about four minutes."

Papa and Daddy's eyes found each other. Daddy said: "No." But Papa said: "Yes. Why not? If all it takes is four minutes to git him out of our hair, lets do it! It ain't gon hurt nothin."
Daddy told Papa that if he felt that strong about Sears driving our car before Mama drove it, he would go along with it. But he wasn't happy about it in the least.

"Me and my children will be right there in the back seat while Sears chauffeur us to his house and back here. I don't want to drive his old funky beat up car." Daddy, June, Doll, T. J., Richard, Charlie and I were in the back seat. Richard sat in Daddy's lap, Charlie sat in June's lap and I sat in Doll's lap.

Mr. Sears questioned: "Let me ask y'all this. What is all y'all packed in the back seat for? I know Im-ma big man and all, but two or three of y'all ken set in the front wit me."

Agitated, Daddy answered him:

93

"Sears, let's go. Chauffeur us to your house and back."

Sears responded: "Chauffeur y'all? By George; Curley you done got me on that one. This is what we gon do. Cruise up to my house, pull in the driveway and drive all the way to the back yard and toot the horn. If my old cripple ass wife is up and in the wheel chair, the housekeeper can push her to the window. I bet you anything that when she see me behind this wheel she is gon shit all over herself. Ha. Ha. Ha. I like this green Chevrolet. Come Monday morning, I'm going to town and buy me a green Chevrolet just like this one. Yeah. This is a pretty car and I gotta have me one."

Sears drove fifteen miles all the way. When he drove to his back yard and tooted the horn he was in for an earth shaking, rude awakening, that left him quite speechless. This is what happened. After tooting the horn, he directed his full attention to the window where he thought his wife would pull the curtain back and peep out the window as usual. He heard his wife laughing and talking to Sugar (Sugar was one of her horses). Straight ahead of him slightly to his right he saw his wife climb on Sugar and Sugar took off running. Mr. Sears mouth flew open and the cigarette that he was smoking simply stuck to his upper lip. In slow motion, with his mouth still open, he turned and caught Daddy's eyes. It was as if he had saw a ghost. He was frozen. Daddy removed the cigarette from Sears's mouth and tossed it out the window. Tears began to roll down Sears face and saliva coated his well groomed salt and pepper beard .

June was curious: "Why is Mr. Sears crying and spitting? He's acting like a mad dog. Ain't he Daddy?"

Puzzled, Daddy answered: "I think it's a possibility that he's in shock. I saw situations like this in the Army. June, help me get him out of the car and lay him on the ground. He's too heavy to carry in the house. T. J., blow the horn until Mrs. Sears come. This man need a doctor. Doll, go tell Papa to go to town and tell Dr. Webster that Mr. Sears is sick and need him right away."

Mrs. Sears came as soon as she heard the horn blowing consistently and went directly to her husband's side. The four of them managed to get Mr. Sears in the house and in the bed. Mrs. Sears washed his sweaty face with cool water. She talked to him trying to bring him out of that state of stillness. She wanted Daddy, June and T. J. to wait there with her until Dr. Webster arrived. Richard, Charlie, and I played in their back yard while awaiting them.

In the meanwhile, Mrs. Sears fell on her knees and commenced to weep with guilt. She then confessed to her husband that she had been walking for over a year. She was devastated for manipulating him to believe the opposite. The reason why she did it was because he brought her stroke on by beating and kicking her to a pulp. Simply because she asked her sister if they could raise one of her children. She wanted to punish him forever for what he did. But after seeing him lying in bed motionless with an uncontrollable deformed face. Her compassion for him moved her which allowed her to let go and forgive him at that very moment. Tears filled her eyes as she suddenly realized that she still loved him. Her trembling voice screamed his name demanding that he look at her! She massaged his face vigorously and had no results. She jumped in the bed and sat on his triple basketball stomach.

She had an idea; "Let me tell you this Sears. I was the one that kicked you in the ass a few nights ago. That was a well deserved ass kicking you had coming for a long time! What are you going to do about it? Are you planning on laying there with your ugly face turned to the side from now on? Let me tell you this Sears. I ain't hardly taking care of no big ass funky man."

After slowly turning his head until her face was in view, Mr. Sears's pitiful red face struggled with a tremendous amount of determination to form a haphazard smile. Excitedly, she blurted out; "It's been years since I saw a smile cross your face. I have to admit it is most beautiful on you."

Dr. Webster arrived, examined Mr. Sears and his diagnoses

were that Mr. Sears had a slight stroke which was due to a lack of rest, sleep and too much excitement. (JEALOUSLY)

The ten of us were finally on our way to Centerville, Mississippi. While driving, Daddy shared his gratitude: "Oooh! I am thankful, happy, blessed and besides myself to have a loving healthy wife, children and In-laws! And I equally appreciate our new car! You know, I feel like I could jump up and clap my feet!

Papa made a comment: "Sears is a darn good neighbor. I remember when the brakes in my truck gave out as I was driving down the driveway and I ran into Sears's truck. I was banged up pretty good, hit my head on the windshield and that brought blood. Sears's window got broken and the glass cut his arm. But he was more concerned about me.
And when Bessie (the cow) got bogged down in the mud after that heavy rainfall, Sears was rat there wit us, helping pull her out. And rat after that, he helped us deliver Bessie's calf. Ooh, that was a mighty long day.
When Sears had his problems and Lord knows he had a plenty of them. We were rat there for him too. But what Sears fail to realize, is a hard working man ought to be able to have the desires of his heart without answering to anybody. It ain't no way they gon be the top dog all the time. Things are changing fast! And they will continue to change for the best!"

Our visit with Trudy was short. She was in the process of writing a letter to a male friend of hers. It seemed as though she couldn't tear herself away from it long enough to visit with us. We left shortly after we arrived. Big Mama said 'you could see the jealously and envy in her eyes.' Anyhow, I was very pleased to leave. I didn't want to be in her house or her company ever again. She was rude and mean to me the last time we visited her.

I had fallen asleep in the car in route to her house. I don't know who carried me in her house and put me in her bed. The rest of the family were in her yard chilling out and kicking it. Trudy woke me up and told me to:

"Git yo bo-legged ass out of my bed and go outdoors and play with them meddling brothers of yours. Night time is for sleeping, not day time."

I sat on the edge of her high bed looking down, afraid to attempt the long journey to the floor. Perhaps Couldnt Trudy saw the fear in my eyes, because she gave me a helping hand by snatching me off the bed and letting go. I fell on my right knee and stayed there crying. My upper lip was saturated with tears and snot. She told me to wipe my face. I used the back of my hands wiping the tears and snot onto my face and hair and that angered Trudy. She in return took off her faded, dirty, funky, greasy, apron and wiped my face. She got a bit of snot on her hand and went berserk. After hitting me in my head and pulling my hair, she talked baby talk: "

Did I hurt the baby?"

I shook my head indicating yes.

She stomped her feet and said:

"Look at me, big eyed heffer! You know good 'n' well that I didn't hurt you. You bet not tell nobody that I did either.

" She pinched me saying: "You bet not let out a holler. I don't like pissy crumb-snatchers in my bed. As a matter of fact, I don't like crumb-snatchers. I hate it when y'all come here. Y'all oughta keep y'all asses at home. Y'all ain't doing me no favor by visiting me. Don't be giving me that 'damit to hell look gal!' Git up and go outside before I chunk my shoe at you. Another thang I bet not catch you wit them lil hands on my hydrant again. Every time y'all come here, y'all run to my hydrant and turn the water on like y'all ain't got no learnin a tall. Yo pappy and mammy need to teach y'all country nigger's not to touch my stuff."

(And to reinforce that she meant business, she bent my fingers back, made an ugly face at me, and poked her tongue at me.) I called her an old crack-pot. Simply because behind her back that's

97

what everyone referred to her as. I stomped my feet and told her that I wasn't coming to her house any more.

She yelled at me asking:

"Gal you done heard somebody call me a crack-pot. Who? Who been calling me that? I want to know rat now."

I suddenly realized that I had repeated something that I shouldn't have, that's why I ran. She followed me to her back yard and faked it.

"I'm so glad that Y'all came to see me today. It make me feel sad when y'all leave. It gets pretty lonely at times. Why don't y'all let me keep Bet Joe for a week or two. We'll sho-nough have us a good time. I love that lil gal. Out of all them chillins y'all got she's my favorite."

Daddy spoke: "We don't leave our children nowhere! You know that Trudy."

While she was busy lying, I took advantage of that time to disobey her. I went to her hydrant and turned the water on. I washed away the stink on my face from her funky apron. After that I'd hold my feet under the running water momentarily and turn it off, glance at Trudy and turn the water back on. After repeating it several times I fled to safety. I stood between Daddy and Mama and held their hands.

Trudy stood on the front porch waved and complimented Daddy and Mama on the car as we were leaving. I looked back at her as we approached the car. Her piercing eyes were definitely on me. Her appearance was shabby and tacky. She had two big safety pins in her ragged blue and red stripe dress replacing the missing buttons. It also revealed the considerable amount of weight she had gained. Her faded printed scarf was loosely wrapped around her head as though it was going to fall any minute. Her dirty ashy feet were bare and in need of attention. Her teeth were brown perhaps from drinking black coffee. Her eyes were red and a bit puffy with a sense of sadness. Deep wrinkles occupied her face. Everyone except me waved to her as Daddy drove off.

Daddy parked in front of Le Blanc's Restaurant. We were famished. Daddy ordered for everyone, and his choice was superb. T-bone steak simmered in tomato gravy with onions, Cajon style fried perch, rice, sweet peas, cheese and macaroni, root beer soda and lemon pound cake for dessert. The owner of the restaurant introduced himself as we ate and asked if everything was alright?

Daddy smiled and told him: "So far so good." And he let the owner know that when the opportune time arose again we would come back. Mr. Jean Le Blanc asked Daddy if someone had told him about his restaurant.

Daddy answered him: "I'm kin to Sadee Francis in New Orleans. She wrote my wife and me a letter and highly recommended this place. She said it was a place to get a good home cooked meal away from home."

Mr. Jean Le Blanc shook Daddy's hand again saying: "Sadee Frances is my first cousin."

After sharing past memorable experiences as children and mentioning names of people which both of them were connected to happened to spark something in their minds that made them recollect that they were playmates as children.

Their mothers were sisters. They lost contact with each other after the death of Daddy's mother, due to the fact that the Le Blanc's moved to Baton Rouge, Louisiana. They were long lost first cousins.

Papa asked Le Blanc: "By any chance, would you be related to Le Blanc the fish peddler? He come by our house every Thursday from Baton Rouge peddling fish. A nice man. He always makes it his business to bring each one of the children a package of Stage

Planks."

Jean Le Blanc's loud joyous laughter filled the entire room collecting everyone's attention. Jean Le Blanc sat to the table and stopped laughing long enough to say:

"Ah! I don't believe this! The fish peddler's first name is Sylvain and yes I am related to him. He's my father. Believe this. He was talking about y'all Thursday night. He refers to y'all as his number one customers. He's very fond of these children. Un, un, un wait til I tell him this. He will be surprised tremendously. My father is a widower. Mama died nearly four years ago."

Jean Le Blanc told Daddy that his money was no good in his restaurant. (Hey now. My relatives don't pay to eat here).

Jean Le Blanc then invited my parents and grandparents to a function happening later on saying: "After dinner the Mc Gee brothers is going to get on that stage and sing. Its eleven of them. The youngest one is fifteen and the oldest one is twenty-nine. Them boys can sing. Ain't no doubt about it. They come here and sing every Friday and Saturday night. I want y'all to stay and have some fun. The children can stay with my daughter. She's nineteen years old. I know she will be glad to have them over."

The Mc Gee brothers were cool, smooth, sharp and their singing was melodious. Papa, Big Mama, Daddy and Mama had a wonderful time. They danced on practically every song.

Papa said: "I didn't know a darn thing about dancing. Mary Ellen kept at me to git up and dance wit her. I did it and had so much fun. The floor was full of people dancing. They were bumping against each other and I don't think anybody noticed that I couldn't dance. Even though I gave it a try. I stood there and popped my fingers and pat my feet on the floor and moved my hips to the music. Um, um, um,"
Before the evening was over the whole joint knew that Daddy and Le Blanc were first cousins. Both of them were the inheritor of

their mother's gift to talk. From that day on my parents went to Le Blanc's at least once a month and enjoyed themselves immeasurably.

Sylvain Le Blanc continued to come to our home on his weekly schedule. Each time he made his stay a bit longer and eventually we became his only Thursday customers and like his son he refused to accept pay. On occasions he'd come by and everyone would be in the field working. Being the kind person that he was he'd let himself in the house, fry the fish and have dinner ready when everyone returned from the field. Big Mama and Mama said it was always a pleasure for him to give them a break from the kitchen.

One day Widow Harris, a friend and neighbor whom lived down the road was sitting on our front porch when Sylvain Le Blanc drove up, unloaded his truck and headed for our front door only to be interrupted by Widow Harris threatening to hit him over the head with her umbrella if he took another step towards our door.

"Just a blame minute. Who are you? And just where do you think you are going? This is my neighbor's house and I will not permit you to enter it. Step back or I will break this umbrella over your head!"

That angered Sylvain Le Blanc: "Pardon me? Mam, my name is Sylvain Le Blanc! The people that live here are my relatives. I have been coming here every Thursday for over three years. Now get out of my way before I drop this heavy box on your feet. Throw that rusty umbrella away before you hurt somebody. You crazy ass woman! Move woman! Just get out of my face."

Widow Harris stepped back and put her left hand on her hip and pointed at him as she started in: "Oh! Excuse me! Mr. Sylvain what ever your last name is! You don't have to bite my head off."

Sylvain made his way to the kitchen rapidly, lit the stove and commenced to run around preparing dinner. Forty-five minutes later he noticed that Widow Harris was still there and she was peeping through the kitchen window. Every time he would turn around she would duck her head. Preparing dinner gave Sylvain the opportunity to cool off.

So he broke the ice: "What are you standing out there in the hot sun eying me for? You ain't got nothing better to do?"

She talked: "About four years ago a man came by my house selling fish. Would you be that same man? I live two miles down the road on the right hand side."

"Maybe it was me, or maybe it wasn't me. I don't rightly know." Was his answer.
He was a tease: "UM, um, um. This ice cold orange soft drink is delicious. Its so cold that its giving me a brain freeze. This fish is tasty too, and that cornbread smell so good I can't wait to take it out of the oven."

Widow Harris made a comment: "You get around the kitchen like you know exactly what you are doing. My husband depended on me for everything he ate. He was a good man but he couldn't fry an egg. Who taught you how to cook? Are you a married man?"

Sylvain: "My wife died about four years ago. Anyhow that's when I became a fish peddler. I had to do something to keep my mind occupied. I miss her dearly. I detest being in my house alone especially at night. Everything in that house reminds me of her."

Widow Harris: "I sympathize with you passionately. For I am experiencing the same thing. My husband left me twenty-eight months ago without a warning what-so-ever. I didn't take it very well either. He went to sleep one night and never woke up. Sometimes I get so agitated with him for leaving me. At other times I am so lonely that I can't stand it. We made plans to go north and visit relatives after we retired. We were both teachers.

We have a daughter and she live in Stone Mountain, Georgia. She want me to sell my property and move there with her and my son-n-law and my grandchildren. I am seriously contemplating on doing it. Its better than the life I'm living now."

Sylvain asked her: " Have you ever been to Baton Rouge?"

She answered him: "Yes. When I was younger. It was a most beautiful gorgeous place."

"Its even more beautiful now." Uttered Sylvain. "I love Baton Rouge. I don't think I will ever move away. It would be a pleasure to take you on a tour of my home town, Baton Rouge, Louisiana."

That excited Widow Harris: "Yes! Indeed! Of course! I would love to accompany you on a tour of Baton Rouge! When can you pick me up? Any day is fine with me. Oh look they're coming from the field. I would consider it an honor to help you set the table."

Widow Harris helped set the table and as she did she took a pinch of everything and it tasted good. She was invited to stay for dinner and make herself at home and that's what she did. She said the blessings. She was the first one to sit down to the table and the last one to get up. She enjoyed herself tremendously. The white bonnet which she was wearing when Sylvain first saw her was folded neatly and tucked away in her pocket. Her long salt and pepper hair was in two braids. Her complexion was extremely smooth. Sylvain thought she was an attractive woman and for the first time since his wife's death he was mesmerized. The joy in his eyes and his boyish body language was so obvious that it was impossible for everyone at the table to focus on dinner. He was the center of attraction. He tried to act natural but it was a hard task to master. He dropped his fork several times. He choked on his soft drink.

In the meanwhile. Widow Harris was sitting next to Mama pinching her thigh and whispering: "Oh Gladys. I like that fine looking man. It was meant for us to meet today! He's taking me on a tour of Baton Rouge. Gladys you know the styles of clothes. I want you to cut out a stylish dress for me. I can sew it together. I want to look nice on my date."

Sylvain Le Blanc and Widow Harris were married three weeks later. She moved to his home in Baton Rouge. She held onto her property in the event her daughter might want to move back some day. Sylvain and his bride continued to come to our home every Thursday. We remained their only Thursday customers. Big Mama and Mama became spoiled and accustomed to those Thursdays. The Le Blanc's and our family brought much joy, love and happiness to one another.

Mama's Driving Experience:

After dinner one evening, Daddy took a knife, a fork and a spoon, then told mama to sit down at the table and relax because she was about to embark on her first driving lesson. By the process of simulation, the knife was the gear shift, the fork was the gas pedal and the spoon was the brakes, he went over his demonstration.

That put Mama in a funk and she pushed the silverware to the side and said:
"Curley I know you mean well. But this knife, fork and spoon business ain't teaching me a darn thing. You told me last night that you would start teaching me how to drive the car today. I had my hopes and dreams up high thinking that's what you would do. Either you teach me how to drive while I'm in the car or forget the whole darn thing. And by the way, where is the stern wheel, the horn and the ignition for the key?"

For one month he took Mama out driving and she did well. She gained confidence in herself as a driver. She'd drive him to and from work a couple days a week. One day after she took Daddy to work, she decided to visit Aunt Lottie (Daddy's sister) and her children whom lived in town. She took Richard, Charlie and me with her. Richard and Charlie sat in the back seat and I sat in the front seat with Mama.

I was a little country girl kneeling on my knees and leaning on the car door with my head hanging out of the window as Mama drove down the street on our way home from Aunt Lottie's house. The radio was playing. Mama was driving at a moderate speed as she made a left turn onto the street that would lead us to the highway that took us home. As she made the left turn half-way across the intersection the door that I was leaning on opened. My feet touched the pavement and I immediately pulled them up. I hugged that swinging door while I hung from it with all my might. Mama slowly moved to the curb and got out of the car and ran straight to me and so did the man that was in the car in front of us. (A concerned white man).

He grabbed me and said: "Don't cry. You're alright. Everything is alright."

Mama told me to turn the door loose several times. But I couldn't because my hands were locked to it.

Richard and Charlie were in the back seat shouting: "Turn the door loose Bet Joe!"

Finally I released the door. My strong powerful hold on the door resulted in my fingernails bending backwards and breaking causing my fingers to bleed. With loving care Mama hugged and kissed me and put me in the car. She then stood by the car and took several deep breaths to calm herself and regain her composure.
She thanked God for being there and protecting us. She sat in the car and talked before driving off again: "They say you learn something everyday. That is a true statement! I learned a valuable lesson today. From this day on the passengers, 'that's y'all or anybody else that's not driving will be seated while the car is moving. Do I make myself clear?"

105

I was some kind of scared. I asked Mama if I could ride in the back seat? She replied; "No! That's not a good ideal because you could develop a phobia. I can see the fear in your eyes, but it will pass! Do the thing you fear and death of fear is certain. It's like this. If you start riding in the back seat because of what just happened you will feel safe. Your fear of riding in the front seat will grow to the point that you may never want to drive a car."

I didn't understand what Mama was saying. She told me that as I grew older I would understand. She asked us not to mention that incident to anyone especially Daddy.

She stopped at the store before getting on the highway to our home and bought some vanilla ice cream for us. As she gave it to us she said: "Every time we go somewhere we'll stop here and buy ice cream before going home."

The next day the three of us went with her to the ice house to get ice for the ice box. Even though I was frightened and nervous I had to sit in the front seat if I wanted to go. I wasn't tall enough to see anything significant, but I knew the car was moving by the different trees which I saw passing by. I acquired the ultimate respect as far as riding in a car was concerned. Kneeling on my knees leaning on the door with my head hanging out of the window was history. My fear diminished completely. Richard, Charlie and I were enthusiastic about having ice cream with Mama every time we went some where with her. It was always a delicious treat. But one day Richard and Charlie messed up our good thing.

We were going home from the Piggly Wiggly and as we approached the ice cream store, Mama said: "Its too cold to eat ice cream today. Y'all been coughing since we left home. We need some hot pot liquor."

So Richard said: "I ain't coughing too much to tell Daddy that Bet Joe fell out of the car when you were driving home from Aunt Lottie's house that day."

Charlie said: "Yeah Mama! Remember that day when you dropped Bet Joe out of the car? We gon tell Daddy if you don't buy us no ice cream."

Mama drove into the parking lot of the ice cream store and turned the motor off. She was furious as she turned around in her seat to face Richard and Charlie. They were looking at each other smiling because they thought they were going to get ice cream. Mama cleared her throat to get their attention. Immediately their smiles vanished as they swiftly moved out of her reach to the floor behind my seat.

After Mama commanded them to get back on the seat she gave them a look that could kill before she spoke: "Im-ma teach y'all a word! 'blackmail' and y'all bet not ever forget the meaning of the word 'blackmail.' This car ain't moving until y'all learn how to spell it and know what it mean."

After they learned the meaning and spelling of 'blackmail,'
Mama continued: "I am your mother. And if y'all ever under any circumstances think of blackmailing me again you better believe that I will whoop the shit out of y'all. Guess what? If y'all get any more store bought ice cream some body else will buy it. I thought it was a nice gesture to treat me and y'all to some store bought ice cream when ever we were out. Apparently, y'all thought I was buying the ice cream so you wouldn't tell your Daddy. Guess what? I told your Daddy that same day. I'm so mad. I should make y'all get out of the car and walk home."

Richard and Charlie put on some kind of show: Richard (Fake coughing profusely) "I don't wont no ice cream. I wont me some hot pot liquor. I'm sick."

Charlie seconded the emotion: "Me too."

Crying he added: "Mama we don't know how to git home. It's a lot of snakes out there and they gon bite us. I don't wont no ice cream. I wanna ride home in the car."

107

Richard started in again: "Mama I don't wanna walk home. Them ghost in the graveyard will get me and Charlie if we walk pass there. I know they will." He waived his right index finger in the air as he confirmed: "We ain't gon blackmail you no mo Mama! Cause you will beat the shit out of us if we do!"

I glanced at Mama and she was holding her hand close to her mouth her lips were turned inward. She was trying to camouflage her laughter because she found Richard and Charlie to be amusing.

Work: Work: Work:

Rising at 4:30 A. M. Mama was in the kitchen firing up the stove preparing to make breakfast. Each day she'd prepare something different from her breakfast menu. Biscuits, flapjacks, grits, rice, or fried potatoes with onions directly from our garden. And from our livestock bacon, ham, sausage and a variety of jellies and jams from our fruit trees. There was home made syrup and molasses from the sugar cane in the field. Depending on the season, after Daddy was off to work, Mama served us breakfast, made our lunches and got us ready for school. Her day was just beginning. Before she joined Papa and Big Mama in the field to hoe the vegetables, she would wash the dishes, skim the milk and clean the house. During the summer season they had the help of June, Doll and T. J..
Usually Big Mama and Mama worked from 7 to 11 A.M.. Then they would make dinner at Big Mama's house. Their only entertainment was the radio which they kept with them while preparing dinner, regardless if they were in the kitchen cooking the meal or on the front porch preparing the vegetables to cook. Being entertained with the stories of Helen Trent and Young Doctor Malone on the radio from Monday through Friday was a contentment they cherished. And on Saturdays, if they didn't go to town they'd listen to Gunsmoke.

Daddy, June and T. J. took turns drawing water from the well. Daddy cut firewood. June and T. J. took it in the house and stacked it by the stove, the heaters and the fireplace. The cows were milked twice a day. In the morning June, Doll and T. J. did it. On occasions, in the afternoon after returning home from work, Daddy helped June and T. J. with the milking, feeding the livestock, the chickens and cutting the grass.

Daddy was an expert at taking the chickens from the coop and wringing their necks so Mama could pluck their feathers, clean them, cut them up and fry them for supper. On Saturday or Sunday mornings before daylight they would go rabbit hunting, catch a rabbit, bring it home, skin it, clean it and cut it up so all Mama had to do was cook it. The three of them went fishing at the creek.

Sometimes Daddy would cook. He was an excellent cook. T. J. was the candy boy. He was always in the kitchen wearing his white apron making peanut brittle. Everybody loved it.

Mama washed the linen and clothes by using the washboard. If we didn't have Argo starch, Big Mama would use the starchy water from cooked rice to starch our clothes directly after Mama washed them. (shirts, blouses, dresses dungarees and can-can slips) As soon as the sheets were dry, they'd take turns ironing them, alternating two irons on the red hot coals in the fireplace. It was my grandparents and parents tradition to always bring the new year in with everything in the house clean, the bed linen, towels, clothes and curtains, etc.

Big Mama churned butter once a week. She had a mean knack for making dill pickles and bread and butter pickles. The crisp crunchiness made them superb.

The Cotton picking Season:

Picking cotton was something the entire family took part in. I can remember being in the cotton field with my family doing what little I could do. According to Papa, every little bit counted. The cotton buds were like rose bushes. Everybody showed me how to hold the cotton bud in one hand and pick the cotton with the other hand without pricking my hand. I was very clumsy. I kept pricking both hands until I couldn't stand it any longer. Anyhow, in about a week, all of the cotton was picked and off to the cotton mill.

The Slaughtering Day In February: (Our own special Holiday)

February was the designated month for slaughtering. It was a two day vacation from work and school. It was an all day event. Some of our neighbors attended and gave a helping hand. By living in the country, this was our way of life. My grandparents and parents would choose a hog and put him in a fenced cage with a wooden floor and put him on a corn diet for six months to rid his system of impurities and fatten him up. After the six months, he was ready for slaughtering. There was a humongous tree that was located on the side of the well, that's where the slaughtering took place every year.

Papa was always the one who killed the hog by hitting him in the head with a sledge hammer. Then he would cut the hog from his nuts to his neck with his butchering knife. The grown-ups along with the children who were big enough to help, were waiting to fill their containers with the hog's organs. June was always the first one in line awaiting the nuts. He liked them so much. He said he could eat them everyday. Getting everything organized, chit-chatting and gossiping was a must among those busy events. To assure harmony, those men and women worked together for two days until everything was complete. The hams, ham hocks, link sausages and slabs of bacon were seasoned and in the smoke house, smoking. The patty sausage, pork chops, ribs, ground pork, salt pork, and the pig feet, was packed in ice in the ice box. The chitterlings, the crackling bread and the remaining edible organs were cooked and shared among everyone that was involved. Papa and Daddy were the hog head cheese makers.

110

Daddy Went to Buffalo, New York: July 1956

In July 1956, my beautiful Aunt Miracle, whom was married to Daddy's brother Shayne, drove to Gloster, Mississippi from Buffalo, New York, on her vacation to visit her mother as well as us. While visiting with us her conversation was directed to us moving to Buffalo.

"You all need to move to Buffalo! Gladys, aren't you tired of living this country life? Curley, you, Gladys and the children should be tired of working in the field and wiping your asses with that hard paper from the Sears and Roebuck Catalogue. I guarantee you all will love Buffalo and you will not regret moving the children there. Things are modern in Buffalo, appliances, water, a telephone and a television at your fingertips in the house. Curley, I can see you sitting in front of the television watching the ball game. The schools are so close to the houses that the children can walk there in a matter of minutes. Colored and white children attend the same schools. Colored and white teachers are teaching in the same schools. I am not saying there is no prejudice people there. You will find that everywhere you go."

Daddy and Mama walked to the back yard while making a decision. He entered the out house and tore some pages from the Sears and Roebuck Catalogue.

He ripped the pages and threw them on the ground saying: "Lets do it!" We'll move north and try our level best to make a living for us and our children. If we don't make it we can always move back here. After all we still have all of this land. Honey don't worry. Papa and Mama are moving with us."

As they sped down the highway in the direction of Buffalo, NY, in her strong confident voice Aunt Miracle said: "I am astonished and overjoyed that you all made this decision. Like I told you, if you don't find a job in eight days I will pay your way back to Gloster on the train."

111

The rest of the family stayed in Gloster, Mississippi. We prayed and stuck together while doing our chores. The thought of Daddy getting a job and sending for us to move to Buffalo, NY was exciting. It was definitely the talk of the town!

Arriving in Buffalo one hour before Uncle Shayne was due for work, Daddy freshened up, had a cup of coffee and drove Uncle Shayne to his job site. (Uncle Shayne didn't drive) He directed Daddy to personnel. Daddy filled out an application and was hired on the spot. He began to work the same day. Uncle Shayne was happy to have his brother work alongside him at Buffalo Steel. They had a lot of catching up to do and that was the perfect place to do it. They were like twins, you didn't see one without the other.

Three months later Daddy came to visit us for one week. A month after that he sent for Mama to come to Buffalo. Five days after Mama arrived in Buffalo, she took the bus to Children's Hospital, filled out an application and was hired as a Milk Lab Technician. Because they missed us terribly, Mama wanted to help Daddy make money so they could save even more and get us there as quickly as possible.

In the meanwhile Papa and Big Mama cared for Doll, T. J., Richard, Charlie, Earl, Emerson and me. June enlisted in the Army. Daddy and Mama were loving parents. They made sure that we had a wonderful abundant Christmas even though they wasn't there. They sent boxes with a variety of toys, clothing, Christmas candy, etc. for the entire family. T. J. took Richard, Charlie and me to the woods with him to pick out a Christmas tree and cut it down. The horse carried the tree home on its back. We gathered our Christmas lights and other decorations from the previous years and together we made the tree beautiful. T. J. did the fireworks on Christmas Eve. He wanted to show Papa and Big Mama that he was responsible. He did well and we enjoyed it. That was our last Christmas in Gloster, Mississippi.

Doll worked diligently helping care for us. She religiously gave

Richard, Charlie, Earl and Emerson hair cuts every other Saturday. She wanted them to look nice for church. She'd put the milk and bread bowl on their head and cut everything that wasn't under the bowl.

She was a majorette in high school and she stayed up late at night until she completed her majorette costume. She also made a costume for the school play which she participated in. Big Mama said she was quite a seamstress at her young age. Doll also worked for Mrs. Sears two days a week. She always took me with her.
T. J. surprised everyone by assuming his responsibilities and working like a man. He'd get up early every Saturday morning before the break of dawn and go rabbit hunting. Often times he let Richard and Charlie tag along with him when he went fishing. It was like a picnic for Richard and Charlie. They sat on the grass and ate whatever T. J. had in the bag for them, ham, biscuits, cheese, persimmons, plums, apples, maypops, etc..

Doll and T. J. began to have disagreements in reference to driving the car. And it escalated everyday. T. J. had no consideration for Doll. He never inquired if she needed the car or if she had any objections to him driving to town every afternoon seven days a week. He'd get out of school and do his chores, then leave for town. He would be back home within two hours and Doll would be agitated.

After he returned home one day she told him: "Give me the car keys. Everyday you take off without telling me anything. I don't think it's necessary for you to drive to town everyday. From now on when you want to go to town ask me if you can use the car. Im-ma tell you right now, you won't be driving it everyday."

He told her: "I am not giving you these keys. I will drive the car anytime I want to."

The next day Doll told Richard, Charlie and me: "When T. J. finish his chores, I want y'all to follow him. If he goes anywhere near that car, call me. I'll be in here sewing."

Our first day on the spying job wasn't what we expected. When T. J. walked out of the front door we stopped playing to watch him. He knew we were on Doll's side and he had many tricks up his sleeve to counteract. He turned the pockets of his britches inside out and walked around the yard as though he was searching for something. Stomping his feet and giving the impression that he was upset with us he said:

"Which one of y'all took that whistle from my pocket?" We denied taking it and he tricked us: "Oh yeah! I think I know where it might be. Under my bed. Hey, I got a nickel for the one who finds it."

We pushed and pulled each other trying to be the first one to get under T. J.'s bed and find the whistle. It was dark under his bed but we tried to find that whistle anyway.

Doll got on her knees and looked under the bed asking us:
"What is y'all looking for"
I answered her: "T. J. said he lost his whistle under the bed. He said that he will give whoever find it a nickel. That's what we're looking for."

I can't began to describe how angry Doll was:
"I told y'all to follow him! He just made a fool out of y'all. He took the car again. I'll get him tonight."

She took her pin cushion and stuck needles in his mattress and made the bed up nice and neat. Her intentions were to agonize him. That particular day he was gone until way past dark. We were in bed when he came home. Everyone was asleep except Doll and me. (My children, my nieces and nephews grew up listening to T. J. laughing and telling this story. I believe it was one of his favorite childhood stories).

T. J. took his shoes off before entering the house and tipped toed to his bedroom. Something was fishy! His bed wasn't a mess, the way he left it. It was made up nice and neat.

He smiled to himself thinking: Doll is up to something!" I must investigate!

He pulled the covers back and saw the needles. He removed them from the mattress and placed them on the dresser. And the fun began.

Doll and I heard his bed squeaking, followed by the loud fake screams which lasted a good two minutes. The fake crying went on for a minute or so.

By that time everyone was awake and feeling compassion for him.

T. J. talked: "This ain't over yet sister, not by a long shot. Tomorrow I'm going to the undertaker in town and use his phone to call Daddy and Mama and tell them that you are down here trying to kill me. All because I want to have a lil bit of fun before I move to Buffalo. My butt is hurting real bad. I can barely walk. Gee, my life is sho-nough in grave danger. Im-ma tell Daddy and Mama to send for me. Im-ma git a job working with Daddy. For all I care, from now on you can be the boss of everything. You can do all the chores. I ain't doing nothing else around here."

He walked out the door and slammed it behind him. T. J. sat on the step and simply raved about his clever performance!

Doll talked: "I shouldn't have put those needles in his mattress! I feel bad about it. Papa and Big Mama will be disappointed in us. We need to get along. I can't do all of the chores by myself. And y'all is to small to do enough that would amount to anything. I'm only one person. Maybe he can have the car every other day and I can have it every other day. I don't want him to call Daddy and Mama. They will worry."

Papa made a decision: "Each one of y'all can use the car one day a week. If y'all want to use it more than that, I suggest putting your differences aside and using the car together. Y'all are sister

115

and brother. Try acting like it! The keys stay with me. It wasn't long before Doll and T. J.'s animosity towards each other dissolved. T. J. didn't follow through on his bluff not to do his chores and calling our parents. They went to town together and looked out for one another.

Doll's schedule prompted her to give notice to Mrs. Sears that she would be quitting work in two weeks. The Sears were sad to hear that Doll would be quitting her job. While we were hanging the clothes on the clothes line in their back yard, Mr. Sears came out there and asked Doll if she knew how to shoot a gun.
She answered him: "No sir!" So in return he told her that he was going to teach her. She replied: "No thank you Mr. Sears. I am a young lady and certainly not interested in learning how to shoot a gun."

He replied: "Let me tell you this, living out here in the country is a must that everybody know how to shoot a gun. You say you gon work here two mo weeks. Im-ma show you how to shoot a gun by then. I'll be right back wit the gun."

She told me: "Mr. Sears is fresh and up to no good! Help me throw these clothes on the line. I want to be gone when he comes back out here. I don't trust him at all."

That fresh bastard was running across his lawn in our direction. He tripped and fell causing his shot gun to go off shooting the electric power line that led to their house. The lights in their house went off. Dusk was twenty to thirty minutes away. We ran home. The following Saturday we were sitting on our front porch when Doll spotted Mr. Sears walking down the road.

She assumed he was coming to our house and told us: "Come in the house with me."

We followed her to our parents bedroom. She got in the closet and laid on the floor instructing us: "Take the coats off the hangers and cover me with them. Go in the kitchen and sit at the table.

Don't answer the door!"

Mr. Sears knocked on the door several times, then let himself in and walked to the kitchen saying: "Let me ask y'all this. Didn't y'all hear me knocking?"

We answered him: "No sir."

He opened the back door and went to the back porch looking around.

He returned to the kitchen: "Let me ask y'all this. Where is Doll and T. J.?"

I said: "Wit Papa and Big Mama."

He said: "I thought I saw Doll when I was walking down the road. They went where wit y'all Papa and Big Mama?"

Richard said: "None of your business."

And I said: "To buy some ice for the ice box."

Then he talked to himself: 'It took all of them to go git some ice? Shit, it seems more like somebody done died. They done left all of these chillins here by they self? Alright y'all tell Doll that I came down here to see her. I'll be back to see her tomorrow. Now y'all stay out of devilment. You hear?"

My grandparents returned home shortly after that. We told them what happened. They were furious and in a state of mental unrest.

Big Mama voiced her opinion: "My instincts have never lied to me. Old man Sears should be ashamed of himself. That sneaky nosey bastard. Always coming around here and grinning in our faces like a chess-cat. Acting like he's so darn concerned about the children, saying 'Let me tell y'all this. I know Curley and Gladys miss their children something terrible. Let me ask y'all this, How long do you think it will be before they send for them youngens to come to Buffalo, New York with them?'

Big Mama continues: "I wonder if Mrs. Sears know that he get lost every Saturday in town. The people are laughing and talking about it. He cruise up and down the streets on the colored side of town eyeballing every woman he pass. Why don't he cruise the streets on the white side of town? I can't stand his doggish ways. I know damn well he ain't lost nothin over there. But you know good-n-well what he's looking for. I guess he feel that he just got to have him a beautiful colored woman. I have big news for him. He ain't gettin a damn thing here. That old bastard need to quit."

Papa told Big Mama that they were going up to the Sears house the next morning and let them know that the previous Thursday was Doll's last day of work.

Mr. Sears: "Well, good morning to y'all. Let me ask y'all this. What brings the two of you up this here way so early? I hope ain't nobody done hauled off and died or something like that."

Big Mama: "No Mr. Sears. Ain't nobody dead that I know of. You know that we rise with the roosters every day."

Papa: "We just wanted to talk with you and your misses. Is she around? Oh good morning Mrs. Sears. I was just asking about your where-a-bouts. I know Doll told you she could work another two weeks, but she can't afford the time. She is bogged down rat now. Its a heap of things going on wit her rat now and she can only do so many things in a day. She got the school play. She have to stay after school for that and the majorette practice. And on top of that she is making her school play and majorette costumes. And there is also Bet Joe and Richard's school play that she's helping wit."

Mrs. Sears: "Please! I need Doll. I can pay more. Let me tell you this. I love having Doll work for us. Let me ask you this. Can she work for us on the week-ends only? I understand the situation quite well. When Doll was up here the other day, she excitedly told me about her play. I sensed that she was bogged down in a lot of things then."

Mr. Sears: "Let me ask y'all this. Did Doll tell y'all anything? What is that gal been saying about me? Y'all tell me now."

Mrs. Sears asked Big Mama if she could help her a couple of days a week. Big Mama apologized to Mrs. Sears for not being able to help her out due to her own busy schedule. Then she turned to Mr. Sears and answered his questions: "Naturally, Doll had a difficult time making this decision. She will miss working for you all dearly. And most of all, she will miss the money. And Mr. Sears, Doll only had pleasant things to say about you and Mrs. Sears. Why would you think differently? And why did you ask us that question?
Anyhow I been thinking on it, Carrie Lou Brooks is looking for a job. Maybe y'all could hire her and see how it work out. That way she wouldn't have to walk to town for a two hour job every other day."

Mrs. Sears answered: "Let me tell you this. Its a funny thing that you mention Carrie Lou. She ran across my mind right before you said that. You know that girl need to be taught some sense, cause she ain't got none. She will have to completely change her ways, if she want to work for me again. She worked for me last summer, I was forced to let her go. Shit, I was tired of paying her to come here and do nothin. Hell. She'd come here and change the radio station to that boogie woogie music and stand at the ironing board, ironing and dancing around, throwing her legs every which-a-way. One day she burned Sears white shirt in the back and didn't mention it. He found out after he went to town and everybody laughed at him. Then he had the nerves to come home raising hell wit me. I had to tell him to get the hell out of my face. Didn't I Sears? Carrie Lou showed me a radio in the Sears and Roebuck Catalogue. Asked me to order it for her. Said she didn't have one at home."

Papa talked: "Mrs. Sears I don't think it is right to put Carrie Lou down. She ain't crazy. She's just happy, that's all. And as for the radio, more folk ought to be like that. Shoot ain't nothing wrong wit listening to the radio and kicking up your heals and dancing. Sometimes when I'm sittin on the front garret, right before the sun go down, I turn the radio on. I declare that music is something pleasing to listen to. I just sit there patting my feet and popping my fingers. If I knew the words to the song, I'd sing rat along wit it. There comes a time when people want to have a little fun. That's all. Being serious all the time just ain't good for you."

Mrs. Sears responded: "Let me ask this. "Did Carrie Lou ever get her hands on a radio to call her own? Oh she didn't! Well she's looking for a job and I need somebody to help me out. She live rat over yonder just a hop, skip and jump away. I can order that radio for her. That-a-way she can listen to it at home. But when she's here working, there certainly will not be any dancing, singing or prancing around."

Big Mama commented: "I'm pretty sure that the job will work out fine with Carrie Lou this time. She is a year older and probably more responsible too. Especially since Manley (her father) ran off with that young woman. Its just her and Sindy Lou (her mother) there now.

Mrs. Sears gave Papa and Big Mama Doll's final pay with an extra six bits. Doll was thankful for that.

Doll's costumes for the school play came out splendidly and her majorette outfit was gorgeous on her. She looked like she had stepped out of a fashion magazine. Her school play was voted the best play of the year. It was a big hit that made her popular and well liked by the entire school.

The Sears's had Carrie Lou come work for them again and it worked out fine. The three of them got through it one day at a time and respected each other.

Daddy And Mama Purchased A Home In Buffalo:

In February 1957 Daddy and Mama purchased a beautiful three story home with a full basement. It was a two family house located in the Cold Springs area of Buffalo, New York and down the street from an elementary school, a church and a corner store. In the opposite direction the house was one and a half blocks away from beautiful Humboldt Park-Way. (Things were looking up. They were shittin in high cotton again).

In April 1957, Daddy sent Mama back to Mississippi to bring Richard, Charlie, Earl, Emerson and me back to Buffalo, New York. June was in the Army. Doll and T. J. wanted to stay until school was out, which was the following month. We took the bus to Buffalo. It was a long, hot, uncomfortable ride. We rode in the back of the bus and the motor was extremely loud and annoying. Three days and ten hours later we arrived in Buffalo, New York.

Daddy met us at the bus station. It was an early, cloudy, cool, Saturday morning. On the way home I sat in the front seat with Daddy and Mama. I was so excited that I couldn't contain myself. They kept telling me to sit down.

Every red brick house I saw I pointed and hollered out: "Is that our house?"

When Daddy turned onto Glenwood Avenue, he announced: "This is our street. Now y'all start looking for it. The address is 515 and its on the right side."

We finally arrived and Daddy drove to the back yard. Mama opened the door and attempted to get out. I couldn't wait. She was taking too long. I crawled over her lap and jumped to the pavement. It was unbelievable! We had concrete in our back yard. Oh my goodness! It was so much to see.

The garage had a basketball rim mounted to it. The houses had three floors and basements, and they were so close together. We were country and accustomed to wide open spaces with no cement or pavement. I was the first one to take my shoes off right there in the yard. Then Richard, Charlie and Earl took theirs off too.

Daddy unlocked the door and gave me the key to our unit upstairs and said: "Honey go up stairs and unlock the door so we can bring the luggage in."

I ran up four steps and thought I was upstairs. But I wasn't. I was downstairs. The door wasn't locked, so I went in and went straight to the cabinet and helped myself to a package of Fig Newton cookies. Then I opened the refrigerator and took three bottles of Coca Cola. By that time the rest of the family was carrying the luggage upstairs.

And I ran to the door and asked: "Where is everybody going? Daddy the door wasn't locked. Hey Richard, Charlie, Earl and Emerson, come here I got us some cookies and Coca Cola."

Mama said: "Girl this is down stairs. We live upstairs. Don't you see all of those steps? Come out of there, close the door behind you and follow me."

I followed her and brought the cookies and Coca Cola along with me. The house was spacious and pretty with beautiful shining hardwood floors throughout. The kitchen was equipped with modern appliances. Just like Aunt Miracle said it would be. Doll and I had a big bedroom with a very nice white bedroom set. My brothers had bunk beds in their rooms. Daddy prepared a pot of delicious vegetable beef soup and a pan of corn bread for us. While we were eating, he told us that his Army buddy, Hog Wash was renting a room in the attic and instructed us not to go in his room and disturb him under any circumstances. After eating, he gave us a tour of the attic.

Richard, Charlie and I went to the back yard to explore and acquaint ourselves with the unfamiliar surroundings. While doing that, we met our next door neighbor, Mr. Houston and had a confrontation with him.

"Hey, what are you kids doing in that yard? Hey! You boys, get out of that tree! What are you looking for anyway? Get away from that car lil girl, or I will call Mr. Holmes. That's his yard, take your mannish asses away from there. Y'all ain't up to nothing but no good."

Richard retaliated: "Shut up mister! You got a big mouth. We ain't going nowhere. This is our back yard, for your information, Mr. Holmes is our father. This is my brother Charlie and this is my sister Bet Joe. What is you doing in that yard? Do you live in that house?"

Mr. Houston stood there staring at us and shaking his head. Then he insulted us: "Well I be damn. So the wind finally blew you country no shoe wearing hicks in? Your Daddy and Mama has been having a fit to get you all up here. I don't see what for. If you ask me, I think they should have left you down there in Glosville, Mississippi. Y'all is country! Let me school you on something. You are in the city now. And in the city everybody wear shoes. Alright? And to answer your question boy, yes I live in this house. My wife Vic lives here too. What's it to you anyway? Oh by the way, my name is Houston."

Mr. Houston wasn't as bad as he pretended to be. His wife Vic, was a nice classy skinny woman, she was five feet tall with blue hair. I noticed her peeping out of their window, while Mr. Houston talked with us and waved at her. She waved back and came out to introduce herself to us. She gave each one of us a nickel and told us where the store was. Ms. Vic also invited us in their house and gave us some leftover Easter candy and a glass of Kool Aide. She welcomed us to Buffalo and the neighborhood and told me that Linda, a girl my age lived in the house on the other side of us and I could play with her.

Later on, Richard, Charlie and I were playing basketball when Hog Wash drove up into the back yard, got out of his car and said: "Well, Well, well. Y'all must be part of the Holmes family. My name is Hog Wash. I live up there (pointing to the attic) and I hope I don't have any trouble out of you."

He laughed a heavy rumbling laugh as his shoulders shook vigorously. He walked to the lilac tree and cut a limb from it with his extremely sharp knife. While cutting it in the form of a toothpick, he began to talk again: "Yeah! I won't hesitate to cut a finger or two off or maybe a hand, if I catch it on the door knob that lead to my room."

He put his six inch long toothpick in his mouth, wiped his knife with the lower part of his white shirt and waved it in the air while gazing at us with a mean, serious expression on his face, it was penetrating. I was frightened and not very comfortable with his actions. Therefore, I stood behind Richard and Charlie for protection. Hog Wash knew I was afraid of him and he laughed that heavy rumbling laugh again. His wide shoulders shook as if he was dancing. After stepping in place several times, he shouted 'Oh' then turned around, shook his fat hippo ass and clapped his hands.

My fearless brother, Richard, interrupted his laughter: "Shut up Mr. Hog Wash! You look pretty silly, laughing like that. I don't see nothing to laugh about. Mess wit me and I'll throw a rock and knock the shit out of you. I ain't scared of you!"

Hog Wash responded: "Boy, you are just like your daddy. You got more guts than the damn law allow."

At that precise time, Daddy stepped out of the back door and said: "Come on in the house. I want y'all to watch the wrestling match with me, I think its something that you will like. Oh yeah, Wash, I see you met my children. Look man, don't tease them, I heard you out here laughing. I didn't know if you were up to no good or what."

Hog Wash told Daddy the biggest lie: "What? Tease them? Now Curley I thought you knew me better than that. I left that old habit in the Army. Give me some credit for something. It ain't no way that I would ever tease these little sweet children." Then he gave each one of us a dime. That was the first and last time Hog Wash teased us. And we got along with him thereafter.

The wrestling match was a real exciting treat. It was quite amazing! Our first time ever watching television, we were most appreciative for it as we sat on the floor watching it closely. Mama made ham and egg sandwiches with lettuce, tomatoes and cheese on them. She popped popcorn and made a pitcher of ice tea. We took pleasure in spending that Saturday afternoon with our parents in our new home, in front of the television, while we ate.

When the wrestling match was over, we watched Sing along with Mitch Miller, followed by, the Lawrence Welk show, followed by Gunsmoke.

Mama said things had changed considerably: "At home in Mississippi, I listened to Gunsmoke on the radio. And here in Buffalo, I get to watch it on television, every Saturday night. I think I prefer watching it on television much better. After listening to Gunsmoke on the radio all those years, I finally get a chance to see what Marshal Matt Dillon look like."

That is the way our first Saturday afternoon in Buffalo began and it continued that way for many, many, many years. No matter what the family was doing, we made it a point to put it aside for that special Saturday afternoon, starting with the wrestling match and ending with Gunsmoke.

Getting adjusted to living in Buffalo was pretty easy. Except for the difficult time we had with this one particular family of three brothers, the Hillips, whom lived across the street from us. They took us for a bunch of pushovers. They were always peeing down our backs and telling us it was rain. They laughed at our unique southern accent.

The first time it snowed, the oldest one of them, Carley, came to our back door with a brown paper grocery bag full of snow. Richard answered the door.

Carley presented the bag to him, laughing as he said: "I know y'all miss the cotton that you left behind in Mississippi, so I brought you a bag of it."

Richard laughed right along with him and that made Carley mad. Because that wasn't the attitude he was expecting. Anyhow the joke backfired and he left with a silly look on his face. He took the bag of snow along with him. Naturally, Richard insisted that he take it.

Five minutes later, Carley returned and asked Richard: "Hey dude let me stay here until my mother and brothers come back from the store. I don't have a key to get in the house and it is freezing outside. If you let me stay, I'll help you shovel the snow."

Richard looked at Carley and questioned him: "Shovel the snow? What snow? There is no snow to shovel! Hey man, do you feel alright.? Cause you are acting crazy."

Carley responded: "Nol, dude. I ain't crazy. Look out the window and tell me what you see." Richard looked out the kitchen window into the back yard, laughed, and answered Carley: "Hey man, that's cotton! Why don't you kick back on it and wait there for your mother."

After a while their jokes and teasing became stale and simmered down considerably. Carley and his brothers eventually became friends with Richard and Charlie. His brothers and I were on speaking terms. But not Carley. He hated me. I was scared of him.

He was always threatening me: "Im-ma kick your ass. I don't like you. And I don't want you living on this street. Take your ass back to Mississippi. I bet not catch you outside by yourself."

He chased me home from school a lot of days, at times, I'd barely make it to the front glass door to slam it in his face. He would stand out there bullying me. And I would stand in the hallway safely locked behind the door, poking my tongue out at him. One day, Mama was cooking dinner and discovered that she needed some sugar to sweeten the ice tea. She asked me to go to the corner store to buy some sugar. (The store was only ten houses down the street). I went to the window in the living room and looked for my brothers, but didn't see any of them. So in return, I told Mama that I would wait for one of them to come home and accompany me to the store.

And she answered me; "I need you to go to the store right now."

I told her that I would go as soon as I called Peggy, (who was my friend who lived down the street from us). to see if she could accompany me to the store.

Mama had a little talk with me that made a lot of sense: "Honey, you came into this world alone and you will most likely leave this world alone. Now is there anything wrong with walking to the corner store alone?"

I walked to the store alone. People were sitting on their front porches on both sides of the street, which made me feel safe. On my way back from the store, I saw Carley Hillips across the street going in the opposite direction. As soon as he saw me he ran across the street and pushed me against a tree. He told me that he was going to kick my ass. He grabbed my sweater and pulled me towards him. I could feel and smell the onion fragrant heat coming from his mouth. Yuck! He scared me so bad that I began to sweat profusely, it ran down my face and burned my eyes. It wasn't hot enough to sweat. Perhaps it was 70 degrees.

He tried to take the bag of sugar from me. I held onto it with all my might, kicked him in the shin and ran right out of that sweater which he was holding on to so tight. I held the bag of sugar to my chest with both hands as I ran swiftly making long strides to my house. When I reached the top step to the porch, I looked back and saw Carley on the corner, which was three houses away. I wondered: 'How did I get so far ahead of him?' It was my adrenaline flowing abundantly.

I stood in the hallway, behind the glass door, shaking like a leaf on a tree, awaiting Carley. He was out of breath when he got there. He went through the same old tacky routine, he had the nerves to beat on the door and jerk the handle, trying to get in. That provoked me extremely! Something down inside of me said 'Fight back! Fight back! For goodness sakes, Fight back!' I didn't take out time to think about it. My back was against the wall. I was angry and fed up with Carley. Either he was going to kick my ass or I was going to kick his ass. I was crazy at that point, and didn't care what the outcome would be. 'kill or be killed.'

I remembered Mama's words: 'A person can't do no more to you than you can do to them.' I opened the door so forceful, that it hit the wall and bounced. I stormed out to the porch and threw the bag of sugar, hitting Carley in the face with it. I ran up to him, spit in his face and kicked him in the shin again. I pulled his cap off, threw it on the porch, stomped it, spit on it, ripped it apart and threw it in Mr. Houston's driveway. Then I called him a bunch of dirty, low down, funky names. The bastard didn't open his mouth. He stood there staring at the floor like he was in another world. He wouldn't fight me so I told him to get the hell off of my porch. He did. As he turned to walk down the steps, something told me to kick him. I didn't do it. I shouted 'BOO' and he jumped as though it scared him. I stood there watching him as he clumsily carried his pitiful sorry ass across the street to his house. The problem was solved. I got Carley off of my back. And it felt good.

It occurred to me that a bully is someone with no confidence in them self, who is always trying to put fear into someone, talking about what they will do to you. This that and the other. Beware of me cause I'm Bad! That is a crock of hot air. Because when you confront them face-to-face its a completely different story. In reality the bullies are the scared ones. I have a great dislike for bullies. (Beware of the quiet ones! Because you don't know what's on their mind or what they will do) .

Mama was upset with me because I took so long coming back from the store: "Didn't I tell you that I needed the sugar immediately? I guess that didn't mean anything to you. Huh?"

I told her in vivid detail what had just happened on the porch with Carley and me.

She was surprised: "You mean to tell me that Carley did all of that? He is such a polite gentlemen around me. Just the other day he helped me bring the groceries in. He told me that he got out of school early, because he didn't feel well. And he didn't have a key to get in the house. I fixed him a sandwich and gave him a glass of milk. He sat right there and ate it. We had a very nice conversation.

Well enough of that. Why didn't you mention this to me, Curley or your brothers? And how long has this been going on? I see why you don't want to go outside unless somebody goes with you. Well this is going to stop right now. It ain't going no further. Im-ma tell Curley and we are going over there and have a talk with his parents tonight. The nerve of him, picking on a little girl."

I asked Mama not to have a talk with Carley's parents, because I didn't think I would have any more problems with him. I was proud of myself for standing up to him. Carley Hillips never bothered me again. When he came to visit my brothers, sometimes we spoke and sometimes we didn't. I had developed a habit of saying: "I hate Carley Hillips!" Mama straightened me out. She told me that it was wrong to hate a person for a childish ignorant mistake they made. She asked me to forgive Carley Hillips and put what happened in perspective and go on with my precious life. I took Mama's advice, although it was not an easy task. I forgave

Carley Hillips along the years. But I never forgot that incident. I never possessed any respect for him. I think it would have been easier and perhaps we could have become friends if he would have extended an apology to me.

The childhood games were the same in Buffalo as Mississippi. My friends and I played Hop Scotch, London Bridge Falling Down, Skip To The Loop My Darling, Little Sally Walker, jacks, and we also jump roped.

At least three times a week mama took us for a walk to her friend Viola's house. It was located on Humboldt Park Way and Hamlin. She also took us for walks to Jefferson and Glenwood Avenue and treated us to a slice of pizza and a Coke. We looked forward to those lovely occasions.

My brothers played with and got along so well with the Renfroe children (whom lived two doors down the street from us) that you couldn't separate one from the other. And they still have that unique, special, rare, strong bond and friendship of a lifetime. Charlie has also been friends with Bill Lee Hillsberry since they were in the second grade. I consider Bill Lee as my brother!

The Bear Sandwich:

Once upon a time, I came home from school hungry and went directly to the kitchen to eat. There was a delicious looking roast beef decorated with onions, carrots and potatoes in the casserole dish on the stove. It simply made my mouth water. I couldn't wait to make a sandwich and taste it. I cut a small piece and ate it. Ah! It was the best. I made a sandwich and went to the living room where Mama and Roy were watching television. I sat on the couch and ate that sandwich and made noise: "Um, um, um, this is good! Mama, I love all of your cooking, but this is extremely exceptional."

Mama remarked: "Yeah! I thought so too. That's one of the

130

best tasting chickens I ever cooked."

As she continued to watch television, I thought to myself: "Wow! Mama has chicken on her mind." I finished eating the roast beef sandwich and made another one. Mama asked me if I saw the bear roast that June left on the stove? I answered: "I didn't see the bear roast, but I saw the delicious roast beef you cooked. Mama it's so good that I made another sandwich. You should cook roast beef like this all the time."

Mama said; "I fried chicken for dinner. It's in the oven. I thought that's what you were eating."

I laughed and responded: "No Mama you cooked this delicious roast beef." And by that time her and Roy was laughing something terrible. Mama was on her knees falling out laughing. (The only time I ever saw her on her knees was when she was saying her prayers.) Roy was on the floor lying on his back laughing and kicking his legs up. I sat down and tried to get into the movie that they were watching, because it had them rolling. Their laughter was highly infectious. Therefore I began to laugh too.

Finally, Mama stopped laughing long enough to say: "Bettye I'm trying to tell you that you are eating bear meat. There is no roast beef on the stove. That is roast bear."

Roy interrupted: "What difference does it make Bet Joe? You love that bear meat. You said it and you made two sandwiches and ate both of them. You licked the bear juice off your fingers. Ha, ha, ha, ha, ha, ha, ha, ha, ha."

My entire disposition changed: "I'm mad at everybody in this house. Especially June. Why would he bring a bear here? My stomach feel funny. I'm sick. Why didn't June put a sign on the bear? I was tricked. I don't even like bear."

I went to the kitchen and wrote a note in red ink: 'Warning:

Caution: Be Careful: This casserole dish contain BEAR: Eat at your own risk.' I went to my room, closed the door and pouted. Later on I heard Daddy, my brothers and some of their friends in the kitchen talking and laughing about my note.

Daddy said; "What kind of bear is this? Is it a Polar bear? Is it a Teddy bear? Is it a grizzly bear?" They continued to laugh and carry on.

It made me angrier. I went into my closet and closed the door so I wouldn't hear them. I fell asleep while laying there and drifted off to Jingle Bell Bear Land, U.S.A.

I thought: 'Where are the houses? I haven't seen any houses yet. It smell funky here. It's not Christmas. Why is Jingle Bells playing? Oh there's somebody!' "Hello. Miss. Can you tell me how to get to 515 Glenwood Avenue in Buffalo, New York? I'm lost!"

"Child, it ain't no reason or time to be asking about some old street in Barracuda, New Yurk. This here place, is your new home. Bear Land, U. S. A. We been expectin you. You greedy dummy. Why did you eat that bear? That was 'White Sky.' And everyone loved him. You are in a lot of trouble child. I hope you have a good excuse for eating White Sky. Look, look, look, they are looking at you in that tub of water. You see that grey bear wit them red eyes? That's White Sky's wife. She saw you in that tub of water making those two White Sky sandwiches. And she been crying since then. You ought to be shame of yo self. Good luck. You are going on trial today."

I had no idea what she was talking about. I was more interested in her: "What kind of woman are you?" I asked.

"Child, what on earth do you mean?" She replied. "What kind of question is that to ask me?"

I answered her: "I don't know? You look different, that's all.

132

Your hair is stuck together with leaves in it. You don't have feet like people and your finger nails are a hundred inches long. Are you a wild woman?"

She scratched her head and said: "Well I guess you can say I'm a wild woman. And might I add, I am a beautiful wild woman."

I wanted to tell her that if she ever came face to face with a mirror, it would surely crack, because she had an ugly mug. Anyhow, she looked at me with a sad depressing frown on her face. I was nosey: "Wild woman why are you crying?"

She asked me if I saw any tears in her eyes? I didn't see any tears.

She shook her middle finger at me and said: "You big eyed dummy, I was smiling at you and I only do that two times a year."

I asked: "Where is all the people? And why are they playing Jingle Bells? It's not the Christmas season?"

She answered: "I'm the only people here. Them bears eat the people as soon as the trial is over. This won't be your home for long. Because your trial is next. Unless you wont to stay wit me and work for Judge Moon. Look, look, look, see that big black bear sitting behind that bench? That's Judge Moon. I been wit him for one hundred years.
Ain't that a blessing? I cook and clean for him. Yup, he brought me here when I was fourteen years old, straight from my honeymoon. I married a man a rat smarter than me. He was a bit older than me too. He was at the ripe old age of sixty four. Well, I might as well tell you what happened. We ran off and got married and were on our way to the big city and happened to stop in the woods and camp and find some food. My husband Lug, spotted a young bear and killed him. He cooked him and we ate him. In the middle of the night, them bears raided our camp and took my poor Lug a-way. And one hour later they found him guilty and soon after that they et him clothes and all. Look, look,

look, you see that red bear leaning on the tree? He the one dat et my poor loving husband Lug. And that Jingle Bells song is played all the time here in Bear Land. And the only time it stops is when there is an emergency."

"Hey chap what yo name?"

I answered: "Bettye Joe Holmes;"

She talked: "That name is kind of old like me. Do you know what my name is? Well, its None Of Yo Business."

I said: "You are right. It's none of my business."

She snapped: "You stupid girl! I told you my name. Now, listen, listen, listen. My name is None Of Yo Business. The bears say they love my name. Ain't that a rat pretty name? Come on, come on, come on, tell me how you like it?"

I insulted her: "It was silly for your mother to give you a name like that. Besides, that's not a name. None of yo business, is a simple slang sentence."

Angry, she reached for me saying: "Come here chap. I'm getting ready to slap some respect into you for talking sassy to me Miss Bettye John Houses, Im-ma make sho that Judge Moon eat you for dinner tonight. And another thang, you ain't gon git no trial either. You don't deserve one. Judge Moon is hungry rat now. Come on gal. He like for his dinner to be on time."

She grabbed my dress and started pulling me and calling for the other bears to help her out. She was losing her grip, because I bit her hand several times. Three funky bears came and picked me up and took me to Judge Moon. He was smiling with his salt and pepper shaker.

He called: "None Of Yo Business, come here please. I want to thank you for such a fine delicious dinner. I know I'm not going to get heartburn, cause she ain't wearing no perfume. You know how bad perfume give me heartburn!" (He stood up and licked his lips and rubbed his stomach, then laughed); "Ha, ha, ha; I feel like its my birthday. Turn the music up."

I told Judge Moon that eating the bear was a mistake and I thought it was roast beef. I was truly sorry and to let me go home. And it was my brother June's fault because he brought the bear there. Judge Moon told me, that June was smart enough not to eat the bear and I was dumb enough to eat the bear. After his speech, None Of Yo Business and the bears began to laugh and clap their hands; and I saw an opportunity to escape and took it. There was a centerpiece piled high with coconuts on Judge Moon's Desk. So I took one and threw it at him, and it went in his big mouth and didn't stop until it landed in his windpipe. Therefore, he couldn't breathe or talk.
All he could do was beat on his chest and that sounded like a drum. The Jingle Bell music went off and None Of Yo Business asked where was Dr. Wind? She was informed that Dr. Wind was on vacation. And Nurse River was visiting with her daughter, whom just had twins. The bears gathered around Judge Moon with the intent on reviving him. I crawled under the desk, between and around the bears legs and when I thought it was safe, I ran.

None Of Yo Business saw me and warned the bears: "Help! Help! Help! Judge Moon's dinner is bout to get away."

Two bears joined None Of Yo Business and they almost got a hold of me. As I ran and cried I heard somebody knocking and calling me from a distance. The next thing I knew, my feet were rising above the ground and I ran through the air staring down at None Of Yo Business and the bears. They were telling me to come back and turn myself in. While they continued to run and jump up, reaching for my feet. They scratched my legs with their long ugly contaminated nails. I didn't have time to tell them what was on my mind because I was busy running. One of those bears managed to catch my foot and pull me towards him.

I cried, kicked and screamed: "Ouch! You're scratching my ankle! stinking bear turn my foot loose."

The knocking and the voice that was calling me were getting closer and closer. 'Bettye, Bettye.' It was Mama's voice.

"Bettye, are you sleep? Answer me girl!" "You've been in that closet for a long time! Are you still pouting ?"

She opened the closet door, I looked in her face and smiled. I stretched my hand out and she grabbed it, pulling me from the closet floor. I immediately closed the closet door behind me and locked it.

"Come on in the kitchen girl and let's have a bowl of vanilla ice cream."

What a pleasant beautiful healthy relief it was to wake up safe at home from that unbelievably devastating horrible nightmare! I pinched myself just to be positively sure that I was awake. I checked my legs, ankles and feet, there were no scratch marks. I was overjoyed and simply loved everybody. After joining Mama in the kitchen for ice cream, I had to ask :

"Mama is there a place called Bear Land U. S.A. that play Jingle Bell music all the time?"

She laughed and answered: "No. There is no such place. Honey, you had a nightmare that's all. You know something; that bear was pretty tasty. Yeah. All of us had a go at it and it's all gone now."

Momentarily, a teeny -weeny thought entered my mind; 'The whole family is going to Bear Land U S A.' But I dismissed that thought immediately.

That was my first and last time eating bear. It was an enlightening experience. I never went to sleep in my closet again.

136

I am thankful that Mama woke me from that devastating nightmare just in time. If she had not awakened me at that precise moment; what would have happened?

The Easter:

It was the Wednesday afternoon before Easter. The school dismissed us early due to a default in the heating system. School would be out for one and a half weeks. It was a vacation we needed to get away from our teachers and chill out. I had the radio on in the kitchen while I made lunch for Richard, Charlie, Earl, Em, Roy and myself.

I heard a noise in the hallway and went to check it out. It was Emerson. He was sitting on the steps that lead to the attic with his head between his knees, crying profusely. His suit and shoes were on the step next to him. I wanted to know what happened to make him cry like that. He said he was tired, tired, tired.

"I'm tired of the Holmes hand-me-down Easter suit tradition. I'm tired of those duhickies in the attic making fun of me and calling me the Easter-hand-me-down-boy.
(I wish they will go home.) I'm tired of Richard showing his brand new Easter suit and shoes to everybody. This is no joke! I want a new outfit for Easter."

"Bet Joe, what do you think about these shoes? It's a lot of things wrong with them. The first year Richard wore them. The second year Charlie wore them. The third year Earl wore them and left the shape of his feet in them. He also walked the taps off. Now the heel is jacked up. Check this out, these shoes are big enough for daddy. I am tired of Mama stuffing socks in oversized hand-me-down shoes to make them fit. These shoes are a perfect example of an antique. And this suit is outdated. These pants has lint balls between the legs. Three people done wore these pants and farted in them. I refuse to wear this suit! I'm not going to church if I don't get a new Easter outfit!"

137

"Bet Joe, I want you to ask Daddy and Mama to buy me a new outfit for Easter. Ok?"

I asked Emerson why didn't he tell Daddy and Mama how he felt. And he said it hadn't bothered him until minutes prior to that when the teasing kicked in and that provoked his mind to wonder seriously about what those duhickies were saying. I tried to boost his morale by telling him not to worry and that he would get a new outfit. I had him help me make our lunch by setting the table. He wanted some potato chips and Teem soda to go with the lunch. So he and I walked to the store and bought it. I told him that he would look nice in a gray suit with a yellow shirt.

And he immediately let me know: " Im-ma boy. Ain't no way I will ever wear a yellow shirt! You can forget about that. I like the way a gray suit and a white shirt sound."

Daddy and Mama got home from work late that day.

I told Emerson: "Let's go talk with Mama about getting you an outfit."

He put his jacket on and said: "I hear my friend Renfroe calling me. I got-a-go."

He took off leaving me to talk with Mama. I told Mama about the situation.

Smiling, she pinched my arm and responded: "Guess what? It's already done. That's what me and Curley were doing after work today, buying suits. It's five suits, five pairs of shoes, five shirts, five ties, etc., out there in the trunk of the car. I guess we were thinking the same thing that Emerson was thinking.

Things change. Nothing remain the same. Last year I had to do a lot of mending to Earl and Emerson's suit pants. So Curly and I decided that starting this Easter, all of our boys would get a new suit for this Easter and every Easter from here on out. Hand-me-down Easter suits are history. How bout that!"

My brothers were outstanding in their new suits and Buster Brown shoes as they performed in the Easter play. We had a white Easter that year. But that was perfectly alright. After church we had a wonderfully delicious dinner. Following dinner, I helped Daddy hide the blue, green, yellow and red Easter eggs in the living room for the Easter egg hunt. Daddy made the hunt more interesting by wrapping a two dollar bill around one of the eggs, he announced. They found all of the eggs except the one with the two dollar bill. Richard, Charlie and Earl came to the assumption that Daddy was joking about the two dollar bill egg. That's why they decided to take a break and eat some of their eggs. Roy followed them.

Emerson kept looking for that two dollar bill egg faithfully and diligently. Richard, Charlie and Earl tried to discourage him by saying Daddy was joking and there was no two dollar bill egg to be found.

A few minutes later, Charlie looked up and saw Emerson smiling and commented: "No you didn't Emerson! You didn't find the egg with the two dollar bill? Did you?"

Emerson continued to smile as he shook his head and threw his hands up. "What can I say? When it rain; it pours!" Then he walked around smiling and showing off his two dollar bill.

That was my best Easter yet. By the way, Emerson's suit was gray, his shirt was white and his tie was gray with yellow poke-a-dots. He was one happy little brother!

Busted Gambling In The Back Yard: Buffalo

One day Richard, Charlie, Baxter, Hunter, Dobb, Alaney, Bill Lee and Alonzo were in the back yard shooting dice and using bad language. My brother in law Bob taught Richard and Charlie how to shoot dice. They liked it and every time Daddy and Mama wasn't home they'd take advantage of it by getting in the back yard with their friends to gamble. On this particular day they were pretty loud, which disturbed one of our neighbors. So to get even with my brothers and their company, the neighbor called the police and told them that it was a lot of people gambling in our back yard. Five police cars came to our house. The policemen rushed to our back yard hoping to arrest some adults. But they only found a bunch of kids gambling and acting as though they were adults. Stunned! The policemen walked to the site where the kids were gambling and spotted some change; several fifty cent pieces, some quarters, some dimes, nickels and pennies. They looked at the frightened faces of those little gamblers and burst into laughter.

After they had their laugh one of them asked;

"Hey which one of you are winning?" None of them admitted to winning. It was an embarrassing situation. The scared little gamblers looked from one to the other hoping that nobody would open their mouth, causing them some jail time.

The policeman told Richard and Charlie, to take their asses in the house and their friends to take their asses home. And that they better not ever hear of them gambling in the back yard again. If they did, they wouldn't hesitate to haul them off to jail.

Somebody told our parents what happened and apparently added a little more than what actually happened. And that fired Daddy up.

He walked in the back door taking his belt off: "Me and your mother just heard about the police coming here. Y'all had a gambling party. Huh? Money thrown all over the back yard? Um huh! Y'all want to flip a coin to see who is going to be the first one to get a whooping? Get over here right now."

Richard raised his hand and said; "Since I'm the oldest, I'll go first." He was very polite: "I'm sorry for gambling in the back yard. It won't happen again. But Daddy, you always say boys will be boys!"

Daddy hit Richard with his new stiff belt. Richard said: "Ouch, that hurt!" Tears ran down his face, as he rubbed his butt.
Daddy said: "By the time I finish whooping Charlie this belt will be broken in good."

Charlie told me: "I'll be right back." He went to the attic. I felt compassion for Richard. He always took a whooping without crying, but that new belt was a bit too much to handle. I began to weep and Daddy said; "If you can't stand the heat. Git out the kitchen!"

Daddy called Charlie to come get his whooping. When he came, Daddy said: "Damn! Boy. Look like you gained ten pounds over night." Charlie didn't cry when he got his whooping. Daddy was puzzled and agitated by it.

He told Mama and the rest of us that he was going to take his bath and not to wait for him to eat. As soon as he disappeared into the bathroom, Mama pointed at Charlie and beckoned for him to come to her.

She grabbed both of Charlie ears and said: "If you ever pull another stunt like that, I will make you strip down to yo draws and whoop yo natural ass! Don't even try acting like you don't know what I'm talking about. I know you're wearing yo snow pants under yo jeans. That's why you didn't cry when Curley whooped you. You better be glad that he haven't figured it out yet."

Daddy solved that puzzle while he was taking his bath: "Charlie, get in here. I have some talk for you, about your sudden weight gain."

We were afraid that Daddy were going to whoop the hell out of Charlie. Charlie walked in the bathroom and closed the door behind him. Mama and the rest of us were nervous as we gathered outside the bathroom and listened. Daddy laughed. Charlie laughed. And the rest of us laughed. That hot bath worked a miracle. We sat around the table and laughed about Charlie's prank as we ate ice cream.

Mama's Surprise Birthday Party:

It was a freezing cold Saturday morning in February of 1959. (Mama's birthday) She pretty much started the day off thinking:

Mama stated: "Good morning everybody! My. My. My. Aren't you guys up early today! Its six thirty. Y'all don't get up this early on school days. Well don't get me wrong; I'm not complaining. Its a good thing to get up early. Your grandmother, always say, 'Early to bed, early to rise, make you healthy wealthy and wise.' I sure wish I could stay home with you guys today. Its seven below zero and the streets are covered with a sheet of ice. Curley is blowing the horn, I better go. Come here, y'all give me a warm hug!"
I offered to make a lunch for Mama, she said she had other plans for lunch. I thought that was strange, because she always took her lunch, on the weekends, due to the cafeteria being closed and I knew she would not go out to lunch in that weather.

On the way to work, Daddy seemed to be preoccupied with something as he listened to the radio. He had not wished Mama a happy birthday.

Mama broke the silence: 'Curley, do you know what today is?"

He answered: "Yeah."

A minute went by and she asked: "Well, what is it?"

He asked: "What is what?"

He started to whistle, with the song that was playing on the radio. That upset Mama. She thought to herself: 'This has never happened before. Curley done forgot my birthday. All the years that we have been together, he brought me breakfast in bed on

142

every single one of my birthdays. It wasn't anything to write home about. (a boiled egg, a day old biscuit with some jelly on it, cheese and crackers, lunch meat with crackers, a banana, pear, apple etc). But it meant the world to me. He would get back in the bed and help me eat whatever it was that he had fixed. Curley, I miss that. That's why I stayed in the bed an extra twenty minutes, waiting for my birthday breakfast. I would have been happy if you would've made me a cup of coffee. I want to know just what in the hell is on your mind that would make you forget an important day like my birthday. Well, its still eight and a half minutes before I get to work. I'll give him one more chance.'

"You never did answer me Curley! Exactly what day is today? Get it right!"

Daddy: Its Saturday. Isn't it?
Mama: What's the date?
Daddy: Ah, ah, ah February the twentieth?

Mama: No. Curley today is February the twenty fifth. Does that ring any special bells?

Daddy: Let me think! Oh yeah, how could I forget. Its one of the president's birthdays isn't it?

Mama was outdone and she began to think: 'Forget it Curley! That's alright! At least my co-workers won't forget my birthday. I wonder what are they bringing? Since it's the weekend, they probably won't bring much. Perhaps Mattie will start the day off with some Freddie's Donuts. Um, um, um, I can't get enough of them. The first thing Im-ma do when I get to work is grab one. I'm so hungry. Let me see; there is only seven of us scheduled to work today.
Margo makes some darn good fried chicken, she probably got up early this morning and fried some. Lonnie makes a mean dish of cheese and macaroni. I am positive that is what she will bring. Now Viola, that girl can't boil water, I don't know what she will bring. Maybe some potato chips like she always do. Well I can

143

dig that. Candy will bring her goulash. I love it. Loraine, will bring her potato salad. Yeah that's hip. It's my birthday! Therefore I won't do much work. I will be busy eating and partying.'

"Well here we are. Im-ma have to walk you to the door honey. I don't want you to slip and fall." Daddy said passionately.

He parked as close to the door as possible and while him and Mama tipped through the parking lot on the glistering slippery sheet of ice with his arms around her, she gently patted Daddy on his behind.

That was embarrassing to him: "Gladys, what are you doing? Don't you see all of these people out here? Quit that. Alright now, you are going to make me fall."

When they got to the door, he leaned down and told Mama to give him some sugar. She bit his lip and told him that he didn't deserve any sugar and rushed in the door. He watched her as she disappeared down the hallway and into the elevator. While he drove home tears formed in his eyes, but he fought to keep them from rolling down his cheeks. He felt miserable for pretending he didn't remember Mama's birthday.

Mama was shocked to find out that there was no donuts in sight. She thought: 'Where are the donuts?'
Being inconspicuous, she looked for them and came to the conclusion that there were none. She checked the calendar and everything was in order. The big red circle around that date with her name was still there. That was an indication that it was her birthday and it was in plain sight. That's what Mama and her co-workers did at the beginning of each year to assure that nobody's birthday would be forgotten or overlooked.
She thought to herself: 'Where is my birthday food? Where did you guys hide it? Come on now, I am famished.'

She asked: "Does anybody know what today's date is?"

144

Candy answered: "Its February the twenty fifth."
And in return Mama casually threw out this question?

"Does this date ring a bell for any of you guys?"
All six of them indicated that it didn't ring a bell or anything else
for them.

Mama had another thought: 'Gladys, three strikes and you are
out. They done forgot your birthday too! Even though its circled
in red on the calendar. As long as I have been working here,
forgetting a co-worker's birthday had never happened. Wait a
minute? Maybe I'm being a little bit too hasty. I'm-ma try one
more thing.'

"I'm getting ready to order pizza. What would you ladies like on
yours?" Mama's intentions were to put them in a compromising
position, so they would confide in her that they had brought food
to celebrate her birthday. But that didn't happen.

They replied: "No. Thank you. We brought our lunch."

Break time rolled around. (On the weekends, they took their
lunch break together.) And Mama's six co-workers brought out
their brown bags and commenced to eat, talk and look at Margo's
twin sons' wedding pictures.

Feeling down and out, Mama excused herself and left for the
Coke machine.

She grabbed a coke, opened it and drank it straight down and
thought to herself: 'Since this is the only lunch I have, why not
indulge in another one!' She got another one and just as she
looked up from the machine she saw Mary Ann, (who worked in
the maternity ward) approaching her.

"Hello Gladys. How are you? Goodness, this has been a long
slow day hasn't it? I am accustomed to being busy. I'm lost with
all of this idle time."

As Mary Ann continued to talk, Mama thought to herself: 'For heaven's sakes, be quiet Mary Ann. I am having a bad day! And I have a bad attitude. Nobody is remembering my birthday! It's a critically serious epidemic. Curley started this darn thing, then my eight children and six co-workers caught it. I am torn up about it. I need some time to myself, after all, this is my lunch break and I want to be alone.'

She interrupted Mary Ann's conversation: "Girl, I have to go the bathroom. I can't hardly hole it. I'll talk with you later ok!"

She went to the locker room and laid on the cot, her body and mind was heavy with rejection. At that moment, she didn't feel loved by Daddy and her children as well. That gave her reason, to think more with teary eyes: 'They have a lot of nerves! Forgetting my birthday! I have a good mind to run away. (After a long silence) Nol. I can't do that. I know what I'll do, I'll call Miracle and invite her to join me for a movie and have a burger afterwards to celebrate my birthday. Miracle love going to the movies. I can count on her. I'll call her when my break is over.'

After taking an extra hour and fifteen minutes for lunch. She rushed back to work and apologized for taking extra time: "Ladies, I was in a deep meditation, and the time flew by. I see that I didn't miss out on any work. You guys are still sitting around and looking at those wedding pictures.'

Mattie inquired: "Gladys, do you feel alright? You look worried. Your eyes are red and puffy. Is there anything that I can do or get for you." Mama thought: 'yeah. What about some Freddie's donuts?'

Mama called Aunt Miracle: "Hello Miracle. What's up? Ok. Well I won't keep you long. I'll get to the point. I'm inviting you to go to the show with me tonight."

Aunt Miracle told Mama that she was baking a ham and preparing dinner. She was expecting company that evening. She suggested that perhaps they could attend the show the following week at her expense. Mama wanted to know: "What time is dinner? Ham sounds good to me. I'll be there. If it's alright with you!"

Disappointed. Mama accepted Aunt Miracle's lame excuse. "Gladys, I don't think you will feel comfortable, because you don't know any of the people that's coming here tonight." Then she rushed off the phone.

On the way home from work, she stared out the car window at the melting icy streets. Daddy asked how was her day at work? (He already knew, because him and Doll talked with her co-workers several times that day.)

But Mama told Daddy: "I had a most wonderful busy day. And the time went by so fast. That's why I didn't call you. The girls and I ordered a pizza for lunch. It was really good. So how was your day?"

She anticipated the thought that there would be her favorite cake (a stack cake with strawberry jam and whip cream between each layer) sitting on the table awaiting her to cut it. She could smell the food, that Doll was cooking. Whatever it was, Mama knew it would be scrumptious. That thought made her smile and she was content until she got home to a cake-less kitchen, with lunch meat sandwiches and pork and beans.

Mama didn't complain, but she thought: 'Um, um, um, this is surely a birthday to remember. I was expecting a little more than a lunch meat sandwich and pork and beans. I see Doll didn't hurt herself making dinner. I'll eat the sandwich. But I don't want these damn pork and beans.'

She wanted to know:

"Doll where is all the kids?" Doll couldn't stop smiling: "They are in the attic with June, Miney, (June's wife) and T. J. They are

147

helping June put up decorations. Some of June's army buddies are here in Buffalo. So June and Miney is having a party for them.

Mama ate the sandwich, and was unusually quiet. After making a cup of coffee, she left the kitchen and went to the living room to watch the wrestling match, but she couldn't seem to get into the wrestling match. Therefore she decided to take a hot bath. On her way to the bathroom, she noticed that Doll was frying catfish and asked:

"Doll, why didn't you tell me earlier that you were planning on frying this fish? You know that is my favorite. I could have waited to eat. Oh boy! that look good. I can't wait to dig into it. Um, um, um, this fish is good, and it's fresh too. I'm going to pile my plate up later and pig out."

Doll told Mama that the fish was for June's party. And she had to take it to the attic as soon as it was ready.

Mama's immediate goal, was to soak away all the stresses, that she had accumulated that day. She scooted down and leaned her head back on the tub. The bath water was level with her neck. And it was most comfortable. She fell into a peaceful sleep and slept for fifteen minutes. She woke up to the music which was playing in the attic. She thought: 'They are playing green onions. I could listen to that record all day. Wait a minute? (As she sat up in the tub) I declare those women voices out there in the hallway sounds like my co-workers, Loraine, Maggie, Margo, Viola, Candy and Lonnie. It can't be. I know darn well they wouldn't be coming to June and Miney's party. They don't know them.'

There was a knock on the bathroom door and Mama asked: "Who is it?"

She heard a faint reply: "It's me."

She inquired: "Me who?

148

The answer came: "It's me, Mama. It's me, Emerson. Open the door. I have to pee!"

She told him: "Come in. The door is not locked. Emerson, where are you going all dressed up in your Sunday suit? I know you don't think you are going to June and Miney's party! Honey, that party is for grownups and you can't go. Why are you looking in every direction except for my direction? Boy, look at me. It is impolite not to look at a person when they are talking to you. Do you understand me? I am talking to you. Boy, say something."

Emerson made a remark: "Mama, I can't tell you where I am going. They told me to keep my lips zipped. That mean I can't say anything." That little bit of information confused her:

"Emerson, I am totally lost. Help me out here. What are you talking about? Who told you to keep your lips zipped? Speak up now. This is no time to be quiet and shy!"

Emerson responded: "I finished peeing! May I please wash my hands and go now? They told me to come right back."

Mama refused to let him go: "Nol. You are not going anywhere until you tell me something.
(There was a long silence as they stared at each other.)

Well, I'm listening."

Emerson finally opened up: "Mama, they told me, Bet Joe, Richard, Charlie and Earl that if we say anything, we will spoil the surprise. Please Mama, I don't want to spoil the surprise. May I go now?"

Mama smiled: "Yes honey. You can go now."

As soon as Emerson exited the bathroom and closed the door. Mama laid back in the tub and kicked her feet splashing water onto the floor, thinking to herself: 'So that's what's going on.

Curley and the children are taking me out to dinner. That is very thoughtful, and sweet. I love my family. Oops, I have to act surprised. Heck, I'll cross that bridge when I get to it. I wish the whole family could go, but that's impossible because June, Miney, Doll, and T. J are having a party in the attic. I am a very happy mother. How could I have been upset with my beautiful family? They didn't forget my birthday! I am going out to dinner. What will I wear? It's time for me to get out of this tub. She went through her closet, looking for something very special to wear. She came up with a neat green and white wool suit and some green boots. She hurried and dressed, while singing, I am going out to-night, cause It's my birthday.'

She was a knockout. Daddy told her that she was the prettiest pregnant woman he had ever laid eyes on. Mama was excited and could not hold her bit of incorrect information in any longer.

Therefore, she told Daddy that his surprise had risen to the surface: "I know that you and the children are taking me out to dinner for my birthday." And she mentioned the difficult day which she had encountered at work. They laughed about it, but Daddy, laughed the hardest.

She was anxious to find out where they were taking her to eat:

"No more secrets Curley! Where are we going? You just said the children are in the car waiting for us. I want to know exactly where we are going!"

Daddy answered her this way: "I will tell you in a minute. But right now I want you to go upstairs and meet June's army buddies. They are a nice group of people to be around."

Mama commented: "I am not particularly concerned about meeting a group of young people at this moment. Maybe I will meet them after we come from dinner. I'm sure they will still be here. Baby, the night is young."

That rattled Daddy's nerves, and he thought: 'Woman, this ain't no time to be stubborn. We have been planning this surprise birthday party for a long time. Now that it's here, what can I do to get you in the attic? Ok. I have an ideal that might work.'

He told Mama that he would be right back. He went to the attic and screwed out two light bulbs, then called Mama and told her that they had a blackout up there. He asked her to bring him the light bulbs and the flashlight. She had the flashlight in one hand, guiding her way up the steps and the light bulbs in the other hand. When she reached the attic and walked a few steps, she asked Daddy where was he.

At that very moment the lights went on. And everybody simultaneously shouted; "Happy Birthday Gladys!" That shocked and scared the wit out of Mama to the point that she jumped and threw the flashlight. Mr. Houston caught the flashlight.

Daddy hugged her and said: "Honey, Let's not fight. Give me those light bulbs before you throw them too." Then he kissed her, wished her a happy birthday and said: "I am glad this surprise is out in the open. This surprise thing, has taken a lot out of me today! I'm hungry. I'll fix us a plate."

Simply surprised and lost for words! Mama turned around smiling as she acknowledged everyone. She felt the special love flowing through the air as she thought to herself: 'What can I say? In my wildest dreams, I would not have imagined something this magnificent. Oh my goodness. Get a load of these fine decorations. It must be a thousand balloons in here and check this out, my name is spelled all the way across the wall with crape paper, ah, that's hip.

This is my first birthday party. I think, I love this! Who thought of doing this for me? I am usually on top of things, nothing get around me. But everybody kept this secret until I came up here. Why did I think, they were taking me out to dinner? Now this is something to write home about! I think, I love this. It is so mellow. There's my children. Yeah. Curley had me going, thinking the children were in the car waiting for us. I see why they got up so early this morning. They have been busy all day. Look-a-here. There's my co-workers, (She laughed as tears ran down her face). That was them I heard talking earlier. I give them an A, for their performance at work today. Everything that I imagined them bringing to work, is on the table. Mercy! Mercy, Here come Mattie with two donuts. (Smiling) One of them must be for me.'

Mattie hugged Mama saying: "Happy Birthday Gladys. Here's the donut that you were looking for this morning. (Laughing) Gladys, you had us laughing all day long. Especially, when you took that fat red marker and traced over the bold red circle, that was already on the calendar. Gladys, we couldn't say anything. Our lips were zipped. Girl I wish somebody would make that much fuss over me."

Aunt Miracle came in carrying her ham saying: "I know I'm late y'all. But isn't it better late than never?" She glanced at Mama and winked her eye. Mama wanted to know what was in the roaster. She told her that it was ham. Mama asked if it was leftover from her dinner?

Aunt Miracle asked: "What dinner are you talking about? Girl. shit. You caught me off guard. I had no idea that you were going to call me from work. Hey. That was the only story that I could think of. It was convincing. Don't you think so? Gladys I been looking forward to this party for weeks. I know we will have a lot of fun tonight. About the show; why don't me and Shayne and you and Curley get away and go next Sunday afternoon!"

Daddy used a serving platter to fix something for him and Mama. She enjoyed her meal to the fullest. As a matter of fact, she ate several times. The food was prepared to satisfaction. Everyone simply loved it. The oversized birthday cake which Doll made was Mama's favorite layer cake. It was superb and vanished quickly. Everyone simply raved about it.

152

The music was great and everyone there danced except for Daddy and Mama. She preferred eating over dancing.

The partying went on as the evening progressed. It was time for the children to leave the party in the grownups hands and go down stairs. Richard, Charlie, Earl, and Emerson were obedient. But I was curious to know what the outcome of the party would be. I sat on the steps and pretty much heard what was going on.

Aunt Miracle announced: "I think most of you know me. But for those who don't know me, I'm Miracle Holmes. Gladys is my sister-n-law. And I am going to *ROAST* her. Why? because she's the birthday girl! I'll only take a few minutes of your time. As you all know; Gladys moved to Buffalo three years ago. And I am the one who started the ball to rolling when I went home to visit my mother. Mississippi is my home too. Well. My husband, (she pointed out Uncle Shayne) would tell me every time that I went home to bring back his brother Curley. So three years ago while driving down there, I thought 'why not!' I didn't have time to beat around the bush. So after a short visit with them I said 'What do you all think about moving to Buffalo, New York? Curley I'll be leaving Sunday, directly after church. And I want you to go back with me. I know you can get a job up there. It's time for you all to move on.'

Gladys was hesitant and threw all kind of stuff at me: 'What, when, where, why, which, how, that's a hard decision to make. We need a couple of weeks to think this over.' I saw right then that I had my work cut out for me. I started off with that damn out house. Considering the fact that it was fresh on my mind, because I had just used it and lost one of my brand new shoes.

Well. It was like this. I was doing my business and looking through the Sears and Roebuck Catalogue and was rudely interrupted by a noise coming from under the other Sears and Roebuck Catalogues, which was on the floor. I saw something long and brown, it could have been a snake or a lizard. Whatever it was, I didn't think it was in there to welcome me. So I jumped

153

upon the toilet seat and my foot slipped, that left me straddling the seat. My right leg dangled over the toilet and my shoe fell splashing something wet on my foot. I was too scared to scream!

I didn't bite my tongue. I Just said out loud: 'If I have to drown; let it be water that I drown in and not this toilet full of shit. I think I must have scared whatever was under that paper, because it didn't waste any time getting the hell out of there.'

Anyhow. I was bellyaching to get through to Gladys: 'Gladys aren't you tired of getting fully dressed to go out to that snake and lizard filled outhouse to do your business and wiping your ass with those Sears and Roebuck Catalogue pages? That's country as hell and old fashioned. I went to my car and got four rolls of toilet paper and gave it to her. (Laughing) This country girl was glad to get her hands on that toilet paper. (Laughing) Her face was blush with a smile as she looked at me and said she was going to save it for a special occasion. (Laughing, laughing, laughing)

Talking about : 'You know. Like when the preacher come over.' I told her to forget about the preacher's ass and think about her own ass.

She said 'Nol. I can't do that. Ooh wee! Toilet paper is very expensive. I bet one roll of this stuff cost a whole nickel. If we move to Buffalo, New York I don' think me and Curley will ever be able to afford enough toilet paper to go around the whole family.'

(laughing, laughing, laughing, laughing)   I can go on and on and on. But Im-ma be nice and step aside so somebody else say something. Gladys I hope you are enjoying your surprise birthday party. I'm telling you that we went through hell and high water to keep this away from you. Sister in law you are a good woman and I am tickled because I had a part in making this a special birthday for you. I am so happy that you are in Buffalo, that I could jump up and clap my feet. One more thing! That big gift wrapped in the pink paper is from me and Shayne. Open that one first. Ok

Gladys. You are like a sister to me! I Love you with a passion."

Aunt Miracle was kicking out some amusing things. But I didn't laugh. I was a bit upset because she was ribbing on Mama. But it didn't seem to bother her. She was laughing too. Daddy was laughing. As a matter of fact I was the only one that wasn't laughing. Mama opened Aunt Miracle's gigantic gift first. And everybody cracked up with laughter! It was one hundred rolls of toilet paper and a Sears and Roebuck Catalogue.

Mama said that was the best birthday she ever had. And she would definitely write home about it. She received a gift from every one that attended the party and was overwhelmed with joy and happiness. She felt like a child on Christmas morning. She also commented that if she could snap her fingers to make her relive that day, she wouldn't change a thing.

Daddy Took The Driving Test:

The time for Daddy to renew his driver's license rolled around again. When he arrived at the Department Of Motor Vehicle facility, he was informed that he had to take the actual driving test. He felt like it was no problem and went for it.

The instructor called him to the car, introduced himself and made some small talk. He told Daddy to relax and they were on their way. Daddy was confident throughout the complete driving test. At the conclusion of the test, the instructor had Daddy drive back to the facility and park. He took a few minutes to write some notes on the test paper and put his signature on it. Then he proceeded to talk with Daddy: "Mr. Holmes you are an excellent driver."

Daddy thought he was done talking: "Thank you sir. I consider myself one of the top ten best drivers in the United States Of America." The instructor said: "Wait a second Mr. Holmes. I wasn't finished talking. I was going to say 'but' Daddy interrupted him again: "But? But what? Let me see that paper!"

The instructor told Daddy: "Calm down Mr. Holmes and let me finish talking. Like I was saying you are an excellent driver. But you need to do something about those rolling stops. Do you realize that you did two rolling stops on this driving test? I could overlook one, but I can't overlook two. I am aware that there were no cars in sight. But you still have to make a complete stop. Therefore, that's why you have to take the driving test again. I will make another appointment for you to come back and take another driving test.

He proceeded to write something else on the test paper. Daddy casually took out his wallet and removed a twenty dollar bill and laid it on the seat. The instructor stopped writing and glanced over to see what Daddy had laid on the seat. He asked: "Mr. Holmes, are you trying to bribe me?" With a serious expression on his face Daddy looked at the instructor and answered: "Bribe you? That's an outright insult! Why would you think that?"

As he reached for his money, the instructor extended his hand: "Mr. Holmes I want to shake your hand. I believe a congratulation is in order. You passed the driving test. You scored 100%."

The instructor tore the original test paper up and did another test paper with 100% written across the top. He signed it and gave it to Daddy. He was happy and twenty dollars richer. Daddy was happy because he didn't have to retake the driving test.
Daddy was a fast learner. He took heed to the instructor's advice and never made any more rolling stops!

The Day Roy Was Born:

June 14,1959, The clock went off at five that morning. Still sleepy. Mama turned the clock off with the intentions of getting back in bed and taking another fifteen minutes of sleep. But the baby was situated on her bladder. And that pressure sent her to the bathroom. By then she was wide awake, hungry and wanted some coffee.

It was a typical morning. Mama made breakfast and fixed Daddy's lunch as usual. They talked while having breakfast. Mama suggested that they have barbecue and homemade ice cream for dinner. That is what she was craving. She jotted down a list of things they needed to make the dinner and planned to stop by the grocery store after work and pick them up. Mama's dinner suggestions sounded like a winner to Daddy. He hurried and filled the soup pot with water and put it in the deep freezer to make sure they had ice for the manual ice cream freezer.

On the way to work Daddy backed out of the driveway then drove right back into the back yard. That was because Mama had to use the bathroom again due to the baby's pressure. After she returned to the car, they were on their way again. She massaged her abdomen hoping the baby would change position and give her a break. She had no luck. So her and Daddy assumed at that precise moment that the baby had a mind of its own and it had to be a stubborn girl. Their assumption turned out to be wrong. That was alright with us!

Mama At Work:

It was an extremely uncomfortable morning at work for Mama. The pressure wouldn't let up. Mama had three weeks to go before the baby was due. Some of her co-workers told her that they had the same feeling of pressure on their bladder during their last month of pregnancy. That particular pregnancy was different for Mama. She never experienced an uncomfortable feeling like that. But it didn't seem to affect her appetite in the least. She ate several times before lunch and was still hungry.

She was scheduled to take the last lunch break that day. The Milk Lab was quiet and the work was caught up. Mama looked for something to do to keep her busy until her lunch break came. She found a stack of paperwork that needed attention and

157

committed herself to taking care of it. While she sat and went through the papers, her mind wasn't fully on what she was doing. She couldn't keep her eyes off her watch. Then she found herself thumping her fingers on the desk and counting the minutes before lunch.

Mama didn't make it to lunch. The stubborn baby with a mind of its own had other plans for her. Her water broke while she was sitting at the desk but she had no knowledge of it until the phone rang. Ring, ring, ring. Mama went to the phone and discovered that her water had broken during her conversation on the phone. She was taken to the maternity ward. Daddy was waiting for her when she got there.

She couldn't believe it: "Curley! What are you doing here before me?"

Excitedly he began to talk: "Your supervisor called me at work and told me that you were in labor and to get out here as soon as possible. So here I am after speeding and running red lights all the way from my job. The way it started was by me getting stopped by the police for running the red light just as I pulled out of the parking lot from the job. Honey I thought he was going to give me a ticket. He asked me where was I going in such a big hurry? And I explained to him that your supervisor called me at work and said you were in labor. He told me to get back in the car and follow him. Honey we were driving seventy miles an hour. I was chasing a cop and it felt good. Unbelievable! I believe we got here in ten minutes or less. He lead me right to the emergency door and we talked for a hot minute.

He was a real nice guy named Marion Miller. That was my first time meeting a man with a woman's name! Anyway, he shook my hand and told me that he hope I have a healthy boy. And that he grow up to be an officer of the law just like him. Wouldn't that be something if we was to have another boy and he grow up and become an officer of the law for real? Oh boy. Wouldn't that be something?"

Just as Mama agreed with Daddy and started to smile a labor pain wiped the smile off her face real quick and forced her to stand up. When the pain subsided Daddy called us again to keep us informed as to how things were progressing. All of us were excited and praying for a sister. Especially me. I rushed to the bathroom and fell on my knees: "Our Father. Please. Please. Please let Mama have a girl? Amen."
We sat around the phone picking out names for girls.

Mama had several more labor pains. Daddy had a hostile confrontation with this particular unprofessional admitting clerk. But most of all they met the most wonderful doctor in the entire city of Buffalo, New York, Dr. Yellen, who immediately became Mama's doctor and delivered my baby brother; Roy Lane Holmes.

When we heard the news of his birth, Doll immediately suggested that his name be Roy Lane. She told us that her professor in high school had a son and his name was Roy Lane. She had anticipated on saving that name for her son. Daddy thought it was a nice name and said Mama would like it too. So Roy Lane Holmes it was.

Daddy came home to take a bath after Roy was born. We crowded around him asking the usual questions how do he look? Who do he look like? What color is his eyes?
Daddy was happy. But there was a sad unsettling undertone in his face that was showing through. I considered it as being in an uneasy state of preoccupation. He mentioned the nice Dr. Yellen many times. He told us that Mama was the first black woman to have a baby at Children's Hospital and the entire hospital was talking about it. He understood that it was expected to be in the newspaper. He was fatigued from drinking coffee and smoking cigarettes with just about every doctor who invited him to join them in the cafeteria to do so.

I overheard him talking on the phone with Dr. Yellen: "I don't know what Gladys and I would have done if you hadn't come along. We were determined not to leave there and go to another hospital. I guess Gladys would have had the baby in the wheel chair right there in the lobby. And I would've cut the umbilical cord with my pocket knife. But then you came to our rescue just in time. Dr. Yellen, you are a blessing to us! What can I do to show our gratitude? Saying thank you doesn't seem like enough.

Oh! I see. I don't believe this! You left your office and was on your way home and something told you to make a U-turn and drive to the hospital. That was fate! It was meant for us to meet.

You know. I expected this kind of treatment in Mississippi. We assumed things were a bit different here in Buffalo at Children's Hospital! I am so freaking angry and hurt for the inhumane treatment my wife and I received from that ignorant sick minded unprofessional woman with nothing but prejudice in her heart for colored people. People working in an environment like that shouldn't let the color of a person's skin get in the way of them performing their job efficiently. That woman has been working with and grinning in my wife's face every day for the last two years. Can you believe that? She is a disgrace to Children's Hospital. She certainly is not qualified to have a job working with people, especially people who require medical attention. Hell! We are here to stay. And nothing in this world will ever change it. The more I think about it, I want her from behind that desk. Hell! If she treat somebody else like that they might not be as nice as I was.

Yeah. Yeah. Yeah. You are absolutely right doctor. I am upset. Wouldn't you be upset if you were in my shoes? Ok Dr. Yellen. I'll try to take your advice and get some sleep. Maybe I will feel better. But you know it's easy for you to tell me to get some sleep. But it's not an easy thing for me to settle down and close me eyes and fall asleep with this depressing, bewildering weight on my mind! I'm going back to the hospital later. I want to be there when Gladys wakes up in the recovery room from that anesthesia. Ok. I'll see you then. Bye."

I totally agreed with what Daddy told Dr. Yellen. I was agitated

160

because of his insatiable state of mind. Also I felt bad and was hurt for what my sweet, kind hearted, loving, considerate mother and father went through. I realized that Daddy was trying to grab a nap before going back to the hospital. But I felt it was a necessity to have a talk with him about what I heard him discussing with Dr. Yellen. I told him that I heard the conversation he had on the phone. And I was curious as to what was going on.

After scolding me for snooping outside of his closed bedroom door eavesdropping and invading his privacy, he commenced to talk: "Don't pay any attention to what you heard me saying on the phone. That's no concern of yours anyway. After all I am human. Getting mad frustrated and blowing off steam is a natural human instinct."

I had empathy: "Yeah! I'm mad too. Guess what; I hate that stupid woman. She tried to keep Mama from having the baby in the same hospital where she work. I am not going to eat any of those Girl Scout cookies that Mama ordered from her."

The thought of me talking like that made him feel bad: "Wait a minute. I don't like you talking that way. It's not good to hate a person! But you can certainly hate their ways. Bring me the Bible I want to show you something. Turn to Matthew 5:44 and read it to me."

I read it: *'Love your enemies, bless them that curse you, do good to them that hate you, and pray for them which despitefully use you, and persecute you.'*
He told me he knew that I understood what it meant. Because that's what Mama was always telling us and that was the way that he wanted me to think and act. He assured me that there was no reason to worry about Mama because she was in God's hands.

He added: "Your mother is a woman of strength and a strong woman." He also mentioned: "We should be proud of her for standing her ground and being the first black woman to have a baby at Children's Hospital. Her courage has paved the way for

161

other black women to have their babies at Children's Hospital as well."

A faint smile invaded his face as he said: "The name Gladys Holmes will circulate in and around Children's Hospital for a while. When she got up this morning we had no idea she was going to make history."

Later that evening he called us from the hospital and Mama said hello to all of us. She said we had a beautiful baby brother with thick black hair and long eye lashes and she could see all of us in him. And that he was a good eater with a firm grip. She was fatigued from that extremely long active day.

Daddy raved about the nine red roses, which was situated in an expensive crystal vase sitting in the center of the window seal, as they entered the private room, Mama was due to stay in until she was discharged from the hospital. The sender forgot to sign the card. That was a mystery.

Mama's six day stay at the hospital was exceptional. She enjoyed it tremendously. Daddy broke a hospital rule every day by coming and going before and after visiting hours. A couple of times he stayed past midnight. Visiting hours were over in the evenings at eight.
Daddy's disposition improved remarkably with each day. And the big day finally arrived.

Doll took a vacation day off work. We had a lot of things planned for that day because Mama and the baby were coming home. (Mama was still craving barbecue and homemade ice cream). It was exciting. We planned to have barbecue, corn on the cob, potato salad and homemade ice cream. Each one of us was assigned to do something. Richard and Charlie cleaned the grill. Earl and Emerson was assigned to take turns freezing the ice cream (turning the handle), I helped Doll out in the kitchen. I put some flowers from the back yard in Daddy and Mama's bedroom as a welcome home gesture. The meat was seasoned and ready for the grill. So little Earl who was overflowing with energy wanted to help out. That's why he took it into his hands to start the grill. He was fast and careless, while taking short cuts. He put some newspaper in the bottom of the grill and forgot to add the charcoal. Then he put some lighter fluid on top of the news paper and lit it with a cigarette lighter. His hand was burned because it was too close to the newspaper when it caught on fire. Doll immediately gave him first aid attention. Then he was off to the back yard again to lend a helping hand with the barbecue.

Everything was ready. Mama was being discharged after Dr. Yellen examined her and the baby. Due to the fact that we had a party line (a shared telephone line with three other families), we were hoping that no one was on the phone. We didn't want to miss Mama's important call letting Daddy know she was ready to come home.

Earl asked Daddy: "Can I back the car out of the garage when you get ready to pick Mama and the baby up from the hospital?"

Daddy answered him: "You don't know anything about driving Earl."
Earl replied: "Yes I do. I know a lot about driving. June and T. J. been teaching me how to drive. I can drive real good."

Knowing how excited Earl was about Mama and the new baby coming home, Daddy found it difficult to say no to him.

So he told him: "Alright. But only if you do exactly as I tell you. I'll let you hold the keys. But Earl I don't want you in the car until I get in it. Alright? Is that clear?"

Earl was willing to do whatever he had to but he didn't. After the phone rang and he knew it was Mama for sure he forgot about following Daddy's instructions.

Earl ran down the stairs and into the garage. He got into the car. And without waiting for Daddy he started the car and proceeded to back out of the garage. He stepped on the gas too hard. And this is what happened. He ran into the garage door knocking it off the hinges. When the car was completely out of the garage energized Earl stepped on the brakes so hard that it made the tires smoke. Then he turned the ignition off and got out of the car to make an account of what damage he had just did.

All of that noise brought Daddy and the rest of us to the back yard. Besides the broken garage door, there was a scratch on the side of the car that extended from the head light to the tail light. Earl traced the length of the scratch with his finger and shook his head like he was disgusted.

Then he walked to the garage door and said: "This ain't too bad. I can fix it." He traced the length of the scratch with his finger again. And said. "I can get some sand paper and smooth this out and spray paint it. It will look just like it did before this happened."

Daddy was pissed. He turned red and was biting his tongue: "Boy! What did I tell you? Why didn't you wait for me like I told you? I thought you told me that June and T. J. been teaching you how to drive and you knew a lot about driving."

We could barely hear what Earl was saying: "They only taught me how to drive forward. I thought I knew how to back up. Daddy I wanted to surprise you and make you happy."

That kind of softened Daddy's heart when Earl said he wanted to surprise him and make him happy. He thought to himself: "Yeah! Well. You surprised me alright. But that's water under the bridge. I cannot stay mad with you for wanting to make me happy. You have been trying hard all day to do something significant that will make a difference. As far as I am concerned you have already made a difference and I appreciate your love! It is obvious and powerful son."

With compassionate love; he told Earl that he was letting him go the hospital to bring Mama and the baby home.

That made Earl's day: "For real? I can go with you? I ain't gon get no whooping? Daddy you mean it? I can hold the baby on the way home from the hospital! (smiling) Ok. I'll sit in the back seat." He sat in the back seat waving and smiling as Daddy backed out of the driveway.

We were sitting around the table in the kitchen when we heard the car drive up. We went to the car to greet them. Daddy helped Mama out of the car and into the house. Earl was in the back seat holding Roy. Doll took Roy and followed Daddy and Mama. We followed Doll. Roy was a beautiful baby, just like we heard he was. We stood in line waiting to hold him. Ah. He was a little bundle of joy. We loved him so much that we used to hold him while he was sleeping. And we didn't give him a chance to cry much. Because every time he opened his mouth and made a whimper we were right there to pick him up. We fought over who was going to change his diaper who was going to feed him etc.

Three months later:

It was time for Mama to return to work. They hired Mrs. Merry who lived down the street from us. She was visiting her son and daughter in law. Husband passed away and her son insisted that she come to Buffalo and stay with them for a while. Mrs. Merry was accustomed to working. She said that was what she needed to keep her going. She was highly experienced. She raised fifteen children of her own. She simply loved children. They were her passion. (Her native home was Kanfield, Arkansas)

She was a tall fairly good looking woman in her late sixties. She loved to talk. She was not a shy woman. The first day she worked she familiarized herself with the kitchen and made biscuits, bacon and eggs for our lunch. When we arrived home from school for lunch the table was set. I said: "Mrs. Merry you

165

don't have to make our lunch. I do that. You are only suppose to take care of Roy." She said: "I am all six of y'all's baby sitter. And starting tomorrow morning I will be fixing yo breakfast too. I will be washing on Monday, Wednesday and Friday. And I want y'all to put your dirty clothes in a pillow case and put them in the back hall way so I can wash them. Follow my rules and we will get along fine."

Daddy had a problem with that: "No!. No way. Ain't no other woman gon wash my draws. Gladys I realize that it would help us a lot if she would wash the children's clothes. But not ours, especially my draws."

That's the way it was. She spoiled all of us. That was cool. We didn't have a problem with it. She'd wait until we ate our lunch before she began. We'd sit around the table and listen to her tell stories about things that happened in her lifetime. Her down home southern stories were interesting and fun to listen to.

She insisted that Daddy or Mama buy a stroller for Roy so she could take him out every day to get some fresh air. Roy got his stroller and Mrs. Merry took him somewhere every day even if it was a short walk to the corner store. The winter didn't stop her from taking Roy out. She was the only person in Buffalo, pushing a stroller down the streets covered with snow and ice. Sometimes people would blow their horn at her and tell her to get the hell out of the street with that buggy. But Mrs. Merry always had the last word. She would give them the finger and tell them exactly where to go.

She had a passion for taking Roy to the Museum Of Science on Humboldt Parkway. They went there faithfully every Tuesday morning. Mrs. Merry told us that it was fascinating to see the expression of wonder and amazement on Roy's face when he saw the Buffalo Bull as they entered the front entrance of the museum. That's what inspired her to keep taking him back.

One day she put a loaf of banana nut bread in the oven to bake,

166

and began to sweep the kitchen and hall way floor. While she was in the hallway the wind blew the door shut, locking her outside in the hallway and Roy inside in the kitchen. In panic she called Roy and asked him to open the door.

All he did was answer: "Huh"

Things flooded her mind: 'The banana loaf is in the oven . I don't want it to burn. Roy is in the house by himself. What if he turn the stove on. My hot coffee is on the table. Etc..'

She left the house in search of a phone. She went to every house on the street and finally found someone home in the next block. They were kind enough to let her use their phone to call the police. They arrived at the house spontaneously. Mrs. Merry explained to them what happened, while they were taking the hinges off the door. Roy, was standing by the door when they took it down, holding his empty bottle in his hand.

Everything was intact and while Mrs. Merry was running her mouth and feeding the policemen some of her banana nut bread and coffee, Roy fell asleep on the floor under the kitchen table. When the three of them noticed that he was missing they panicked and searched the entire house for him. The three of them were calling him and disturbed his mid morning nap and he answered them: "Huh"

Mrs. Merry was in the mirror checking out her hair when we got home for lunch. She told us that episode scared the heck out of her and aged her a good twenty years. She also told us that she would swear on a stack of Bibles that she didn't have that much gray hair when she came to our house that morning.

Mrs. Merry loved to come to our house so much that she came on her days off and hung out with Mama. If Mama had to go shopping or anything Mrs. Merry went with her. Mama said she was a very lonely person therefore she did not want to be at her son's house all alone. After watching the soap operas with Mama for one day she took an interest in watching them every day.

After working three years for us Mrs. Merry said something was missing in her life. She couldn't get used to living alone. (Her son and daughter in law was there but that didn't make up for her loneliness or take the place of a man.)

According to her since her husband passed away. She had been entertaining the thought of getting married again: "I am very much alive and I have a whole lot of living to do."

Because she had so much to give, she needed a man of her own to love and make a fuss over. She also wanted a man to love her and make a fuss over her as well. She was a charming woman who knew what she wanted and went after it.

She called the man that was best friends with her late husband and asked him to marry her. He accepted. She said he was a good catch and she didn't want other women getting the same idea. After all he had only been a widower for three weeks.

She talked: "I knew his wife. She was nice. I guess. We used to see each other in church and speak. I never heard anything bad about her. She used to wear nice store bought clothes. But you know what? She's dead now and Im-ma fill her shoes. His name is Jonah W.

He is pretty well off. Ain't nothing wrong with me bragging. The second time around for me is going to be the best. I loved my husband. But I missed out on a lot. We were dirt poor. I didn't complain cause I loved him and my children. But I won't go through a situation like that again. I won't waste money. But I sure do plan on getting some of the things that I always wished for. Y'all know what I'm trying to say.

For instance. A brand new wool coat, some nylon stockings, some silk underwear and a store bought night gown with lace on it. Ah. Why is y'all looking at me like that? Hey! If you knew what was going on in Kanfield, Arkansas, you wouldn't look at me that way. It's them damn church women. They are baking my intended husband cakes, pies and all kind of sweets. The next damn thing they will do is try to move in with him. And I ain't gon let that happen."

She moved back to Kanfeild, Arkansas and married Jonah. And they communicated with us for years.

My Siblings:

Edward June Holmes (June) In Gloster, Mississippi

June was my oldest brother. And I looked up to him and followed him around all the time. I was his shadow. People used to say: 'If June was to fart that gal will smell it before he do.' He was always around looking after me and protecting me. I never heard him raise his voice. He got along with just about everybody. I believe that his favorite things to do was go hunting and horse back riding with his friends. June taught me how to tie my shoes. He also taught me my A, B, C's and how to read and print my name.

One clear, sunny summer day, June told me that he was going to take me horseback riding. That was a real treat and the best thing I had heard in a long time. I had never rode a horse before. I went to Big Mama's house and told her that I was going horseback riding with June. She was sitting at her sewing machine sewing, and told me to try on a red blouse that she made for herself but after washing it and hanging it on the clothes line, the heat from the sun shrunk it.

My lovely grandmother had a talk with me: " I am tired of you ripping and running around with no blouse on climbing trees and jumping off the porch and not to mention spitting and arm wrestling with your brothers. You are a Tomboy. Just the other day Mrs. Sears said you were a Tomboy and yo middle name should be Tomboy. I didn't like that one bit. But you know it started me to thinking and I came up with an idea. You are a girl. From now own you will be doing girl things"

Her blouse was huge on me. But she had a solution in mind. She sewed a ribbon on each side of the blouse, put it back on me and tied it in the back. She took it off again and shortened it. While she was working on the blouse, she mentioned that June was driving her to town the next day and she was taking me along

170

with her to buy some material to make blouses for me that would fit properly. After finishing the size 2XXX red blouse, Big Mama put it on me again. It came to my ankles.

Crying, I told her: "This ain't no blouse. It look like a long dress. The only thang that I like about it is the red color. Big Mama Please don't make me wear this ugly thang. You don't like me no mo. Do you? Its too hot for me to wear this blouse. I wanna be a Tomboy."

She gave me a piece of gum that was still in the silver wrapper. I chewed the gum, forgot about that long red ugly dress and skipped to the corral and crawled under the wooden fence. June was busy brushing the horse. Just as I began to walk in his direction Bessie (the cow) started to make a big fuss about something. I really didn't pay much attention to her. I was Happy-go-lucky and in my own little world because I was getting ready to take my first horseback ride. And the next day I was going shopping in town with Big Mama. Anyhow Bessie was determined to get my full attention. And that's just what she managed to do. She was jumping and kicking the barn wall with her hind legs. I was glad that blame cow was tied up to the barn, because she scared the wit out me acting like that.

She mooed to the top of her lungs and made sounds that I simply didn't think was possible for a cow to make. Although she put fear in me I was overwhelmed with compassion for her. I couldn't stand it. I truly believed she was in chronic distress. That's why I walked towards her in my big red dress. I thought if I untied her, she would be fine and dandy.

June shouted: "She's going to break away from the barn. Run Bettye Joe."

That confused me. I ran in Bessie's direction, and that aroused her even more. By time June was running towards me. And my senses sparked me to change my directions and run towards him. At that point, he was shaking his head indicating no and

171

pointing at the fence that I had just crawled under. Before I could get a clear understanding of what he was trying to tell me, Bessie broke away from the barn, pulling darn near half of the barn wall on the rope that was tied around her neck.

She was acting like a darn fool! Jumping, bucking, kicking her hind legs, ramming her head into the ground and screaming in a high pitch tone. Perhaps that was her way of dealing with her frustration. Anyhow she gave me one last quick stare before she took off after me. As I recall, it was right then when I finally realized and understood exactly what June was saying to me. Surprised, scared, spell-bound, hot and sweaty I stood there watching that humongous two-thousand pounder make the ground shake as she made her way towards me.

June shouted: "Bettye Joe. Git the hell out of here! Run. Run. Run fast. Run Bettye Joe. Run like hell. Run like hell to save your life.

I heard June loud and clear that time. And that's exactly what I did. I headed for the fence running like hell to save my life.

Bessie caught up with me just as I fell on my knees with the intentions of scooting under the fence to safety. I was extremely happy. Because that big clumsy cow defeated her purpose. She was crazed and determined to kill me. But due to a slight misjudgment she rammed her head into the fence instead of me. The impact was so powerful that it broke the pole that was imbedded in the ground as a point of foundation for the fence. While wiggling her head trying to free herself her mouth and nose inadvertently pushed me under the fence away from her boundaries and insane violent attack.

I arose to my feet and continued to run. Papa and Big Mama's house was closer than ours. Immediately after I put my hand on the door knob and turned it to open the door to the kitchen I heard something jump on the porch and run. I dashed into the kitchen slammed the door, locked it, rushed pass Big Mama and scooted under her kitchen table. Something was trying to open the locked door.

Frightened and trembling I pleaded with Big Mama: "Please don't open that door Big Mama. Please don't open it." She opened the door! What a cheerful relief! It was June! I thought it was that crazy ass Bessie.

Big Mama asked: "What on earth was all of that racket out there? I was hanging out of the window trying my best to catch a glimpse of something.
But I couldn't see a darn thing. The sun was glaring in my eyes. Bet Joe I heard you screaming to the top of your lungs. Come from under that table! I want you to tell me just what in the world would make you scream like that?"

June told her about the gruesome Bessie ordeal. Speechless, Big Mama fixed us a bowl of milk and bread. While I was eating mine her quivering hands palpated my extremities searching for injuries.

Smiling she said: "I am grateful and thankful to God that you came out of this un-harmed. I see that this red dress did one good thing. It protected your knees from getting scarred up. Take a look at these dirty knee prints on this dress."

While un-braiding my hair as I ate she cleared her throat several times trying to be a strong grandmother while fighting back the tears. "I, I, I just don't know what I was thinking about. Putting that red dress on you. I knowed all the time that you were goin out there to the corral wit June. What is Curley and Gladys gon say? How will I ever live this down? Oh my goodness. Where are my manners? I'm being selfish thinking about myself."

"To this day I ain't never been able to figure out why red make cows go crazy and attack. This red dress is the reason Bessie tried to hurt you. Just the other day you were out there crying because June was teasing you about Bessie being slaughtered come slaughtering day. I guess Bessie burgers and Bessie steaks sounds

173

pretty good to you rat now. Huh? My sweet little blessed granddaughter:"

I answered; "I hate that big fat cow real bad. She got mad and went crazy and almost killed me. All because you gave me this big red dress. Big Mama do you know why Bessie didn't kill me? Because I ran like hell to save my life. Ain't that the truth June? Big Mama I think it is a very good plan to slaughter Bessie. That-a-way you and Papa and Daddy and Mama ain't got to go to the Piggley Wiggley to buy steak no mo. We can have Bessie steaks all the time."

I was teed-off with Bessie from the day before that incident occurred. I found a pink new-born hairless mouse in the barn. I named it Little Pink. I was going to take Little Pink home and play with it. I took Little Pink outside for Bessie to see it. Bessie fooled me when she leaned her head down to my hands. I thought she was going to take a closer look at Little Pink. She ate Little Pink instead. That peed me off and I slapped her so hard that it made my arm and shoulder hurt. Then I spit in her face. The following February we had Bessie burgers and steaks galore.

The Old Brown Rusty Bike:

June found an old brown rusty bike in our watermelon patch and brought it home.

I asked him was it for me and he said: "You better believe it little sister."

One of our neighbors told Papa that four white boys found their way to our watermelon patch and one of them was riding that old brown rusty bike. He also related to Papa that those boys had to make three trips to the watermelon patch to steal twenty-four watermelons.

The neighbor laughed and said: "Yeah! They made one mo trip

174

to have a smashing good time eatin them watermelons. When they got a belly full, I declare, they went to acting like they ain't had no sense! Them boys was throwing watermelons every which-a-way. That is when I pointed this shot gun straight up in the air and pulled the trigger. Smiley, the but of this gun caught me in the chest with a blow and knocked me on the ground. When I straightened up I didn't see hide nor hair of them boys. Ha. They ran off and left that old rusty bike. I don't thank they will come back."

That was my first bike. Even though it was old, rusty and bent out of shape, I felt like it was a brand new bike. Learning to ride it was not easy for me. But after many, many, many attempts, a sprained ankle, and being flipped over the handle bars, I finally got the hang of it. Being very patient, June finally taught me how to ride that old rusty brown bike. I simply rode it until it fell apart. I cried because I truly loved that old rusty brown bike. June was absolutely without a doubt my *favorite* brother.

June's Hot Sauce Game:

We had been living in Buffalo about eight months when June started something. One Saturday morning he put four quarters and a bottle of hot sauce on the kitchen table and said: "Whoever eat a teaspoon of this hot sauce without drinking water will get a quarter. I will go first."

June ate the hot sauce and took a quarter. Richard was next. He ate the hot sauce and cried because it was extremely hot. Charlie procrastinated.

He'd put the hot sauce in the spoon and walked around the kitchen saying: " Im-ma eat this hot sauce. Nol. Ain't gon eat nothing. Cause y'all keep rushing me!" That's what he did every Saturday.

After a month Richard became accustomed to eating the hot

sauce. Therefore, he ate two teaspoons of hot sauce. June did the Same.

Three months later Daddy and Mama had a talk with Richard: "Richard you are eating something on Fridays or Saturdays that's giving you diarrhea. That's peculiar! This has been occurring for three months or longer. We are worried. Perhaps you can shed some light on this situation? What are you eating on these days that the rest of us are not eating?"

Charlie told. "It's that hot sauce that June pay Richard fifty cents to eat every Saturday morning.

June told Richard: 'Eating this hot sauce give you the shits. But don't worry about that. The shits will stop sooner or later. The important thing is this hot sauce will make hair grow on your chest.' That's what June said! But Richard been eating that hot sauce for five years and he still got the shits. And you better believe ain't no hair on his chest."

Daddy and Mama mumbled: "What are we going to do about Charlie's mouth? Perhaps we should make him wash his mouth out three times a day with some Tide. And Clorox."

Charlie heard what they said and quickly changed the subject: "Daddy are we going to watch the wrestling match today? Cause its almost time for it to come on."

Daddy had a conversation with June about his hot sauce game and from that day on June's hot sauce game was history. Even though he still gave Richard fifty cents every Saturday.

Dolly Mae Holmes Gilchrist: (Doll)

Doll is my only special *favorite* sister.

Doll used to dress me up and take me places with her all the

176

time. She would comb my hair, braid it and on the ends of my braids she'd put pretty colored plastic clothes pins or some cute wide ribbons. She made sure that the white part of my black and white shoes were polished and clean. My can-can slips were starched to her satisfaction, so they could make my pretty dresses stand out beautifully. She tried diligently to encourage me not to bite my finger nails. All of her friends would say I was cute and gave me candy or a nickel and that spoiled me terribly. I relished the Saturdays which she took me to town. I will always treasure this particular Saturday, during the Christmas season when I accompanied her to town. We walked down the street on the white side of town and admired the gorgeous decorations as we appreciated the Christmas carols. We also engaged in my first movie. It was incomparable! That was better than Santa Claus bringing me a baby doll for Christmas. She always shared secrets with me. At night after going to bed we'd talk about our activities of the day, tell jokes and laugh. That was our thing.

The First Time Doll Took Me To Choir Rehearsal:

As I remember. The first time that she took me to choir rehearsal: It was a blessed, cloudy, late Saturday morning. We were the first ones to arrive at church. So we stood around outside until it started to sprinkle. That forced us to go inside the church and wait for everyone else to get there. We sat on the front seat while she talked with me.

She pointed to the piano and said: "From now on when we come to church I won't be sitting with the family because I'm the new Piano Player. I'll be sitting on that bench at the piano while Reverend Clinton preach. That's a new bench and it's padded too. I hope it's more comfortable than these benches. Guess what Imma do to keep from getting nervous? Daddy told me to drink some cold water. He thinks that will aide me in staying calm and collective. I will keep a glass of ice water right there on top of the piano to sip on."

The church quickly filled with the choir members and they were anxious to get started.

Doll gave me her note book and some bubble gum and told me to sit very quietly while they practiced the songs. I obeyed her well until I came across my very first enemy, Georgia, Georgia came from the opposite side of the church to pick on me. She pulled my hair, grabbed my arm, twisted it and pinched me.

Then she said to me; "That's my mother singing. Now you be still, sit up and shut up. Give that bubble gum to me and listen to her sing. You bet not tell nobody what I did." Little Miss Georgia was in for a rude awakening.

I in-return pulled her hair. (I learned something from her, a new pinching technique that brought excruciating pain. Naturally I tried it out on her.) With my index finger and thumb I took a portion of her arm and held onto it tight as I twisted it just like she did me. And it worked wonders. She cried more than I did.

After that I spit on her, bit her hand and said: "That is my sister playing the piano. And if you pull my hair and pinch me again she will give you a good spanking." Angrily I stormed over to the piano interrupting the song talking loud. I told Doll what that mean girl did and said to me. She had me sit on the bench with her and they rehearsed the song again. Every now and then during the remainder of the rehearsal I'd glance over and catch her eyes on me and make ugly faces at her. The choir members told Doll that Georgia was a bad egg and a little trouble maker that needed a good dose of discipline to straighten her out.

The Day I Borrowed Twenty-Five Cents From Doll Without Asking

When Doll got her first pay check from Children's Hospital in Buffalo she was very happy as she waved her twenty-five dollars in the air and said: "I ain't never got this much money in two weeks before. I'm rich."

A couple of hours after that I was visiting my friend, Linda who lived next door. We wanted some orange sherbert. Neither one of us had any money. The sherbert cost three cents each. We anticipated that if we had ten cents we could splurge and buy three sherberts and with the other penny we'd buy nine peach stones (candy) Having a whole sherbert along with a half one and the peach stones was an exception.

I volunteered to go home and ask Doll for the ten cents. I asked everyone where she was. No one knew. I searched everywhere for her. She wasn't home. But her purse was. So I decided to do a little simple thing. Go in her purse borrow a dime and tell her about it when she returned home. But that's not what happened.

I went in her purse and there was no chump change in it. All she had was that twenty five dollars. I had a wonderful Idea. Take the five dollars to the store and spend a dime buying what Linda and I had contemplated on buying. I'd take the $4.90 back home and put it back in Doll's purse. No problem! A very simple thing.

This is what I did. Linda and I went to the store and bought what was on our agenda. On the way home. I began to think. I should borrow this fifteen cents too. That will make a quarter which I borrowed. I can have sherbert, peach stones and money for the next five days. This is such a good plan. It's settled. I'll just put $4.75 back in Doll's purse. She will understand. After all I'm borrowing this money. I'm not stealing it. I will pay her back when I get a job.

I put the money back in her purse and went back to Linda's house to enjoy our goodies. After that I went home intending to tell Doll about the money I borrowed. I was on my way to our bedroom and she was on her way out of our bedroom.

I said: "Doll I borrowed"

And she said: "Bettye, I have been robbed." I asked her: "What

179

do you mean you have been robbed?"
She said: "Take a look at this. This is $4.75. A quarter is missing.
A thief went into my purse and took my five dollar bill and left
this $4.75. I should call the police and have them come here and
take fingerprints. They can tell me who that shiftless sticky finger
thieving thief is. (That scared the shit out of me. And gave me an
instant headache. Therefore I thought to myself; 'keep your mouth
shut)!' She was highly upset. By that time the whole family was
in it trying to figure out what happened.

Naturally I took my advice. I was ashamed and too
embarrassed to admit the truth then. I knew what it was like
having six brothers tease you. I didn't want them to tease me
about that. My conscious bothered me to the point that I didn't eat
for several days. It took away my cravings for orange sherbert for
a year. I kept that fifteen cents for six months. Because I was too
scared to spend it. I was glad that Mama didn't think to feel my
heart. Because if she had it would've gave me away big time.
(When we were children and did something we wasn't supposed
to, Mama would investigate and play detective by feeling all of
our hearts. The one with the fastest heart beat was the guilty one.
And it worked every single time. It was better than a lie detector's
test. After our hearts gave us away we'd come clean crying.
Yeah. It was me but it was an accident, etc. Actually all Mama
wanted us to do was tell the truth.)

That was a lesson very well learned. To this present day I am
polite and particular. I always ask for what I want and don't
assume anything.

June, Minie And My Sister Gave Jean A Bridal Shower:

On a beautiful Sunday afternoon directly after church June and
Minie had Jean (Minie's sister) over for a bridal shower. During
that particular time June and Minie were newlyweds living down
stairs from us.
Minie and I stayed up until 12:30 a.m. that morning making

salads for the shower. We made a variety of salads, a German chocolate cake, a lemon meringue pie and a casserole of goulash. Minie was a superb cook and a perfectionist. 'Being just right, look good and taste good' was her motto.

My friend Linda and I were helping her. Aunt Miracle brought her crystal punch bowl set for Minie to use. It was brand new. Still in the box. As the three of us unpacked it we took time to admired its beauty and daydream a little.

Minie said: "This is so pretty. I love this floral design. Aunt Miracle is a sweetheart for bringing this over for me to use. I'm almost afraid to use it. I would hate for something to happen to it. We have to be very cautious and not let anything happen to this set. One day I will own a beautiful punch bowl set like this. Aunt Miracle bought this set about a year ago and it's still in the box. I would never keep anything this beautiful hidden and tucked away in a box to collect dust. Oh yeah. I used to think Aunt Miracle was the meanest person on Peckham Street. On the way to school one day, I was upset with Jean so I laid in the snow and kicked my feet and threw snow balls at her. Aunt Miracle was looking out her window and she beat on the window and told me to get up or she would come out there and whip me all the way to school. This is truly a small world. She's my aunt in law now. I'm married to her nephew."

Mama and Aunt Miracle also helped out by making coffee and arranging the food on the buffet around the punch bowl in the dining room. Minie used Mrs. Sears punch recipe. (Lemonade and Coco Cola) She used her creative imagination and added color to it. (fresh juicy strawberries and orange slices). Then she went a step further and added hot ice to give it that cool steamy romantic effect. The crystal punch bowl resembled a picture with the punch and fruit in it pushing the steam upwards. It was extraordinary and breathtaking. The beautifully arranged buffet set up was in favorable taste. Everyone raved about it.

Jean's friend, Century, made arrangements for a male dancer to

181

come over and dance for Jean. The cute guy came there dressed in a black cowboy outfit.

Linda and I were excited as we talked: "We are going to have fun. Century told Jean that he is going to dance and strip. I can't wait. It's going to be an extraordinary treat for us."

Mama was the only one who had a problem with that. She said: "Excuse me ladies. My sister in law Miracle, Bettye, Linda and I are going to tip out of here and go up stairs and watch television while this young man is performing."

Aunt Miracle immediately told Mama: "Gladys speak for yourself. I ain't going nowhere. Wild horses couldn't drag me away from this bridal shower. I intend to stay until the end. I'm mad at my husband anyway. Yeah. He went to a bachelor's party on a Saturday morning and came home at two-o-clock the next morning with lipstick and make-up on his white shirt. This happened a few years ago. Hey. Y'all laughing at me. But I feel like it happened yesterday.

Shit. He left home at nine-o-clock that Saturday morning all dressed up in a suit and tie. Told me; 'Miracle the guys are out there blowing for me. I'll be home in an hour or two. I wish it was a way I could get out of going to this bachelor party. You know how I hate parties.' Seventeen hours later he came home tripping over his feet. I was sitting at the kitchen table. He walked right pass me and went to the bedroom. I had my wig on the wig stand sitting on the night table. Thinking it was me, he used his hands while talking to the wig to help him explain the lies he was telling. He acted like he was cool and knew sign language. 'Hi baby. You ain't sleep yet? I missed you. I'm glad to be home. I ain't never going to another bachelor's party. It was boring as heck.' Then he leaned over and kissed the top of the wig and said: 'good night. I love you.' Then he had the nerves to fall across the bed before I could ask him about the lies he'd just told the wig. That man was out cold. I wanted to thump him on the head and wake him up. But something deep down inside of me said 'He's home! Ain't that you wanted?' Yeah. I was cool.

I was content because he was home. I got in the bed and fell asleep besides him but that man wouldn't let well enough do. He woke me up twenty minutes later talking and laughing: ' Stop that. Quit it now. You gon get in big trouble. Ha, ha, ha, ha, ha, ha, ha. Yes baby. Ha, ha, ha, ha, ha.

No. I told you I ain't married. Ain't never been married. Ha, ha, ha. Yeah. I'll marry you.' Yeah! I went and got the broom and when I finished with him he was sober and too scared to go back to sleep. Thought he might tell some more stuff on himself .

I didn't notice the make-up until the next week when I took his clothes to the cleaners. I acted a fool. I went straight to his job to make him leave with me. He had the nerve to tell me; 'Woman you must be crazy. I'm not going nowhere with you. I get off work at 3:30 P. M., that's when I'll go home and not a minute sooner. The truth about that lip stick and make-up business, I don't know how it got on my shirt. You don put the shirt in the cleaners. I didn't see nothing on the shirt when I was wearing it. Where is your proof? Ha, ha you ain't even got no proof.' He tried to make me look stupid in front of his co-workers and I didn't like it. I punched him in the face with my fist and he slapped me. I raised so much sand until his boss said: 'I'll pay you for the rest of the day. Please just leave with that crazy woman.'

We rode around pouting for a while and I looked at him. The first thing I saw was his nose. Child it was red and big as my fist. You better believe that every time he go out I check his shirt and his draws too." After Aunt Miracle's enlightening story, Linda and I followed Mama upstairs. One hour later Minie asked Linda and I to come back down stairs to help her out. She assured Mama we would be in the kitchen washing dishes. We were, at least one third of the time.

When Linda and I went to the living room to get the dirty plates and cups, the cowboy had just finished eating. He moved the reclining chair to the center of the living room for Jean. Aunt Miracle was talking with him; "My name is Miracle. And yours? Ha, ha ha. Just call you the Cowboy? Alright Cowboy. Anybody ever told you that you're a fine young good looking hunk? Oh they did. Are you married? No. Why not? Do you have any children? That's what I like. A young man that ain't tied down to nothing or nobody! If you don't mind me asking, how old are you Cowboy? You're kidding. (Looking back at everyone and winking her eye.) I'm thirty three. Only three years older than you. (In actuality she was forty years old.) Alright now. Watch it. Don't be bumping up against me like that. (She took his hat and put it on.) You're getting ready to start something that you can't finish Cowboy. (using seductive body language) Honey hush. Ha, ha, ha. I don't know if you can finish it or not."

"Hey this chair is big enough for Jean and me. She is practically my daughter. I don't see why I can't sit with her. There's no room on the couch for me. Y'all can forget it. I ain't about to sit on the floor for nothing."

Aunt Miracle had humor for any occasion. She made us laugh. Jean was a good sport. She shared her chair with Aunt Miracle. It was extremely difficult for Linda and I to stay in the kitchen with all of that laughter and music going on. Cowboy could dance! He directed the majority of his attention to Jean. He placed his hat on her head, ripped his pants off exposing his two sizes two small black bikinis and sat straddling her lap facing her. He grabbed both of her breasts and asked her if she really wanted to get married. She blushed and giggled uncontrollably. Cowboy stood up, turned around and flopped back down on her lap with his back facing her. He reached back to take her hands and put them inside of his bikinis. Jean was self-conscious. Therefore she pulled her hands away. Aunt Miracle was anxious and didn't hesitate to grab Cowboy's buns.

Aunt Miracle talked to him: "Come back here. Don't ignore me Cowboy. Come on baby. It's time for you to sit on my lap. Hey. Stop pushing my hands back, they are cold. Put them back inside

184

of these tight black bikinis so they can stay warm. I'm getting married next week. So what you got planned for me Cowboy?" The party was hilarious.

Back in the kitchen Linda and I were finishing the dishes and Linda dropped the last cup to the punch bowl set in the sink and broke it.

That made us nervous and she said: "Minie is your Sister in law! Tell her you broke it."

I said: "No! I'm not supposed to lie. Besides Aunt Miracle is real nice but she can be mean especially if she find out about her new cup. Minie can be mean too. I don't think we should mention this to anybody."

Linda agreed: "That make sense. Let's put it in a paper bag and I'll put the bag in my purse and throw it in the trash at my house. All the cups except that one are back in the box. Let's tape it up before Minie comes back to the kitchen."

Minie took the tape off the box and recounted the cups: "Hey. It's one cup missing. We got-a find it. Maybe someone threw one in the trash by mistake. Bettye check the trash can while I check the rest of the house. Linda go up stairs and see if Mama took the cup up there."

The cup was broken accidentally. Linda and I were afraid to tell because we knew how Minie felt about the punch bowl set. After all we were the ones who helped her unpack it.

Minie kept the punch bowl set for another week in hopes of finding the other cup. After returning the punch bowl set to Aunt Miracle before Minie could tell her that one of the cups vanished in thin air Aunt Miracle said: "Minie you just march right back to the car and put that box in it. I'm giving you that set. Oh my goodness. Minie that punch bowl set was fabulous in your house. And that's where it belongs. I bought that set a little over a year ago on a spur of the moment and brought it home only to put it in the closet. And that's where it stayed until I took it out last week."

"Minie I had so much fun at your house. Ha, ha. Oh boy. I still have a hangover from it. Ah. Guess what? I'm no longer mad with Shayne. Ha, ha, ha. Yeah. Well. I have a different insight on things now. Life is short and precious. And it is certainly unfair to hold a grudge and be angry with your husband for going to a bachelor's party. I told him that. Ha. He got up and spit in the fireplace and said: 'It's about time you knock that foolishness off. Heck. It's been way over three years since that happened Miracle.' So we're in love again. I'm very happy about it."

My Sister Took Us For A Ride:

In the summertime a lot of Buffalonnians would drive or walk up and down Jefferson Avenue, especially on the weekend! One beautiful Sunday in July Linda and I asked my sister to take us for a ride. We went to visit her friend Jerry. Jerry and her two year old twin daughters were on their way out for a walk and we accompanied them. We drove down Jefferson after leaving Jerry's house.

Linda was a tease and a flirt, she asked my sister to park by this couple that was walking down the street. She wanted to say something to that guy. Not knowing what Linda had in mind my sister parked at her request.

And Linda talked: "Excuse me Baby. You look good in that suit. That's why I instructed my chauffeur to stop. I want to know you. You are so cute! What's your name? 'Antonio'. Antonio I dreamed about you last night. Check this out. It's hot! And I'm all yours. Do you want to ride to the Water Front with me? I promise we'll have a lot of fun. Excuse me Miss! But out. I'm not talking to you. I talking to yo boyfriend."

Antonio was all smiles. That's why his girlfriend slapped him.

186

And called Linda dirty low-down names and threatened to beat her up, as she took her high heel shoes off and threw them towards my sister's car. My sister sped off in a hurry. We laughed all the way home.

My sister gathered her composure after that showdown and told Linda. "You better hurry up and believe that you will not be riding in my car again. Even if it's an emergency!"

Thomas James Holmes: (T. J.)

T. J. was a genuinely wonderful brother with a beautiful personality. He was on the quiet side with a unique humorous quality that was captivating. He loved his family dearly and displayed that love on numerous occasions. He was very proper. There is no doubt about it. He was definitely my *favorite* brother.

The Anklet:

T. J. was always around protecting me and taking up for me even if I didn't need or want it. Like that time when I went shopping and bought an anklet. I tried it on when I got home. Daddy and Mama thought it was cute.

Mama reiterated: "That is so cute. Where did you buy it? I think I'll get one for myself."

Later that day I was on the porch down stairs talking with Doll and kicking it while awaiting Linda's arrival. We were going for a walk on Jefferson. T. J. drove up and parked. On his way into the house he couldn't help but noticed my anklet because that's what Doll and I were discussing.

He stopped: "Bettye, where did you buy that thing? I hate to disappoint you. But you are not going anywhere wearing that anklet. So you might as well take it off right now."

Doll said: "Leave her alone T. J.. That's in. That's the style. It's dynamite with that outfit she's wearing. Hey. I'm going to buy one when I get my pay check. (Smiling) Oooh. Im-ma be saying something."

T. J. said, "I don't care if that's the style. Or if it's in. There is no way in this world that a sister of mine is going to wear an anklet. What? Do you all want me to spell it out? Gee whiz. Both of you guys are dumb and out of touch with things. That's what those prostitutes on William Street wear. That is their trade-mark.

Doll you can forget about buying one. Save your money for something else. Bettye like I told you, you're not going anywhere wearing that anklet. I'm going up stairs and tell Daddy and Mama. We'll see what they say about this."

Daddy and Mama said I couldn't wear the anklet. T. J. was happy and I was upset with him. But I got over it.

What A Hefty Hearty Sunday Breakfast:

T. J. was an excellent cook who enjoyed cooking: The kitchen was his and only his on Sunday mornings to make a very special breakfast which was a   pot of spaghetti and meatballs. The spaghetti and meatballs were superb. The recipe was a concoction that he created on his own. I can still remember the smell and that sweetish taste of the sauce with those crunchy peppers, onions, garlic, tomatoes, and tomato paste. His meatballs consisted of ground chuck accompanied by the tender meat from the pork neck bones, which was formed neatly into round meatballs that simmered in the sauce for two hours with a bit of Italian sausage mixed in.

He would carefully fold the sauce and meat balls in with the spaghetti followed by a thick layer of grated Mozzarella cheese and a touch of finely chopped green onions. To go along with it was a butter mixture which consisted of crushed garlic, oregano, grated sharp cheese and cayenne pepper on lightly toasted Italian bread. It was a hearty breakfast fit for a king.

T. J. Loved To Party On Friday And Saturday Nights:

T. J. was known for dressing up and going dancing on Friday and Saturday nights. He used to say he was a swinger. He was a good dancer and a music lover as well. He'd get dressed, put on his cologne and play some records because he had to brush up on some new dance steps before he left home. He had all of the latest music but he loved the Duke of Earl so much that he played the taste out of it. He did the twist, the mashed potatoes, the stroll, slow dance, and he did the fast swing dance also. His favorite people to go out and dance and party with was my cousins: Joe, Annie, Mary and some of their friends.

T. J. had unsightly razor bumps from shaving. But he found a solution to quiet and tone those bumps down. Mama's liquid makeup mixed with rubbing alcohol was the perfect answer. It made his complexion stunningly smooth and clear. One day Mama was in his room looking in the dresser drawer for some Vicks Vapo-Rub to apply to my chest because I had a cold. Surprisingly she stumbled upon her makeup, the makeup she had been searching for. She opened the bottle and discovered the makeup was mixed with a lot of rubbing alcohol. She wondered why would T. J. put rubbing alcohol in her makeup?

Then she laughed and said: "That's why T. J.'s face appears to be smooth and pretty every week-end when he goes out." She put some on her face and asked me how did it look.

Then she put it back in the drawer where he had left it and said: "We won't mention this." I agreed with her but the first time T. J. made me mad, I teased him about wearing makeup. He continued to use that solution until he was introduced to Blue Magic Shaving

Cream.
When T. J. Confronted Robert Earl's Bully:

T. J. was living on Brooklyn Avenue at that time. He had just returned home from work and began to sharpen his knife so he could peel his potatoes for dinner when ten year old Earl came over with a bloody nose crying: "A junior high school bully Albert, beat me up.

T. J. quickly left the house in hopes of finding the bully who intimidated Earl. He was in luck. The five feet eleven inch tall bully was waiting on the corner for T. J.. Because Earl told him that he was going to get his big brother and bring him back to beat him up. The confident bad boasting bully and three of his friends were ready to duke with T. J.. T. J. asked which one of them beat Earl up? The bully walked up and admitted it was him and asked T. J. what was he going to do about it?

T. J. said: "I'm getting ready to show you right now." He jumped up and kicked bully Albert in the abdomen knocking him against the tree. Then he hit him with the front and back of his open left hand. Directly following that he captured him around the neck with his right arm. T. J. was still clinging on to the knife that he was in the process of sharpening when Earl came to his house. So he used that to his advantage. He bullied the bully.

Albert was terrified. He told T. J. how sorry he was for beating up on Earl and taking his money and offered to give Earl's money back. T. J. told Earl to go in the bully's pocket and take all of his money.

Albert was scared and talking fast: "It's OK lil boy. Take all of it. I don't care. T. J. Please don't hurt me. Can I go Now?" He reiterated. "I'm sorry that I beat yo lil brother up and took his money. It won't happen no mo."

T. J. laid down a strict rule for Albert Hooks. He told him not to come to our neighborhood again.

Albert said: "Please. Cut me some slack. Let's face it. That is impossible. Ain't no way I can move. I live in this neighborhood. You see that pink and grey house down there on the corner? That's where I live. We're neighbors."

T. J. told him: "You should have thought of those things before you messed with my little brother. I'm going to correct you on a couple of things. This used to be your neighborhood. That pink and grey house down there on the corner used to be where you lived. We used to be neighbors. You have one week to pack up and move out. After that I hope I don't see you again for your own good."

Oh by the way I heard about this a few weeks ago. The lady who live next door to me sent her son to the store with three dollars to make change so she would have lunch money for her five children to last the week. You took the money, ruffled him up and sent him home crying. I don't get it. Why do you pick on little children and take their money? You are almost a grown man."

Albert said, "I don't know. It's fun. I guess. I like having money in my pockets everyday. I guess. I guess it kind of started when I took money from my lil brothers and sisters. I guess, it's all in fun."

T. J. replied, "You guess, you guess, you guess. Well. Ah. I guess, you better be out of this neighborhood in three days. I guess, what I say goes. Now get out of my face."

The bullying Albert sobbed like a baby and used the bathroom on himself. He knew T. J. was just about to release him. He was eager and more than willing to go somewhere and hide from the large crowd that was watching. His bullying reputation days was shot to the curb. With the intentions of walking away he didn't give T. J. a chance to remove his arm from around his neck. He turned his head to the left very quickly. The left side of his neck glided smoothly on T. J.'s razor sharp knife from the back of his jawbone just under his left ear to one inch from the right ear. It wasn't a deep cut but it required medical attention. Albert was gratified that things didn't turn out worse. Therefore he moved to Detroit Michigan to live with his father that evening.

Three years later: He returned to Buffalo, NY and looked T. J. up and invited him to dinner. Puzzled and overloaded with questions. T. J. accepted Albert's invitation.

Albert told him: "Man I came all the way back to Buffalo to shake your hand and thank you. Until I met you, all my life people let me push them around. Nobody stood up to me and it became a way of life for me. I had no respect for my mother. She always said I was a no account good for nothing.

"I went home the last time you saw me and called my father to see if he would let me come to Detroit and live with him. He told me to catch the first thing smoking. I took the bus that left at 9:45 that night on the way to Detroit Michigan. When I got there he already knew what happened with you and me. My mother told him. From the bus station he took me to school and got me registered.

Driving to his house he told me that until I got a job after school I would be taking my lunch to school because he was on a tight budget. He told me not to make any plans for Wednesday evenings, Friday evenings and all day on Sundays. My lunch consisted of one cold weiner split down the middle on two slices of plain bread and a half of an apple which he fixed every night. That went on for three weeks. I didn't like the school. I didn't like the kids. I couldn't take any more of those plain cold dry weiners. I couldn't go to the store like I was accustomed to because I was broke. I quit school and he said: 'We're getting up at 4:00 in the morning. We're due to start work at 5:30. I have been working there since before you were born. Ain't never missed a day or been late. I expect you to follow suit.' I never had a job before that. He took me under his wings and taught me.

And to this day we work side by side. He's my boss now. But he doesn't show favoritism. I like it that way. I was given a chance to know and like him. He is the best friend I ever had. I'm active in church and enjoy going three times a week. That's where I met my wife. We have an eleven month old son."

Albert continues to talk: "T. J. I guess I just want to say I'm truly ashamed for the circumstances which brought us together for fifteen or twenty minutes, three and one half years ago. But I am glad that I met you. It was meant for us to cross each other's paths. You made my dream come alive by persuading me to leave Buffalo. You see my father was the one essential ingredient that was missing in my life. I always wanted to live with him but my mother wouldn't permit it. He taught me well. It was difficult at first. I fought, rebelled and talked back.

After attending Sunday School, Bible Study and Church for about a year I finally got the hang of it. I was at work one day and it hit me on the head like a ton of bricks and opened up my mind. It was a Miracle from Heaven. I developed an appetite and thirst to know God's word. I have changed for the best. Guess I can say I'm a good boy now. Thanks to you T. J..."

I Fried An Old Roasting Hen:

My parents and Roy went to Mississippi to Daddy's sister's funeral. T. J. was designated as the cook and I was the dishwasher. Feeling confident about cooking a meal on my own I approached T. J. and told him that I wanted to cook dinner by myself. He asked me what was I planning on cooking? I gave him my menu, fried chicken, mashed potatoes with gravy, biscuits, broccoli, and ice tea. He thought it sounded pretty good and told me to go for it. He went to the back yard to wash his car, leaving the kitchen to me. He told me to holler if I needed any help.

The chicken was extremely difficult to cut up. Unlike the chickens I cut up before. I seasoned it the way Mama did and

193

began to fry it. Richard and Charlie sat at the table and did their homework. Usually they'd watch television afterwards. But they stayed in the kitchen to keep me company. They told corny jokes. They sang the beans good for your heart the more you eat the more you fart song. The first time I heard it, I thought it was kind of funny. But they kept singing it over and over. And that irritated me profusely.

Three hours later dinner was finally ready. I fixed everyone's plate. We said our blessings and commenced to eat. No one's teeth could penetrate that golden brown good looking chicken. It was some kind of tough.

T. J. took the butcher knife, cut a piece of it, chewed it and said: "This is like chewing a piece of car tire. Wait a minute. What kind of chicken is this?" He took the flashlight and went through the trash in the back yard and found the wrapping from the chicken. He returned to the kitchen and said: "Hey girl. You want to know why this chicken is tough? And why we have to wait another three hours before we can eat? Because this is an old roasting hen! I was wondering why it was so big and plump when you were frying it. He rolled his sleeves up and got it together. He cooked the hen in the pressure cooker and went a step further by making dressing. Dinner was ready in less than an hour. That old roasting hen was falling off the bone tender and simply nothing but delicious. T. J. said that was the best tasting hen he ate since he left Mississippi. He wrapped a portion of it and put it in the freezer for Daddy, Mama and Roy to have when they returned home. Then he gave me the wrapper form the hen and said: "Girl. You need to read! what does this wrapper say?"

I read it: "Roasting Hen."
He continued: "Just because it look like a chicken and it's the size of a chicken and it's wrapped like a chicken doesn't mean it's a chicken! I'm surprised you didn't fry that young turkey. Gee. Girl. I hope you learned a lesson today."

I asked: "Besides that. What do y'all think?"

194

T. J. said: "I think it's way past everybody's bedtime." I was expecting a compliment. Especially after all of the work I performed. Gee.

Richard Noble Holmes: Richard:

Richard had a really great overwhelming attractive personality. He had a considerable amount of love and compassion for the needy and the handicapped. He would take out time and talk with them take them out to eat and give them money. I remember one year it was exactly two days before Thanksgiving. Richard and I walked to Tim Tell's Cleaners on Jefferson Avenue. We counted our money before leaving the cleaners. I had thirty cents and he had forty eight cents. We planed to put our money together and buy some goodies to take home and share with the family while watching television.

Before we could take ten steps from the cleaners a man dressed in a dirty, greasy trench coat with dirty, greasy hands, approached us asking for money. Richard took his forty eight cents out of his pocket and gave it to the man. He took it and put his hand on Richard's shoulder and said: "Thank you son. God Bless you."

He turned and walked down the street ahead of us. He continued to look back at us like he wanted to say something. Therefore we increased our pace and was five to seven feet from him. At that point he smiled and dropped some dollar bills on the sidewalk. Then turned and walked fast. Richard ran and picked the money up then called to the man: "Hey mister, wait a minute. You dropped your money." The man ran so fast that we couldn't catch him. He disappeared into the dusk. We went straight home and told Daddy and Mama what happened. They counted the money. It was five hundred and fifty dollars. They told us that the money was a blessing in disguise. And because Richard cared and gave his last so freely with true love from his heart, he was blessed with that money. They explained it to us this way. "You grow what you plant." In other words, 'You reap what you sow.' Richard asked Daddy and Mama to buy a color television so Charlie, Earl, Emerson, and himself could have it in the attic. He gave me fifteen dollars. The remainder of it was to go in the bank and remain there for a rainy day. Actually! Richard was my *favorite* brother.

I Remember When Richard Was Born:

I didn't like him because I couldn't sleep in the bed with Daddy and Mama any more. Mama told me that I was her big baby and Richard was her little baby. Therefore he had to sleep in the bed with her and Daddy. And I had to sleep in the bed with Doll. She said I could help her take care of Richard. I got off to a bad start on the wrong foot helping Mama take care of Richard. One day she made him a bottle for lunch to take the place of her nursing him due to the fact that she was busy canning fruit.

The pressure cooker was on the stove with seven quart size Mason jars full of fruit going through the canning process. They needed her undivided attention right then. Anyhow Richard woke up much quicker than she had anticipated. Mama took the bottle to him and propped it up on a pillow so he could suck it. She put my hand on it and told me to hold it like that so it wouldn't fall over. I did that for a while. But Richard was smacking and making a lot of noise sucking that bottle. That made me curious. I wanted to know what that milk tasted like. So I tasted it and it was sweet and delicious. I couldn't help myself. I kept sucking that bottle and Richard began to cry. I put my finger in his mouth and he sucked it. When the bottle was empty, I put it back in Richard's mouth. Mama walked in the room and checked the empty bottle. She couldn't believe that he drank the entire bottle. When she picked him up to make him belch she felt his stomach and said: "I don't believe this. Your stomach doesn't feel full. I put five ounces of milk in that bottle and that was way too much milk for you. Where did all of that milk go?"

196

I was very honest. I opened my mouth, held my head back and put my hand in it. After nursing Richard she put him back in the bed and picked me up, hugged me and said I was a knock out. Apparently that meant I blew it and I was fired. Because after that happened she didn't ask for my assistance anymore. But I offered it anyway. One day I was energetic with nothing to do. As I looked around the room I asked my self a question. 'What can I do to make myself useful?'

Big Mama and Mama were in the kitchen shelling peas listening to a story on the radio and talking. Therefore I went to the bedroom to check on Richard. He was wide awake and fretting. That was an opportune time for me to do a good thing. I picked him up by his head with both of my hands and took him to Mama so she could nurse him. As I was carrying him to Mama in that fashion, she looked up and saw me. "Bettye Joe, what are you doing? Give me my baby before you kill him." (I was two years old).

In the midst of that commotion Reverend Clinton stopped by. Big Mama told him what happened. She said I was a baby toting a baby by the head. Reverend Clinton was concerned and checked with Mama to see if Richard was alright. Richard was just fine. So Reverend Clinton joined Big Mama in the kitchen and told her not to get him wrong because he didn't want to offend us. But that was 'D' most funniest thing he had heard in all his days on earth. Big Mama tried to demonstrate how I carried Richard. She said he was swinging from side to side as I struggled to carry him. Reverend Clinton was laughing and cutting up and being really silly. I didn't know I was supposed to pick a baby up and carry him in my arms. Richard was the first baby I ever tried to pick up. But as I grew and Mama taught me, I became her excellent little helper.

Richard And Charlie Had A Secret Part Time Business:

Once upon a time my brothers, Richard and Charlie decided to let me in on their secret business.

Richard: "Here's two dollars Bet Joe. (whispering and smiling) We got something going on. Snatching purses! Every body's doing it. That's all they talk about in school. At first me and Charlie wasn't going to do it. But we changed our minds. A little extra money won't hurt anybody. See. Don't it feel good to have that extra two dollars in your hand.?"

Charlie (spoke in his normal tone) "Yeah. We got two purses from the two old women down the street in that green and white house, with the swing on the porch. Bet Joe you know the house I'm talking about? I think they're sisters. They're always together. We got nine dollars and sixteen cents all together. (laughing) We're going out again tomorrow night."

Richard: " Bet Joe I want you to be on the look out for us. Keep the back door unlocked so we can come in. I don't want Daddy to catch us. He'll whoop us and put us on a punishment. You know every time he go to the bathroom he lock the back door cause he thinks we're in the attic. Ok. It's like this. Me and Charlie will give you one dollar every time we strike it rich."

The purse snatching adventure went smoothly for two long weeks. It could have went longer but Mama the hard nose warden inadvertently found the haphazard hidden purses in the basement while she was washing. She called me right-a-way. "Bettye Joe get down here in the basement right now."

"Do you know anything about these purses? It's fifteen purses here and there is I D in all of them. I don't know what to make of this! Well don't just stand there! Say something! "

I asked: "Where did they come from?"

She answered me, "I was hoping that you could shed a little light on this."

I told her: "Come to think of it those purses were probably there

198

when we moved here Mama."

Mama: "No. This basement was empty when we moved here. You know that. I got a feeling in the pit of my stomach that somehow these purses are connected with your brothers and you are protecting them. OK. Let's see. It could be that your brothers are bringing girls down here. Oh. Hell no!! That can't be! Look at this picture I D; this woman is older than dirt and she's as ugly as homemade sin. Im-ma go through these purses tonight and see if I can find some phone numbers. So I can call these women and find out what in the world their purses are doing in my basement. What kind of connection do these women have with my young boys? All kind of things are flooding my mind about these old Buffalo women. Are my boys pimping them?"

Warden Mama was up half of the night investigating and she came up with a phone number for every purse. She called those women and made arrangements for the fifteen of them to meet at our home the next day at five-o-clock P.M. She didn't mention that to us.

The next day at four-forty-five P.M., the doorbell rang. The fifteen women came in. All of them were white, old and kind of nice. Mama had displayed the purses on the couch in the living room. Everybody retrieved their purse and thanked Mama. Mama knew that Richard and Charlie took the purses. Because the two sister in laws, Holly Green and Maple Green who lived down the street in the green and white house with the swing on the porch, just happened to mentioned the fact that Holly Green fell on the ice after her purse was taken. And those charming, polite, little crooks, Richard and Charlie came back, picked her up and walked both of them to the security of their front door.

Being amateurs on their first job they simply gave them selves away. This is what happened.

Richard: "Ut. This ice is slippery. Miss why don't y'all put some salt out here to keep from falling? You could fall and break something. Hold her arm Charlie. She ain't doing nothing but slipping and sliding."

Charlie, "OK. Richard I'll help her to her porch. Go help the other lady alright?"

Richard and Charlie apologized and the women accepted the apologies gracefully. It was Mama's plan to pay them back and take the money from Richard and Charlie's allowance. But those women had been on the phone all that day brainstorming and making plans of their own. They were very wise. Mama always said; 'you grow wise with age.'

They were due back approximately $56.92 which they refused to take. All fifteen of those women were widows and needed all kind of work done in their houses from the basement to the attic. Washing the walls, painting and cleaning the basement, attic, closets, refrigerators, stoves ovens, fireplaces, carpet etc.. Shoveling the snow, taking the trash out, fixing loose floor boards in the attic, etc.. It took us seven months to complete all of that work. We wore our school clothes the first day of punishment. That was a big mistake. We came home covered with dirt from head to toe. We had anticipated on doing everything except taking out the trash in fifteen days. We were in for a big surprise. What a way to learn a lesson!

Those widow women had their stuff together. They made lists of everything that was to be done. Some of them had a list of twenty things that needed our tender loving care. As we worked down the lists, they checked behind us to make sure that we did the tasks right before starting the next task.

Those fifteen jobs was intended as a lesson and a punishment for following the crowd and breaking the law. It was some good in it because we had a chance to get to know and like all of them and they got a chance to know and like us as well. They were warmhearted, lonely women, who needed someone in their life to make a difference, somebody to share a little bit of their life with. We touched their hearts and they touched ours. The reason it took seven months to complete all the work was due to the fact they wanted to talk. We respected them and listened to what they had to say. They mainly talked about the times they spent with their husbands. And how their children grew up and moved away. Some of them never had children. Sometimes they got misty eyed. Their pictures was a treasured precious thing to them and they loved showing them off. The Green sister in laws were always in their front window waiting for us to pass by on the way home from school. They'd wave to us and sometimes call us to the door and give us a bag of peach stones and Mary Jane candy.

Some of them baked and cooked for us; (Pumpkin walnut cookies, banana nut bread, gingerbread, peanut butter cookies, zucchini bread with pineapple etc.) They also had ice cream, potato chips and candy. They loved to see us coming and hated to see us leave. One of the women, Mrs. Wayola, made some fresh corn beef and cabbage for us. It smelled awesome. We wouldn't eat it because she didn't have any cornbread to go with it. We had never heard of corn beef, cabbage, potatoes, green pepper, onions and carrots, cooked in the same pot. That was a strange dish. I asked her: "Do you eat corn bread?"

She answered me: "Corn bread? Young lady I don't know nothing about making corn bread. Oops I spoke too fast. There is one thing that I know about making cornbread, it need yeast to make it rise."

I taught her how to make corn bread and she taught me how to cook fresh corn beef. Before the seven months were over those women competed against each other for our attention.

Richard Took My Job:

Daddy gave me the job of washing his work overalls. The second week I washed them I found a fifty cent piece in them and immediately took it to him. He gave it to me. The same procedure happened for five weeks. Then one day Mama said to me: "How

201

long is it going to take for you to catch on? Don't you know by now that Curly is leaving that money for you on purpose? That's his appreciation for you washing his work clothes."

That extra fifty cents along with my allowance enabled me to save enough money to buy a pair stretch of pants and a pair of boots. While I was shopping for my boots and pants I saw a beautiful black Derby hat that went perfect with my outfit. I immediately set a goal. I promised myself that I would wear that Derby home in two weeks. Naturally. I was depending on that extra fifty cents every week. (Mama always told us; 'Don't count your chickens before they hatch).' I didn't take heed to that. And that wasn't the only thing I did. I told Richard. And I should have known better. (Mama always said; 'Don't let your left hand know what your right hand is doing).'

Anyhow what I usually did on Saturday mornings was get up at seven and wash Daddy's work clothes. At six-forty-five, Richard came to me smiling, cracking his knuckles and saying "I got up at six this morning and washed Daddy's work clothes. Bet Joe you were right. An extra fifty cents means a lot. Im-ma add these extra fifty cents to my allowance every Saturday and when I have enough money I'll buy a nice double breasted overcoat."

I stood there watching him grin and listening to him make future plans about the money from the job he had just stole from me. And I said to myself: "You stole my job. I don't like you. I am very angry. I have to wait two weeks longer to get my Derby. I should slap the shit out of you."

Mama was getting ready to leave for work. So I followed her to the car crying the blues about how my sneaky brother got up at 6:00 and stole my job. Mama was a real good problem solver. She asked me how would I like to get one of my Christmas gifts three months early? I answered: "yes" and she told me to come with Daddy when he picked her up from work. We went shopping. I got my Derby and my brothers got jeans, sweaters and gloves. We were all happy and ready to rock and roll.

During the course of that day I calmed down and kicked the madness. My love for Richard was restored and I realized that I wasn't an only child and Richard had as much right to wash Daddy's work clothes and earn a little extra cash as me or any of us. I was glad that I didn't tell him that I didn't like him. That would have made me feel bad later on. And it would have put a damper on his enthusiasm. Besides Daddy and Mama taught us to love one another no matter what a situation may be.

Richard grew up and was drafted in the Army for two years. He traveled and saw different parts of the world. Missing that life style enticed him to enlist in the United States Marines. He served eight years with them. During his service with them he traveled throughout the world and met all kinds of people and learned something about their culture. He ate different cultural foods. He had the joy and contentment of a lifetime traveling the world. He fell in love with many women around the world but married none. At least not until he came home to the good old U. S. A.. He then married a native Californian divorcee with two children. He was a talented artist and calligrapher.

Charlie Bruce Holmes: Charlie (Juice)

Once upon a time in the month of April, in Mississippi, Mama got sick and Miss Duck came to the house. She told Richard and me that if we would be quiet and stay outside she would kill two birds with one stone, make Mama feel better and give us the baby that she had in her black bag. That was not a problem. We stayed on the front porch and waited patiently. It was a very long wait. Big Mama fixed supper for us and we ate it on the porch. The bright sun went down and darkness settled in. The next thing I remembered was waking up at Papa and Big Mama's house the following morning to the smell of fried ham, fried potatoes with onions and coffee. Richard was in the kitchen having breakfast with Papa. I asked Big Mama, "Did Miss Duck make Mama feel better and leave the baby that she had in her black bag?" She informed me that Mama was all better and Miss Duck kept her word and left us a beautiful baby brother named Charlie Bruce Holmes.

My excitement caused me to chock on my spit and cough for the longest time. After Big Mama fed us, dressed us and combed our hair, the opportune time to go see our new baby brother arrived. Charlie was very cute and real small with long eyelashes and thick eye-braws. Big Mama said he could fit in a shoe box and have enough room left for his clothes.

She also said: "Well I declare. That boy has the same facial image of Bet Joe. Surely. They will grow up and look like twins." Mama agreed with her. That made my day. So from that day he has been my most *favorite* brother. He was sassy and always looked out for me when I was in need of his protection. For example: Charlie and I went to visit our closest neighbor Miss Louella Mae. Miss Louella Mae was a super mean woman. Our parents warned us not to go anywhere near her house. They said she didn't like children. And she was always saying: "I will kill a baby If it git in my way." She lived alone. Anyhow Miss Louella Mae had the prettiest best tasting, plumpest, juiciest, sweetest, peaches in the whole wide world.

One day Goodness and Mercy touched her with love and kindness. Therefore she brought three baskets of those wonderful delicious peaches to us. Mama and Big mama made peach cobblers. We had peaches and cream for breakfast. Big Mama and Mama canned twenty-four jars of peaches. They made peach jam. Daddy had peaches in his lunch. We had peaches, peaches, peaches, until one day they were all gone. They were so good that once you started to eat them they immediately became habit forming.

As I remember it was a hot summer day when Richard, Charlie and I were in this big, bushy, shade, tree trying our best to keep cool. When I said: "How bout we go git some peaches from Miss Louella Mae? They will cool us off."

Richard answered: "Not me. Shoot. That crazy woman hate children. If you want some peaches, you go git them. Me and Charlie will wait here for you."

Charlie commented: "I'll go with you and help carry some peaches back Bet Joe. Richard If you don't go wit us you ain't gittin none of em ."

Richard said: "Reverend Clinton don't go see her. He said she is a real fruit cake and it just ain't safe to go around her"

Charlie and I were a brave pair and off to Miss Louella Mae's house to gather some peaches. We arrived at her house and knocked several times but she did not answer the door. We could hear something or someone moving around in her house. And we could also smell the stinking food that was cooking. The aroma was unfamiliar to us. Her screen door was locked and covered with some kind of white plastic preventing us from seeing what or who was inside. We called her several times and there was no response.

The faint breeze carried the fragrance of the peaches as it blew pass our nostrils. And that captured our attention bringing us to the trees. The peach trees was amazingly arranged in a neat row on the sides and back of her house. They were beautifully laid out in the shape of a U. Keeping in mind the fact that we went there in good faith to ask Miss Louella Mae for some of her awesome peaches, we had a serious conversation after taking that breathtaking tour through her peach orchard. I told Charlie that Miss Louella Mae was quite busy and that was the reason for her not coming to the door. And after all she had ten thousand peach trees and would not mind if we took a couple of her peaches.

Charlie asked me, "Do you want to know what Miss Louella Mae said to Papa when he told her that three baskets of peaches was a whole heap of peaches? She said, 'Mr. Smiley, I am glad to give y'all these peaches. Shucks I ain't gon miss them a tall.

205

Shucks I got a plenty of peaches.' Shucks, if we take some peaches she ain't gon miss them a tall."

Those big peaches were weighing the limbs down waiting for us to pick them. All I can say about that is it was an irresistible situation that we took advantage of by picking six of the biggest peaches we could find and left for home.

It was impossible for us to climb the tree with the peaches. Therefore Richard joined us on Papa and Big Mama's front porch. Richard and Charlie were on the porch eating their peaches and I was jumping up and down on the bottom step as I ate mine. When all of a sudden the chickens in the chicken coup began to scatter and cackle. Then Miss Louella Mae rushed out carrying a chicken in each hand. What a surprise that was. Charlie and I thought she was at home. I wondered what was that noise we heard moving around and who was cooking that stinking food in her house? Oh my. She was more surprised than we were. Her eyes looked as though they were going to pop out of her head.

She asked us, "Where did you chillens come from? I didn't see hide nor hair of y'all when I came through here a lil while ago. Now wait just a damn minute. Where did y'all git them peaches from? I know damn well that they didn't come from them sorry peach trees that belong to y'all. Y'all ain't got to say it but I know them is my peaches. I can recognize that smell anywhere wit my eyes closed. See I have my own special stuff mixed up together to produce my tasty peaches. I got me a good mind to git a switch and give you a good licking Bet Joe. You are the ring leader in this gang. You better be glad that my hands are full. What would yo Big Mama and Papa say about y'all stealing my peaches? Y'all ain't nothing but a bunch of damn thieving scoundrels."

Miss Louella Mae scared me talking like that. But Richard and Charlie was fearless and ready to fight a battle.

Charlie had a sassy attitude: "You ain't nothing but a grown damn fool. You ain't gon give my sister no licking . I will shoot you where the sun don't shine with my nigger shooter. Richard and Bet Joe will shoot you with their nigger shooters too. I ain't playing. What would Big Mama and Papa say about you stealing our chickens? Put em down! You damn sneaky scoundrel. I said put them chickens down. Every day Big Mama and Papa count the chickens and there's always one or two missing. Papa said he is tired of this chicken stealing. And it's time for him to go to town and tell the sheriff. You is the one who's been stealing em.

(With his hands on his hips he spit on the ground.) Saying: "Well! I'll be a monkey's uncle. You ain't about to turn them chickens loose. Huh? I'm going to the field rat now and tell Papa that you stole them chickens. What is you gon do when Papa go to town and tell the sheriff? You better believe. Yo ass is going to jail. Papa, Big Mama, Daddy and Mama said you is a crazy ass fool. They don't like you. Me, Bet Joe and Richard don't like you either. Papa saw you stealing that sack of watermelons the other day. He said he started to shoot you where the sun don't shine with his shot gun."

.

The three of us began to shoot at her with our nigger shooters. She continued to run and hold onto the chickens. It was as though they were glued to her hands.

Charlie wasn't done talking; "You crazy ass snag-a-tooth heffer. Marble, (our dog) catch Miss Louella Mae and bring her back here." But due to the fact that Marble was in her twilight years the most she could do was trot very slowly behind Miss Louella Mae. She ended up getting away. Marble was exhausted when she came back to the house. Therefore she leaned on the shade tree. She didn't have enough energy to lay down.

The next day a very peculiar thing happened. Somebody brought four baskets of Miss Louella Mae's peaches and put them on our back porch and they also put four baskets of peaches on Papa and Big Mama's back porch. Papa and Big Mama laughed and said, "That old crazy ass woman met her match when she crossed Charlie's path."

Somehow Charlie's sassy actions changed her and brought her very best to surface. Miss Louella Mae admitted to Papa and Big Mama that she had been taking the chickens for at least six months due to the financial crises she was forced to face when her brother got married and left her alone. Papa and Big Mama were the best understanding, compassionate loving grand parents anyone could ever wish for. They sympathized and emphasized with her and came to an agreement For two chickens a week she would keep the peaches rolling in. The family opened their hearts and supplied Miss Louella Mae with whatever food she was lacking. Sometimes she would accompany us to church and join us for dinner afterwards. Once we got to know her we realized that she wasn't a crazy ass fool. She was a bit cantankerous though. Mama said that Miss Louella Mae was going through a stage that people usually go through when they get that old. She loved Charlie so much that she called him her boy.
She also called him by his whole name 'Charlie Bruce Holmes'

She said: "I'm going to will my peach trees to Charlie Bruce Holmes." We never found out what that strange noise was that came from Miss Louella Mae's house.

Charlie's Unique French Fry Sandwiches:

As I recall this one typical day Charlie was in the kitchen making French fries. After they were done he put them in a bowl and seasoned them with apple cider vinegar, ketchup and hot sauce. That was our usual way of seasoning them. But that day Charlie created something different. He made French fry sandwiches.

Everybody except me were cracking jokes about those French fry sandwiches.

Richard said: "Charlie, what kind of mess is this? Ain't nobody gon eat this stuff. I'm taking my French fries off the bread."

Earl said: "I never have ate a French fry sandwich and I never will. I don't like the way that sandwich look."

I asked: "Charlie Have you ate a French fry sandwich before?"

He said that was his first one. And the idea came to him when he was peeling the potatoes.

Emerson went to the cabinet and took a can of tuna out and said: "I want me a tuna fish sandwich to go with my French fries. Bet Joe make me a tuna fish sandwich."
After Roy pushed his sandwich down and made a highly visible imprint of his little hand he said: "I'm hungry! But I am not eating this sandwich. I like meat, lettuce, tomato, mayonnaise and mustard on my sandwiches. Here Charlie you can have it back. I don't feel up to eating a French fry sandwich today. (Laughing, laughing, laughing) Here come Bill Lee Hillsberry. Use him for a guinea pig Charlie. If he eat it I might consider eating mine."

Bill Lee adored the sandwich: "Hey man. Man this is good. Who taught you how to make this? Hey man. Make me another one. Never mind. Give me Roy's sandwich. Its different. I really like this Charlie. I think I'll go home and make my family some French fry sandwiches. Ay. Y'all stop right now. Git off of Charlie's back. You guys are jealous cause you didn't think of this French fry sandwich idea first. (bobbing his head and jostling around.) What are you looking at Earl? Do you want to go in the back yard or what? Alright. Man. Don't mess with me. Baby Roy. With your proper self. Your word don't hold no clout around here. And please Baby Roy don't volunteer me to be a guinea pig unless a girl is involved. Alright?"

Charlie was breaking small pieces of his sandwich, eating it and licking his fingers like that was the best food he ever ate. Since I was the oldest one of the bunch, I took time to think. Daddy is always saying; 'Don't knock a person for trying, be open minded and commend them for trying.' That's when I became open minded. I thought about the day when I was visiting my friend

209

Linda next door. We were famished and she made lunch. She took some old corn bread from the refrigerator and heated it up in the skillet. She burned it because the stove was turned up too high.

Then she put tuna on it and said: "two for you and two for me. I'll put them on the same plate so I will only have one plate to wash." I turned my nose up and thought to myself, 'I'm not eating that. It smell like cat food. Wow! Linda's mother keep their cat's food in the refrigerator. Wow! They eat cat food!' It turned out that I had formed an opinion too fast. Linda's corn bread tuna sandwiches were actually made with real tuna and they were pretty good.

I had a little talk with my brothers. "Listen to this. Let's not be too hasty. Charlie worked hard peeling the potatoes to make all of these French fries. Think about this. We are always saying we're tired of hot dogs we're tired of tuna and spam sandwiches. Etc. That's why Charlie came up with this unique French fry sandwich. It's different. Besides how will you ever know what it taste like if you don't taste it? Bill Lee like it. So. let's say our blessings and eat."

The sandwiches was different but very satisfying to our taste buds. Earl was the first one to finish eating. He couldn't stop raving about the sandwich. As a matter of fact he peeled some more potatoes, Richard cut them up, I fried them and we enjoyed another French fry sandwich. We had French fry sandwiches every single day for months. By then we had perfected it by adding cheese, scrambled eggs and crumbled bacon to it. Charlie had all the kids in our neighborhood making French fry sandwiches.

Robert Earl Holmes: (Earl)

Richard, Charlie and I thought Miss Duck was the nicest person on earth when she came back to our house to kill two more birds with one stone. Richard said when he grew up he was going to get a black bag and be just like Miss Duck, kill two birds with one stone. As usual we were quiet and obedient while Miss Duck took care of Mama. Big Mama came outside and announced that we had another brother: "I was hoping for another girl but it's a boy. Five boys! His name is Robert Earl Holmes. Earl is a little sweetheart and look more like Doll and T. J.. He has blond curly hair, green eyes and long fingers and feet.

Earl developed a warm gregarious personality at a young age. He involved himself in working with and helping people and did considerably well. He was a conversationalist of good taste. He was well liked. Earl was the type of person that would be there for you whatever the occasion was. He would share his last with you and he loved his family dearly.

Earl Encouraged Me To Break The Finger Food Habit:

I ate greens and bread with my fingers until I was sixteen years old. That old habit was extremely hard to break. I was the only one in the family who still did that. I always started out with a fork and ate everything on my plate excluding the greens and bread. I ate them with my fingers. And that irritated Earl.

I came in the kitchen when Earl was eating some greens and bread and fixed some for myself. I began to eat with my fingers.

Irritated, Earl jumped up from the table and got a fork for me: "Here Bet Joe. Please? For Pete sakes. Eat your greens and bread with this fork. Eating greens and bread with your fingers is outdated. Can't you see that's old fashioned, country and very much not lady-like. What is it about you eating greens and bread with your fingers anyway? Oh! They taste better when you eat them

211

with your fingers. Bet Joe that's a myth you've been hearing all your life. But in reality you get the same identical taste with a fork. Your fingers don't have any kind of magical flavor that make greens and bread taste any better than they did when you first put them on your plate. Take a minute to think about this. Alright let's have a firm handshake on it. Daddy say a weak flimsy handshake ain't worth a plug nickel. You agree to use a fork for your greens and bread from here on out. OK. No ifs, ands, or buts."

I was enlightened and impressed with what Earl said to me. I was most appreciative for him looking out for me and for his display of love and concern. His lesson in etiquette was astounding. Surely that made him my precious *favorite* brother.

Earl Came Home Holding The Seat of His Pants:

On one extremely hot summer day Mama and I were sitting on the porch upstairs trying to keep cool with the fans that I had just made with shoe box tops.

As we sat there fanning we heard a faint voice in the far distance saying: "Daddy. Mama."

Mama looked at me and we simultaneously said: "That's Earl." We leaned over the banister in hope of seeing him but the thick trees prevented us from seeing anything. We stood there waiting as his voice got closer and he was finally in sight. Earl was squatting and walking wide legged holding the seat of his torn shorts with both hands. I ran down the stairs and helped him walk up the steps. Mama joined Daddy in the living room where he was eating watermelon and watching television.

Crying, Earl said: "Daddy, Mama, come here. Look. I cut my wee-wee and my balls is hanging out"

That shook them up. Daddy asked: "Earl! My God! What

212

happened boy?"

Nervously Earl explained what happened. "I was climbing the fence at school with my friends trying to get away from some big boys that were going to beat us up and my foot slipped when I got to the top of the fence. And my shorts got caught on the fence. And (still crying) they ripped. And my draws ripped. And the fence cut my wee-wee."

Daddy grabbed Earl and ran to the kitchen and pushed everything off the table and laid Earl there. In the meanwhile Mama ran to the bedroom to get one of the new white towels that she was saving for company from the trunk. She put cold water on it and wrapped it around Earl like a diaper. Then they were off to the hospital. Before they got in the car Mama remembered that she had left her purse and told me to bring it to her. Daddy told her: "Honey we ain't got time to wait on your purse let's go!"

The rest of the family sat around the kitchen table praying and waiting for them to return home. It was a long wait. The sun went down and nightfall made its way. The phone didn't ring. We kept picking it up to make sure no one was talking, (Due to the fact that we had a party line and shared it with three other families.)

Finally they came home and Earl looked so pitiful. His eyes were red and swollen from crying. Daddy gave us a rundown on what happened at the hospital. "They took Earl in as soon as we got to the hospital. After the doctors examined him they told us that Earl caused quite a bit of damage to his scrotum sack and testicles. They also said his testicles were hanging by a thread. They took him to surgery and repaired the damage. After surgery they informed me and Gladys that Earl would be fine and dandy.

Robert Earl And The Screen Next Door:

Earl was walking down our driveway on his way to the YMCA, when the window screen from next door fell on his feet. He bent down to pick it up and heard a woman's voice: "Love give me that screen please. Every time I turn the blame fan on that darn screen jumps off the window." She was hanging out of the window reaching for the screen. Earl dropped the screen and was mesmerized by the sight of that woman. She was wearing her birthday suit.

"Hello love. Hello. Hello. Hello! Are you alright? Did that screen hurt you? My name is Trouble. I'm your new neighbor. (Pointing to her ears and making a comment to herself, I don't know any sign language. I think this cute little boy is deaf. What a crying shame!) Little boy are you deaf?" Earl continued to stare in disbelief until Trouble finally got his attention.

And The only thing that came out of his mouth was: "Huh."

Trouble said: "Listen up love. I'll give you a dollar if you help me put this screen back in place." Earl's feet was glued to the ground. But he nodded his head indicating he was willing to help her. Trouble directed him to get a trash can from our back yard, bring it to the window and stand on it so he could help her put the screen back in place. After it was complete excitedly Earl went back in the house with his easy earned dollar. He was smiling. I thought he was smiling at me. I smiled at him in return and asked if he had changed his mind about going to the YMCA for his swimming lesson. There was no answer. He stood there and kept smiling as though he was in a different world. That alarmed me. I noticed the dollar in his hand and inquired about it. That question brought him back to reality and while still smiling he mumbled something. I didn't understand what he was saying. Simply because he was still smiling too hard.

I was forced to tell him: "Wait a minute Earl. I did not comprehend. Start over again. And stop smiling. You look like a clown trying to talk and smile at the same time."

His smile was cut considerably as he started over: "Bettye, I just saw a bucket neck woman." His wide smile returned as he continued: "The most beautiful woman I ever saw. I am on cloud nine. You know the woman that moved next door two weeks ago. The one that you and Peggy went to the store for last week. Um, um, um. I am in love with her."

I responded: "Shut up Earl! Trouble ain't nothing but a topless dancer that work in a bar on Chippawau Street. Every man in Buffalo done saw her tits. I heard June and T. J. talking about her. They said all kind of men touch her butt and she don't even care. They told me that I can't go to the store for her any more. Boy you ain't nothing but a nine year old runt. Anyway you can't even spell love."

Earl was in wonderland: "Trouble ran her fingers through my hair and called me a little blond curly head cute-tee-pie. How old is she? She said she was going to wait for me and marry me. Trouble. I love Trouble. How old do you have to be before you can get married? Im-ma write her a letter tonight and draw her a picture. I made a song up in my head about her. Listen to it.

'I fell in love with a pretty woman. She said she was going to marry me. Do do. Do do. Her name is Trou-ble. Do do. Do do. She gave me a dol-lar. And it made me hol-lar. Do do. Do do. I, I, I, I, got the Trou-ble blues. I can't go to the YMCA and take my swimming les-son. I might drown. Cause I ain't got no con-cen-tra-tion No con-cen-tra-tion. Trou-ble in on my mind, on my mind. I got the Trou-ble blues. Do do. Do do.'

"It will sound good if I play the piano and sing it. Im-ma marry her Bettye. I can't disappoint her. She called me 'Love' How do this sound? 'Trouble and Love'

My little brother had a big crush on Trouble for two weeks. After I'd iron his shirt and jeans, he'd take the shirt and lay it on

215

the dining room table and shake Daddy's cologne on it before putting it on. Trouble complimented him on the fragrance the first time he wore the cologne. That encouraged him to continue to wear Daddy's cologne. Earl thought he was a teenager. Anyhow the same time everyday for the next thirteen days Trouble's screen fell off her window. And every time it happened reliable Earl was always in the vicinity willing to help put it back in place at no cost.

Trouble was anxious to get to the bottom of her screen falling mystery. She set a trap by nailing the screen to the window. When it was that time of the day Trouble hid behind the apple tree in her back yard and awaited the soon to be incident. Her little secret admirer Earl had a humongous magnet tied to Mama's missing clothes line. He went to the window, threw the magnet and pulled the clothes line like he did the previous times. Nothing happened! He yanked the magnet several times without any results. He was too busy yanking the magnet to notice Trouble walking down our driveway.

Therefore he jumped three feet when she put her hand on his shoulder saying: "Hey Love. What in the world are you doing with that gigantic magnet and clothes line? No!. Don't tell me. Let me guess (Laughing) for the last thirteen days you have been spying on me faithfully trying to catch me in my beautiful birthday suit again. You are a determined young man. That flatters me. But I got some serious talk for you green eyes."

Trouble didn't squeal on Earl to Daddy and Mama. She took the matter in her hands and had a talk with him that was stern and fearing. Whatever she said to him, I know for sure that it knocked him off his plush comfortable cloud nine causing him to fall out of love with her Immediately and leaving his feelings bruised.

As I recall Earl came to me and said: "Bettye Joe, do me a favor? Never. Ever. What-so-ever. Under any circumstances. No matter what, mention the word Trouble to me! What kind of name is that for a woman anyway? She has bumps all over her face.

Her fingernails are too long. There is a cute girl in my swimming class. She has smooth skin and she bite her fingernails. She's only twelve years old. I like her. He invited me to accompany him to the YMCA and watch him swim. His instructor said he was doing well.

Earl's Stay In California:

Earl lived in California for seven years. During his stay there he attended the El Segundo School Of Cosmetology in the city of El Segundo, CA. He also worked as a full time private Nurse Assistant for a paraplegic patient. After his graduation he went on to work as a Certified Cosmetologist in Redondo Beach, CA.

Earl was approached by one of his clients and offered a job working for her at the Willowbrook Community Project Committee. She was impressed with his genuine friendly personality and knowledge. She felt that he would be an asset in her office. Therefore she offered him a position as an Assistant Committeeman. Earl was honored that she offered him a job working for her with a doubled salary. He accepted the position, learned fast and excelled quite well on his assignments. 'Assistant Committeeman Robert Earl Holmes' was on the door that led to his office.

He worked diligently with city councilmen, the mayor, city officials, and representatives of the City of Compton, CA. It was his proposal and diligence that achieved the funds to develop and implement the Willowbrook Park in the city of Compton, CA on El Segundo Boulevard. The park was a solution for people in the surrounding communities to have a safe place to go for recreation, for adults as well as children. The park was very well constructed with equipment necessary for children to utilize by playing and exercising. The park accommodated barbecue pits, picnic tables, benches, bathrooms, a walking trail and the ultimate was a pond stocked with fish for fishing, etc.. Sometimes we went there on Sunday evenings from church just to reminisce.

Earl had a strong passion for the welfare of the elderly. He possessed a special quality for helping the elderly homeowners acquire funds to refurbish their homes. He also helped the elderly non-homeowners and the homeless get in new apartment homes. They showered him with love and appreciation by baking a variety of desserts.

He often laughed and said: "My favorite dessert is peach cobbler. I'm still waiting for someone to bring me one."

Earl Moved Back To Buffalo:

The fact that he couldn't get Geneva out of his mind (which was the love of his life) not to mention his family also, is what persuaded Earl to pack up his belongings and move back to Buffalo, New York. Earl and Geneva were married soon after that. Their precious lovely daughters are: Kamilah, Tiffany, Le Rondra, Veronica and Santori.

If The Walls Could Talk:

September 1995 : Earl and I Reminisced:

I was moved by Earl's wit as we reminisced sitting at the kitchen table. We had a discussion on if the walls in that house could talk, it would have a million and one stories to tell. And the first story it would probably tell would be pertaining to when we first came to Buffalo.

" (Yup, I remember when those country people came up here from Gloster, Mississippi. It was the year of 1957. They talked funny and everything. Sometimes I had a difficult time understanding what they were saying. They would go to the attic and run all the way down the stairs to the basement and back to the attic again. At least one of them would get confused practically every day for a whole month by going down stairs and raiding the refrigerator and cabinets. And their mannerism towards me was way out of order. I wasn't used to that kind of treatment. I had been standing here for ninety-eight years looking pretty when they moved here. Oh my. that boy Richard brought a green crayon home from school and drew something on me that resembled a man and some trees. Then Charlie took the crayon and went across me making little green circles. After that he laid on the floor watching television with his feet propped upon me. Emerson, ha, that boy was the worst one. Every time he got his hands on an ink pen, a pencil or crayon, he'd run straight to me and get busy. One time he had something on his hands that looked like mashed potatoes and gravy and he wiped it on me. Then took the crayon and smeared it. I wondered, 'how long will these country people be here?'

Emerson also had a bad habit of leaving the house without telling anybody. (I guess he thought he was still in the country). Anyhow he always went to visit the Stenhouse's, who lived three houses down the street. Mrs. Stenhouse would let Emerson play with her children's toys in their basement.

Emerson would return home saying, 'Mama, I went to play in Mrs. Stenhouse toy store. I had big fun.' It was apparent that Emerson being from the country was accustomed to limited home made toys. He was mesmerized by the toys which the Stenhouses' had in their basement. Therefore he thought it was a toy store.

Those boys and their friends snuck girls in the attic on school nights all the time. And for the longest time the kitchen served as a neighborhood snack bar and a place for arm wrestling for their friends. That girl Bet Joe, Bettye Joe, or Bettye, had no clue what a telephone was for. Every day she would go to the window in the dining room, fall on her knees and call her friend, 'Linnn da, Linnn da.' That piercing voice used to get on my nerves.

She came home in tears one day telling Gladys that she went around the corner on Celtic and met some new friends, Sue Ella, (T. J.'s future wife) and her sister Bertha.

They asked her what was she eating and she responded: 'A chiken sanmich.' Their father was sitting on the porch and overheard her.

So he called her, 'Come here lil girl! What is you eatin?'

She told him the same thing; 'A chiken sanmich.' He laughed and laughed.

Then asked his next door neighbors whom was sitting on their porch : 'Y'all come here. I want y'all to hear this. Lil girl. Tell them what you is eatin.'

She told them: 'A chiken sanmich.' All of those grown people laughed at her. She ran home to Curley and Gladys and told them what happened. Naturally, they were upset.

Curley said: 'I'll go over there and knock his damn teeth out.'

Gladys reasoned with him: 'OK Curley. The man won't have any teeth. And Bettye will still be saying chiken sanmich.'

They straightened the matter out by teaching Bettye how to spell and pronounce chicken and sandwich. After all she was their baby girl.

The next time she went to visit Sue Ella and Bertha, their father laughed and asked her; 'Lil girl what was you eatin the other day?'

Bettye looked at him and said: ' I was eating a chicken sandwich!' He was out done: 'Heck No. That ain't the way you said it the other day.'

I have to make a comment on this. Those seven Holmes boys was something else when it came to that pool table up there in the attic. Everybody that went up there lost their money shooting pool. That's all Im-ma say about that. That boy T. J. was known for writing girls telephone number on that fine antique priceless china cabinet. In the 70's, Gladys kept up with the style, by straightening Emerson and Roy's hair and she braided it on many occasions.

Ha. What about that time when T. J. hit Alaney? yeah! He was on the phone talking trash to a girl. I guess she liked what he was saying cause he had been talking that stuff for a long time. Anyhow the door bell suddenly interrupted his conversation and he heard someone running up the stairs. The door to the living room opened and in walked Alaney   He spoke and kept walking.

'Ay T. J.. What's up?'

T. J. was pissed.   He got off the phone and rushed to the bathroom saying: 'Gee. I can't stand that do-hickie!   I can't believe he's back over here after I had that talk with him the other day. Gee. (beating his fist in his hand) I can't stand him. Ooh!'

He grabbed the plunger and hurried to the attic.   That nosey Bettye Joe was right behind him.

T. J. made it to the attic just in time to stand outside the door and hear Alaney say: 'Ay! I'm back. Y'all can kiss yo money goodbye. Cause I'm taking it with me. So y'all might as well put T. J's. Play Boy library back under his mattress before he come up here and Jack y'all up. Hurry up. Get to it. I don't have all day. No thank you. I saw all of them the other day. I'm waiting for next month's edition.'

T. J. opened the door and shocked all of them. (Dobb, Calvin , Renfroe, Bill lee Hillsberry, Alonzo, Albert, Richard and Charlie)

Then he directed a question to Alaney: 'Look do-hickie? What did I tell you the other day?'

After thinking. Alaney said; 'You told me not to come over here to shoot dice any more. And if I did I would be a dead duck. I thought you were playing. You were serious? Mr. T. J.?'

221

T. J. said: 'Tell me if you think I'm playing now.' He lifted the plunger to strike Alaney. Alaney ran and caught Richard from behind and held him as though he was performing a Heimlich Maneuver. Richard broke away and pushed him back.

He asked Richard: 'Is that the same plunger that y'all always use to unstop the toilet?' Richard told him: 'Yeah man. That's the only plunger we have.'

In return, Alaney said: 'Mr. T. J., don't hit me with that dirty plunger. I won't come over here to shoot dice anymore. I promise.

T. J. said: 'Too bad you didn't take heed to my advice. Its too late to negotiate now.' He hit Alaney with the plunger and that knocked him on his knees. While that was going on everybody else left the attic running like a bat out of hell.

Alaney stayed on his knees for quite a while. He was afraid to get up because he thought T. J. would hit him with the plunger again. T. J. told him to get the heck out of there and never come to the house again. Leaving his coat behind, Alaney left quickly without giving himself time to stand up straight. He was bent from his waist as he ran. Ha. That was the last time I saw Alaney.

I remember the day that Bettye and Richard had a scuffle after school. Bettye picked Roy up from the babysitter and fed him. Then she put the pot of soup on the stove to heat it up. After that she washed the dishes, swept and mopped the floor. Finally the soup was ready. She fixed Earl and Emerson a bowl of soup. Then she started to fix her a bowl of it and along came Richard. He was in a bad mood. Perhaps he had a miserable day or something.

Pushing Bettye: 'Git out of the damn way. Im-ma fix my plate first. Who do you think you are? Always fixing your plate first.' Both of them were standing at the stove holding their bowls, pushing each other, trying to be the first one to fix their bowl of soup.

222

All of a sudden, they knocked that big pot of hot soup on the floor and a portion of it splashed on Bettye's foot. She had a fit and ran to the bathroom and filled the tub with cold water to soothe her burning foot. She copped an attitude with all of those boys and went to her room to pout. Yup. Those boys would make Curley mad at times and he would haul off and hit me with his fist and say; "If I hit them right now, I'll kill em."

I would think: 'Those hard head bad ass boys. Go on and kill em, and stop hitting me. I am tired of you getting mad at them and swinging on me. I am not a punching bag.'

I miss the Holmes Family! After all of those years and what they have taken me through made me a Holmes home. You better hurry up and believe I consider myself a member of the Holmes family."

Earl and I Continued To Indulged In Sweet Rich Memories: September 1995

Earl and I relived the time when June came to the house and brought Mama some tea. June said: "Mama I brought you some tea."

Mama answered him: "Good! I can take a break from this quilt and have a cup of it. My back is getting a little stiff from sitting at this sewing machine. Come on Bettye. June brought me some tea. Let's have a cup of it. You too T. J.. You need a break from that darn liquor."

Back in the kitchen, June pulled a tea bag out of his pocket and gave it to Mama. She took it, read it and said: "Sleepy Time Tea. Huh! We'll have sweet sleep tonight. Ay. The water is hot. Where is the rest of the tea June?"

"That's it old girl." June answered.
"What? You got to be kidding. Shit. Boy you mean to tell me that you drove fifteen miles to bring me one tea bag. I don't

223

believe this." Mama responded. T. J. laughed and teased June. But his teasing didn't bother June at all. He just laughed right along with T. J.. As a matter of fact we all laughed. And that was only the beginning.

T. J. teased June about that one tea bag for a long time.

One Saturday afternoon June came over: "Ay T. J. put your shoes on and let's ride."

T. J. asked; "Where are we going?"

June answered; "I was thinking about stopping at the liquor store and then ride around for a while then end up at Mocca's Pizza on Clinton Street"

T. J. made a remark; "I'm not up to drinking liquor today. I'd love to have a cup of tea."

June responded angrily: "Shit! You sound like a damn broken record. I'm tired of listening to it. Lay off me about that damn tea bag. You done told everybody in the family about that tea bag .

Sue Ella (T.J.' s wife) came up behind me in the grocery store yesterday and tapped me on the back: 'Excuse me Mister.' I turned around and she started to laugh: 'Boy you ought to be ashamed of yourself. T. J. told me about that one Sleepy Time Tea bag you drove fifty miles to bring Mama.'

T. J., you ain't got nothing else to talk about? If I would have saw you yesterday you wouldn't have went to work today. Why? You better believe that right now you'd be recuperating from me beating the hell out of you! I'm leaving."

As he was leaving, T. J. asked him to wait until he put his shoes on and brush his teeth because he was coming with him. By June being teed off he ignored T. J. and drove away. In return T. J. took his shoes off again and stretched out on the couch with the intentions of enjoying some relaxation. A little while later June pulled up in the driveway and blew the horn.

T. J. joined him and they were off once again to indulge in their weekend tradition. It was a tradition that the two of them created. (To get a bottle of liquor and drive around while sipping on it. And end up at Mocca' Pizza on Clinton Street.) They would buy two slices of pizza and sit in the car while eating it, talking, sometimes arguing, drinking their liquor and making remarks about the people that drove into the parking lot to buy pizza. An hour or so later they would get another two slices and repeat the same thing. After having three slices of pizza they would call it quits and go home.

Earl talked: "You remember that time when Arold Dobb came over here carrying a neatly folded bag and asked Richard and Charlie to go with him to play a trick on somebody. They went to Mr. Butler's house and Arold took out some matches and said: "Charlie put this bag on the floor by the door. Richard I want you to ring the doorbell right after I strike this match and the bag catch on fire. Then we'll run to your driveway and hide." They ran to our driveway and hid behind the hedges, waiting for Mr. Butler to answer his door. The bag was blazing when Mr. Butler answered his door. Therefore, he immediately stomped the bag until the fire was out. That's when he realized the bag was full of shit and it was all over his shoes. He was so angry that he took his shoes off and threw them in the street. He tried for years to find out who put that bag of burning shit on his porch."

Emerson Holmes: Em Mississippi

Emerson was always quiet and precise from a baby. The entire family was worried about him because we thought he would never talk. Mama blamed it on the hospital because he was the only one of us born in a hospital and he was the only one of us with eczema. Big Mama agreed with her. She also mentioned the fact that doctors like to perform experiments on patients. And they

225

probably performed some kind of an experiment on Emerson which turned out wrong and damaged his vocal cords.

One day in church, Sister Prince told Big Mama that her twelve year old grandson had eczema and he never uttered a word. She said he didn't even cry. Daddy told Big Mama to disregard what that old meddlesome woman told her. He said Emerson would talk when he was good and ready. In the meanwhile he bought a medical book and read up on an assortment of remedies to coax Emerson into talking. Everyday he'd come home from work and try something different. One night he tried the scare tactic by leaving Emerson in the kitchen by himself with the light off. The lights were off for several minutes. Emerson didn't make a sound.

When Daddy opened the door to the kitchen and turned the light back on, Emerson was standing by the table cool and calm with a big smile holding a half eaten biscuit in each hand. Daddy tried all kind of teas. Somebody told him to massage Emerson's neck and throat with duck grease. Daddy jumped right on it. He chose a plump duck from the back yard prepared it and cooked it. He massaged Emerson's face, neck and throat with that duck grease. Somebody else told him to sing to Emerson. When he started to sing Mary Had A Little Lamb and pat his feet Emerson left the room in a hurry and closed the door behind him. He could still hear Daddy singing in the next room so he went to the porch and set on the step to wait it out. Daddy gave that singing his best, but it was absolutely terrible. It would have reminded you of a comedian that was trying to mess up a song just to get a good laugh. That's why Papa told him to stop clowning and sing the song the right way.

Daddy would sit Emerson on his lap after trying each remedy and tell him to say daddy. But Emerson wouldn't say a darn thing. He just smiled and shook his head.

Emerson's first three years was a difficult trying time for all of us. He was a very happy baby who loved to eat. We spent a lot of time with him trying to get him to say something daddy, mama, a good word, a bad word, anything we didn't care. The most we could get out of him was a big smile. He was very well behaved. He enjoyed playing in the back yard throwing rocks at the chickens. He loved to help out with the chores. Feeding the chickens and holding the clothespin bag for Mama when she was hanging the clothes on the clothes line, were the ones which he preferred.

He was extremely spoiled. But we only had ourselves to blame for that. Every time one of us would put him down, another one of us would pick him up.

Mama used to say: "For Heavens sake, put Emerson down and give him a break. He can walk. There ain't nothing wrong with his feet." All of that attention was amusing to him and it probably made his day.

Early one morning Emerson was in the back yard playing when all of a sudden he busted through the kitchen door and slammed it behind him. His cheeks were red and he was out of breath.

Daddy picked him up and asked: "Emerson what is it? What happened? You look as though you just saw a ghost."
Daddy wasn't expecting Emerson to answer him. Therefore he was in for the most precious blessed surprise of his life!

Emerson: "Daddy! The dog got at me! I was very scared! I was throwing rocks and hit her in the head with one of them. It was an accident! No joke. Honest. Cross my heart. You better believe I ain't telling nothing but the truth."

Emerson shook his head and smiled. That literally left us speechless and in a state of shock. It was simply unbelievable to hear Emerson talk and use complete sentences. It was so natural! As though he had been talking all along. Daddy ran to the back yard and called Papa and Big Mama. He told them that Emerson was talking up a storm. They rushed to the house in disbelief. Emerson spoke to them: "Good morning Big Mama and Papa.

227

How are you this fine blessed day? Don't just stand there looking at me with your mouth open and your hands on your hips. Say good morning Emerson."

Big Mama was overjoyed and began to cry and praise God for that wondrous miracle. She said that was something to write home about. The kind of news they needed to celebrate. She asked Emerson what did he want to eat.

He told her: "I want some chicken. I want some ice cream. I want to turn the handle all by myself. I want some sweet peas with potatoes in them and some greens and some squash and some okra and some corn bread and some red soft drink." Then he said: "Big Mama I don't want Marble to live here anymore. I don't like her. She tried to bite me. Will you and Papa take her to live in Roy Rogers Creek, with that old yellow bastard? (the stray cat). Put her in a flour sack with some rocks in it and throw her in the water like you did that old yellow bastard that ate your egg pies, drank your buttermilk and pissed in your face when you were chasing him out the door." Emerson was certainly my *favorite* brother.

We had a joyous pleasurable celebration.

Mr. Sears came by to drop some rabbits off and let Daddy know that he heard about Emerson talking: "Curley, Let me tell you this. I went huntin this mornin and caught more rabbits that I can eat. I brought y'all two of them. Yes-sir-re-bop. I heard about that there boy of yoin talkin. You just-a-grinning. You tickled to death. Ain't you? Well if you ask me, it was about time that youngen open his mouth and say somethin. Let me ask you this. Just what did he say anyhow? The way you grinning, I expect he said daddy. My wife said that was good news. She told me to pass that on to y'all. Um, um um, ain't it funny how fast news travel."

Daddy thanked Mr. Sears for the rabbits and told him that boy of his said a heck of a lot more than daddy.

Daddy told Mama that Mr. Sears claimed he went rabbit hunting early that morning and caught more rabbits than he could eat. Then he pointed out: "These rabbits are still warm. Mr. Sears came straight here from hunting. Why don't you fix that old buzzard and Mrs. Sears a plate of food. Oh yeah, wrap one of those chess pies up. You know how they love them. I'll have June and T. J. take it to them."

Many years later in Buffalo; (1992) Emerson and I were driving down Main street, (in Buffalo) on our way to do some errands for Mama. He saw a girl at the bus stop and pulled over.

Emerson spoke in a very soft voice: "Hello. How you doing girl? This is my sister Bettye. She's visiting from California. Ain't she cute Bettye? Man she's fine."

She spoke to me: "Hello Bettye. How are you enjoying yourself here in Buffalo?"

Emerson asked: "Where are you on your way to? U B. Come on I'll take you there. I'll feel bad if I leave you out here in the rain. Oh your girlfriend is meeting you. Do you guys ride the bus together every day? You do. When can I see you again? Right here tomorrow the same time. You know what? I can't make it tomorrow. I'll be at work. I'm supposed to be at work now but my machine died and it was going to take the rest of the day to bring it back. So my supervisor sent me home. The good thing about that, is I get paid for the rest of the day.

Anyway, what are you doing this weekend? Can I see you? I'd like to take you out to dinner and a movie. If that's alright with you. Can I cook? My friends call me 'Em' the chef. No problem. I'll cook dinner for you. Bettye put my phone number on this piece of paper for her. My name is Emerson. What's yours? Lindy? Um, I went to school with a girl named Lindy. Lindy, may I call you tonight? Bettye write her phone number down. For me."

Emerson drove off slowly and without taking his eyes off Lindy, he inadvertently ran the red light and had the nerves to get mad at the police officer that was behind us. The police officer was also staring at Lindy.

Emerson talked: "Hey Bettye, you see how that pig is looking at Lindy? He dig her. I don't like that shit! I'm thinking about asking her to be my girlfriend. You know what I mean sis?

Ay. Check this out. What in the heck is these people blowing and pointing at me for? Oh no. Bettye, why didn't you tell me that I was running the red light. I can't stop now cause I'm in the middle of the intersection. Darn. Im-ma get a ticket for sure. Oh man! I should have stayed at work. I might as well pull over and park. Maybe if I tell him that Roy is a State Trooper he won't write me a ticket. Hey. What's wrong with that guy? He didn't even stop to give me a ticket. What is he thinking about and smiling like that for? Check out his big ass chin. That big ugly bastard! (Emerson was laughing, joking and happy because he didn't get a ticket.) Somebody should report him. Cause he's doing a lousy job giving out tickets."

Roy Lane Holmes: Roy

"Roy is the BABY! Capitalized period! You will come out better by craving ice cream or candy." That's what Mama told me, when I told her that I was craving for a baby sister.

From the age of four Roy became my little psychiatrist and mediator. Most of the time I went to him for his help when I wanted to go out on a date or attend a dance at the Memorial Auditorium. The Memorial Auditorium was the place where all the singers came to perform every other Sunday evening. It was the stylish thing to do in Buffalo, NY.

Although I was too shy to dance in public, I simply had to be there. I usually went with my friends Linda and Peggy. The dance would last from 7:00 to 11:00 p. m.. I'd get home at 11:30 that evening. And for that reason Daddy and Mama were apprehensive about giving me permission to attend all of the dances, because Sunday was a school night. They told me that if the dances were held on Saturday evenings, it would have been a different ball-game. They were a bit strict too. Anyhow whenever they said no, Roy managed to persuade them to say 'yes' most of the time.

I always used the same old stale routine. I had a stubborn pouting problem when they said no. I would go in the kitchen and find something constructive to do while I pouted. Give the stove a thorough cleaning, organize and rearrange the cabinets, spot clean the walls, anything that kept me busy.

Then I'd call Roy; (this particular Sunday morning) "Roy could you come in the kitchen for a minute?"
Roy: "Alright Bet Joe what is it this time? Talk fast. Because I have to be back before the commercial goes off."

I asked him: "Please. You gotta help me. It's a matter of life and death. I already told my friends that I was going to the dance. Peggy's mother is taking us. They will be here at 6:30 this evening. And your parents say I can't go. Could you talk some sense into them so they can change their minds and let me go? Tell them If they let me go to this dance I won't ask to go to another dance."

Roy: "OK. I'll talk with them later. I'm watching Hansel And Gretel right now."

I asked: "Could you ask them right now so I'll know what to do?"

Roy, "Bet Joe take a look at the clock. It's only 8:45 in the morning. The dance doesn't start until 7:00 this evening. Let me give you some good advice sister. Drink a glass of cold water, relax and let me handle this. I'm just a little kid who want to

231

finish watching Hansel And Gretel. OK? Give me a break. Don't stress me out. I don't need that. I'm too young for grey hair and stress."

I depended on Roy to come through for me with his magical flair. And he did. He is positively without a question my *favorite* brother. Roy's sense of humor has been awesome from a very young age. In a situation where most people might get angry, upset and crack, it was Roy's character to make the best out of a bad situation and break into an infectious laugh.

He developed an interest in walking on his hands and did that for years. It was a unique thing to do. He was the most musically talented of us all, as well as being a good singer. His music equipment was set up in the attic.

Roy and several of his school mates formed a singing group. They would come over and practice singing for hours. Their music had a great sound to it. In the summertime, the attic windows were open and the music rode the air attracting people to the sidewalk in front of our home to hear Roy sing. It was a summer treat they looked forward to. They danced to that pleasing music. At times girls screamed Roy's name. I thought he was going to be a famous singer for sure. Therefore, I contemplated on being his manager.

After he graduated from high school, he went on to college and forgot about music. And one of those college days, Roy just didn't want to get up and go to school for nothing. So Mama gave him that extra ump to get going.

Mama: Roy Honey. It's 6:30. Time to get up.

Roy: I can sleep another half hour. I'm not due for my first class today until 8:30.

Mama: Roy honey, Wake up. It's 7:00.

Roy: I'll sleep another half hour.
Mama: Roy honey, get up. It's 7:30.

Roy: Ok.

Mama: Roy I thought you got up fifteen minutes ago. It's 7:45.
Get up you're running late.

Roy: It's 7:45? Why didn't you wake me earlier? You're right I
am running late. I'll just stay home today. I hate being late.
Everybody turn around and look at you funny when you come to
class late.

Mama snatched the covers off Roy to get his undivided attention.
She got it too.

Roy: Mama it's freezing in here. Put that cover back on me and
turn the heater up. I'll lay here until it get a bit warmer.

Mama: Boy get your ass up before I get mad! Here! Drink the
rest of my coffee. You're going to school today. Better late than
never.

Roy: Ouch. That hurt. You have never talked to me like that
before. Did you have a bad night?

Mama: Yeah. You're right. I haven't talked to you like that
before. But I get tired of being nice. Sometimes you have to say a
bad word! Do you realize how many times I attempted to wake
you this morning?

Roy: Yes Mam.

Mama: No. I did not have a bad night. Go on and drink this
coffee. It will wake you up.
Roy: Mama you know I don't drink coffee.

Mama: You can finish sleeping when you get home from school.

Is that clear boy? It was your choice to attend college and it's my duty to see to it that you are there everyday. One day you are going to thank me for this. You ain't gon learn a darn thing in that bed sleeping.

Yeah, your little friend Mickey Eastman work from 3:00 to 11:00 at night. He get off work and come over here pass your bed time and want to party. Yeah um huh. Y'all was still playing chess when I went to the bathroom at 4:00 this morning. When I mentioned to you about going to bed and getting some sleep cause that's what you needed. You had the nerves to tell me: 'Mama jus, jus, just be cool. I have it under control. Its no big thing if I don't get eight hours of sleep every now and then. I can get two hours of sleep and go to school feeling refreshed.' Do you feel refreshed? I guess you won't do that again. Will you?

Big Mama's Visit to Buffalo: 1958

The Handkerchief:

Big Mama visited us in Buffalo a year after we moved there. She spent a lot of time with me talking mostly in the evening when everyone else was busy watching television, reading the paper or doing homework. We'd clean up the kitchen, make some lemonade and sit at the table and talk for an hour or more.

I distinctively remember one particular evening when Big Mama told me of the story behind the handkerchief which she had been wearing pinned to her bra since her wedding day. Her lips were turned inward as she bit them trying to fight back the tears as she unbuttoned her blue print dress which she made and removed the handkerchief that was pinned to her bra. Her hands trembled as she revealed a handkerchief with a faint border of pink faded roses. In a very shallow shaky tone she said; "My mother gave me this money wrapped in this very handkerchief on my wedding day. Let's see, that was one year one month and twenty four days before your mother was born. That would be your great

234

grandmother. She couldn't afford to give me her last but she did it anyway. I know it put her in a hardship. She loved me so much that she didn't care about the hardship which she would face for weeks to come. It pleased her heart to give me something to save for a rainy day. Um. She squeezed my hands real tight and told me not to worry because it was more where that came from.

I not only worried about it, I felt guilty. But after fourteen months of scraping and scraping, I managed to save three dollars. Which I gave to her. It made her very happy and she took a handkerchief from her pocketbook, wrapped the money in it and pinned it to her brassiere.

I'm thankful for that rainy day never came where I had to use this money. I guess you're wondering why I have this handkerchief wrapped in two more handkerchiefs. Well to put it plain, I don't want this one to be soiled. I know you won't understand this but my mother's precious hands handled this handkerchief and the money that's wrapped in it. That is one way of holding her dear to me and keeping her alive in my heart. I'll keep it pinned to my brassiere until I die. Then your mother can have it. And maybe she can keep it in this same handkerchief and pass it on to you or Doll and you all can pass it on to your children. Like a souvenir. By then it will surely be worth a whole lot more than it is now. This money is pretty old right now. It is from the early nineteenth century.

Girl, you ask more questions than the law allow. But that's good. How will you know if you don't ask. You think it's odd or strange for me to still be emotional when I speak of my mother?

So you want to know why I still cry when I think of my mother whom died so many years ago? Child. You have a whole lot to learn. You don't stop loving or forget someone that's dear to you just because they die. They will always be alive in your heart if you allow it. Time will never make you forget about your love ones. As time goes on you will adjust and digest the fact that you will no longer see their body or have a conversation with them.

But it will always be something that will remind you of them. A taste. A smell. Something that someone might say. Sometimes you will cry when you think of them. Sometimes you will laugh when you think of them. Sometimes you might get angry with them for dying. Because you miss them so much. Or you just might think about them long and hard! You will talk about them quite often. Their spirit will almost always be with you. Sometimes you will get a strong sense that it is with you. My little granddaughter, at times the spirit will come to you in a dream.

It's like this. My mother passed a portion of herself to me. She taught me how to read and write. She taught me how to sew, cook, wash, iron, clean the house, how to treat people and how to work in the field. I could go on for hours telling you what she taught me. But the point that I am trying to make is that everyday by using some of these fine qualities that my mother taught me, makes it impossible to forget her. She lives through me. I am her offspring. And I know that I'm only separated from her temporary. I will see her and my father again, by walking in a Christian-way, down the narrow road. The way that Jesus intended me to walk."

Big Mama Took Us To Lunch:

One day Richard, Charlie, Earl, Emerson and I came home for lunch from school and Big Mama took us to the Deco Restaurant on Jefferson and East Utica. On the way there her and I held Emerson's hands and Richard and Charlie held Earl's hands. The six of us walked to the restaurant and were seated.

Big Mama ordered hamburgers and milkshakes for us. When we got our hamburgers, Big Mama inspected them and told the waitress that they was the saddest example of a hamburger she ever laid her eyes on. That they were stale, dry, three days old, thin as paper with no seasoning hamburgers. And she wasn't going to let us eat it because it would surely make us sick. Then she told the waitress that she wasn't going to pay for them either. She also added: "My daughter wrote me a letter and told me about

236

people up here in Buffalo, New York paying tips when they go out to eat. Well y'all can forget about me. Cause I ain't paying no tip. The only tip you will get from me is how to make a good hamburger."

The manager came out and said he would make us some fresh plump juicy burgers. He did. And Big Mama said they were much better and graciously thanked him.

After we were done eating Big Mama had us stand in a line and introduced us to the waitress and the manager. She told them that she was visiting us from Gloster, Mississippi

The manager danced around and said: "Lady, you're kidding me. I'm from Hattisberg, Mississippi. Born and raised there. And I've been to Gloster a many times. I used to go to the ball games at the school house there." They talked trying to find out if they knew any of the same people. But they didn't. Anyway he invited her to come back and chat with him before she left going back to Mississippi.

It totally slipped Big Mama's mind that we only had one hour for lunch. After we left the restaurant she wanted to go to all the stores on both sides of the street. The shoe stores, the clothing stores, the hardware store, the drug store, the fire sale store, and the grocery store. We had fun that afternoon hanging out with Big Mama trying on shoes and clothes and browsing through the stores. She bought a variety of goodies and told us that we'd have them later. We assumed later meant at home. Big Mama had another pleasant surprise tucked under her sleeve. She took us to the Apollo Show to see Old Yeller. We enjoyed the movie along with our goodies. That was a surprise and a wonderful treat to be treasured for a lifetime.

As we walked home form the show Big Mama told us: "I want Y'all to remember this. Every time you get a nickel in your hands don't run to the store and spend it. Don't let it burn a hole in your pockets either. Hang on to it tight. I want you all to always do your very best. Help Curley and Gladys out around the house by picking up after yourselves, keeping the kitchen clean and taking out the trash, things of that nature." Then she opened her purse and gave each one of us a dollar bill and a nickel. Skipping school and spending the afternoon with Big Mama was tremendous! We did not want it to end.

The next day, Big Mama took us to the principal's office and told her why she kept us home from school. She told her everything that we did. The principal was a mean lady by nature. But she was very polite to Big Mama. The next day Big Mama walked us to school and took the principal a slice of her pound cake. The principal loved the cake. She wrote Big Mama a letter asking her to bake a pound cake for her. She offered to pay Big Mama two dollars for it.

That week Big Mama baked six pound cakes for the principal and some teachers as well. She earned twelve dollars for the cakes and two dollars for tips. She was gratified for it and said: "Y'all better believe. I am not saving this money for a rainy day! Me and Smiley will splurge on every cent of it."

Big Mama was a very lovely outstanding person who always spoke her mind. She was for-real, with a get to the punch don't beat around the bush attitude. That was the only way she knew how to be.

She generously passed her good cooking genes and her hardworking genes down to my siblings and myself as well.

I remember and appreciate all the knowledgeable inspiring things which she taught me. And I loved her tremendously and will always treasure that wonderful sweetheart of a woman in my heart.

It was very emotional for everyone when the time for Big Mama to return home to Papa arose. She loved Papa with a passion and he loved her with a passion. Papa was an exceptional husband, father, father-n-law and grandfather. Big Mama used to say he was a small man, but mighty strong. Although he was a quiet man, he had no problem speaking his mind. When he spoke, everyone would stop whatever they were doing and listen to what he had to say. He was firm, serious and his common sense showed through. Him and Daddy were very close. They worked together around the house as a team and got along well. He loved and treated Daddy as though he was his own son.

Mama Talks About The Day Roy Was Born: (August 1992)

I spent the summer of 1992 in Buffalo, New York with Mama. She was recovering from a stroke. I was doing whatever I could to make her recovery a speedy one. Her physical therapist came to see her three days a week and I helped in between. We had bad days, but most of all we had good days. We were very relaxed and talked about all kinds of things.

One Saturday evening Emerson and his wife Essie attended a Buffalo Black History affair at a local down town hotel. When they returned home he came upstairs and told me all about the affair.

"Hey Bettye we went to a black tie event tonight. It was well organized and professional. The hors d'oeuvres was saying something. I tried some caviar with champagne for the first time in my life. It taste a little fishy and salty but after I added some pineapple dip it was alright. Hey it's something that I can get used to. I wouldn't have a problem with acquiring a taste for caviar. I like the way that sounds. You know what I mean? Champagne and caviar. Wow!"

"We were served a full course meal. And everything was just right. The way the food was seasoned was awesome. I commended the chef for a delicious and perfect meal. I met a lot of professional people tonight. And all of them were hospitable, polite and down to earth. It was a friendly mellow atmosphere.

239

I'm glad me and my wife went."

Emerson overheard two black women talking as they read from a Buffalo Black History Book. "Gladys Holmes was the first black woman to deliver a baby at Children's Hospital. I would love to meet her and shake her hand. She came all the way up here from a hick town called Gloster, in the state of Mississippi and paved the way for the black women in Buffalo, New York. This book says she gave birth to an 8 pound 7 ounce son, Roy Lane Holmes on June 14,1959. She was a courageous woman. I wonder if she still live in Buffalo?"

Emerson was astonished to hear the extraordinary things about Mama. He interrupted them. "Hello. Excuse me for cutting in on your conversation. But yes. Gladys Holmes still lives here in Buffalo. She's my mother. Roy Holmes is my youngest brother.

My name is Emerson Holmes. I knew my mother was the first black woman to have a baby at Children's Hospital. But I had no ideal it was written in the Buffalo Black History Book. Wow. I don't recall her ever mentioning this to me."

Mama was using the bathroom with the door partly open listening to Emerson talk. Usually she'd join a conversation no matter what. But not that time. She just sat on the toilet very quiet. I went to the bathroom door and both of us glanced at each other for a moment in silence and she turned her head. I sensed that Emerson's conversation was a little uneasy for her.

I thought to myself, after I change her into one of her pretty gowns, perhaps that new green one. (She loved to wear beautiful night gowns and pajamas. She also loved beautiful bed linen.) and get her in the bed. I'll fry some fillet catfish strips and make some green tea for our snack. And eventually I'll get back to this conversation. Because it is important that she discuss the day that she made history and the events that took place. I knew it wasn't exactly a pretty picture. But I wanted her to share it with me anyway.

My plans went well. We ate catfish strips and cole slaw while watching television and talking. There was a western movie on and somebody in the movie said something that sparked in Mama's head taking her back to her childhood and she laughed and said: "That remind me of Martha and Maggie when we were children. That's the kind of things we used to do and boy we had fun while it lasted, cutting up and acting crazy.

Bettye this is quite a snack. I know what's up your sleeve. Curley used to say you were full of questions and you just had to know every little detail. I guess being inquisitive is your nature. (Laughing) I remember the times when you would follow me around in the kitchen. You always wanted to help out and taste the food. You would be in my way more than a help.

Stepping on my feet and at times I almost tripped over you. One day I was making some chicken and dumplings and some stewed apples for supper. And I was standing at the stove tasting everything and you pulled on my apron begging me to let you taste it. So I let you taste the chicken and dumplings first.

After tasting it you looked up at me and said, 'Mama, what is this I'm tasting? Ok. Put some milk and butter in it.'

After you tasted the stewed apples you said, 'Ok. Put some salt and pepper in it.' Girl; you were a knock-out."

"Bettye ah my mouth is kind of dry. Why don't you make me a cup of coffee? And don't forget the saucer and spoon. Oh, put it on the table in the dining room. Why don't you help me to the dining room while the water is heating up?"

I made the coffee and put it in a fine china cup and placed the cup in a saucer with the spoon on the side just the way she liked it. (She always said coffee taste better when sipped from a china cup.) Yes. She was happy and ready to rock and roll.

She stirred her coffee and tapped the spoon on the edge of the cup before placing it on the saucer.

She blew her hot coffee and slowly sipped it then said: "You're gathering all of this information. (smiling) Are you writing a book or something?"

I answered her, "T N T"

And she inquired, "Yo baby. Yo baby. Yo! T N T? What is this T N T business?"

I answered her, "Tain't No Tellin." We laughed. And she shook her index fingers at me and said I was a knockout for sure.

Mama: "I was in the Milk Lab watching my watch and thumping my fingers on the desk while awaiting my co-workers to return from lunch so I could go. Girl, I was hungry! The phone rang and I answered it. 'G-o-o-o-d morning! Gladys Holmes speaking. How may I help you?' It was my supervisor Mrs. Barrett, asking me to stop by her office after lunch concerning a raise for me. That was good news for me and just as I started to laugh, I felt water running down my legs. The first thing that came to my mind was, 'Oh my God!' I am standing here peeing on myself. And its a whole lot too. My shoes are overflowing. I told Mrs. Barrett about it and tried to excuse myself from the phone. But she wouldn't let me go.

Mrs. Barrett kept on talking, "Gladys, I don't think anybody has a kidney big enough to hold that much pee.

I think your water has broken. And that baby will be here today. Stay right there and be calm. I will have a nurse come take you to the maternity ward. And I will call Mr. Holmes and let him know so he can come on out here."
I never did hang up the phone. I just stood there holding onto it until the two nurses arrived. It seemed like it took them forever to get there.

And the first thing they said to me was, "Gladys why are you standing there holding the phone. You should be sitting." I told them that I didn't want to get the chair soaked.

When the nurses finally got me to admissions in the maternity ward Curley was already there. As soon as I saw Curley the first labor pain hit me and I leaned over and made some tight fists. And he ran over to me, knelt and put his arms around me. When the pain subsided he went to the admission desk and presented his insurance information to the clerk.

Sometimes it's a good policy to be cautious of who grin in your face. Well my good friendly co-worker and lunch buddy Nancy Hatch, the nice lady whom I supported by buying girl scout cookies, candy, peanuts, or whatever she was selling to help her children out in school. We had lunch together everyday and on occasions we'd share our lunches. She had a knack of running up to me every time I saw her. Three or four times a day rubbing my stomach talking about she knew I was having a girl. Anyhow you get the picture right? Girl. I got something to tell you to-night. Nancy Hatch was working at the admission desk that day. And her treatment towards Curley and me was hostile, immature, predigest, a disgrace to Children's Hospital and also un-called for.

Nancy Hatch pushed Curley's insurance card back in his direction.

He picked it up and asked; 'Do you need my social security number along with this?'

She said, 'I don't need your social security number Mr. Holmes. But I do need you to take Gladys to another hospital to deliver the baby.'

Curley said, 'excuse me, Isn't this Children's Hospital? Oh it is. Oh. What? Did they stop delivering babies here? Oh they didn't. Well who in the hell are you to tell me to take my wife to another hospital to have our baby? Woman you must be crazy. You sound like a damn fool.'

Nancy knew she had pushed a wrong button because Curley was upset. As she was telling him to calm down. Another pain hit me and I stood up. She ran and put her hand on my shoulder asking me to please sit back down. That's when she told us that it just wasn't allowed. So Curley asked her what was she talking about.

She responded, 'You know, Mr. Holmes you know.'

Curley said, 'Woman, I don't know you and I don't know what you are talking about. Cut through the chase and get to the point. I ain't got no time for a damn guessing game. My wife is in labor.'

Nancy said, 'Gladys, you know I like you a lot. But colored people, they're not allowed to deliver their babies here at Children's Hospital. That's against their rules. And I have to enforce the rules.'

That frustrated Curley and made me very angry. He snapped at her, 'There's an exception to every rule. Rules were made to be broken. Shit! Stupid woman! This seems to me like a damn good day to break your rule! I refuse to leave Children's Hospital and take my wife to another hospital to have this baby! We are going to have our baby right here! My wife and I are in **'Distress!'** But I don't expect you to apprehend that! '

Nancy didn't hesitate to respond in a nasty tone, "That will never happen. I will see to it. She asked Curley who was my doctor. He told her that he called my doctor's office and found out that he had a heart attack while visiting relatives in Rochester, New York.

For the third time she reiterated, 'You must take Gladys to another hospital to have the baby. Her labor pains are coming fast.' At that point a crowd of people was standing around. I knew some of them.

By that time Curley was candy apple red, (pausing, looking down and shaking her head) he was tenacious, hot and spicy too. He picked up the phone and told Nancy that he wanted to confront the hospital administrators and demanded that she get them on the phone immediately.

That scared her. The jitters accompanied by confusion crept upon her as she kept repeating herself. 'I don't know the administrators phone number.' And the same time she asked, 'Who is Gladys' doctor?' Dr. Yellen yelled: 'I'm her doctor! Dam-et! What in the hell is everybody standing around looking like a bunch of damn fools for? This is a hospital! Get to work dam-et! Or be in the unemployment line tomorrow!' Everybody scattered."

"And in a precise steady commanding voice he instructed the nurses, 'Get her prepped and in the delivery room. Move it dam-et.' Then he took my hand and introduced himself and said, 'I'm your doctor from now on. Relax and don't worry about a thing. You **will** have your baby here! I'll see you in delivery momentarily. But right now I want to speak with your husband briefly.'

I was off to be prepped and on to the delivery room while Dr. Yellen talked with Curley and exchanged phone numbers. He apologized for the embarrassing position which Curley and I encountered due to the cold unprofessional attitude of the prune face admitting clerk. And he offered to buy Curley a cup of coffee in the cafeteria after the delivery.

Roy came fast, fast, fast. Exactly twenty-nine minutes after I left the admission desk, Roy was born. I had my first spinal shot. It was quite a different experience from having babies in Mississippi. I woke up in the recovery room while Curley was sitting in a chair by the bed. His head was resting on the back of the chair and his hands were covering his face.

I reached over and pinched him on the thigh and he sat up. His

245

eyes were red and puffy. I knew he had been crying. Then I started to cry. I was so hurt because the admitting staff treated us like something you would scrape off the bottom of your shoe and discard it down the toilet. And what made it so bad was I knew them. Had I not known them, perhaps I would have dealt with the situation in a different manner by acting ugly.

Anyway, Curley held my hands tight and told me to dry up those tears. He said it was water under the bridge and history. And the mean things that was directed to us only hurt us that one time, but it will hurt the people that said them every day for the rest of their life. We agreed that the right thing to do was pray and forgive those people, because they were lacking common sense. People with common sense would have handled the matter in a professional manner.

He kissed my hands, my forehead, my nose, my cheeks and my lips and said; 'Honey, together we are going to forget those hurtful things which are behind and press toward the mark. Cheer up because everything is going to be fine and dandy!'

He preceded to enlighten me on what happened while I was in the recovery room. He told me that it seemed like everyone that worked in the maternity ward knew us all of a sudden. The doctors and nurses were extremely nice and polite. They were shaking his hand and congratulating him on the birth of our beautiful healthy seven pounds six ounce son, Roy Lane Holmes.

They let him know that their compassionate concerns was with us. He was getting a lot of positive feed-back from the hospital staff. 'Mr. Holmes there's going to be a write-up in the newspaper this evening about you and Mrs. Holmes. Your wife made history today. She's the first 'black woman' to give birth to a baby at Children's Hospital. She stood her grounds. She has opened the door for other black women to follow suit'

He stood up to show me his pants pocket which was bulging with phone numbers. He laughed and told me that we had a

246

pocket full of friends. Every staff member that he came in contact with him jotted their phone number down and gave it to him saying we could call them anytime. He told me about all the nice doctors that took him to the cafeteria for coffee, donuts and a cigarette. He appreciated all of that attention because it took his mind away from that bitter, angry, vicious storm that was brewing inside of him. It also gave him the opportunity to rethink, regroup and cool down. He realized how blessed he was to be in the shoes which he was in and how far we had come. The love which he possessed for me and his children persuaded him to let go and let God!

I appreciated the passionate concern which Curley received too. Because before I was rushed from the lobby he was biting his lip. He had some crazy looking eyes and he was rubbing his hands together. He was ready to swing on anybody and wouldn't have cared who it was. As the nurse turned my wheel chair to take me from the lobby, I looked at Curley and thought; 'Lord please, Curley is mad, upset and want to kill somebody. Bless my husband with Peace and Harmony. He's in your hands.'

From the recovery room I was wheeled to a private room. I don't know who paid for it, but we didn't. There was a beautiful bouquet of nine red roses in an expensive crystal vase situated in the middle of the window seal.

As a matter of fact, that was the first thing I saw when I entered the room. I thought Curley bought them, so I thanked him; 'Ah baby you are such a sweet husband. But why didn't you save the money for something else and get some flowers from our back yard?'

He said, 'Honey, these roses are gorgeous and you know that red roses are the only flowers that I like. I wish I could take credit for them being here, but I didn't buy them. Here's the card let me see what it says. How bout that. Congratulations Curley and Gladys. But it doesn't say who sent them. That's odd. They neglected to sign it. I wonder why?'

247

My stay at the hospital was great. The hospital staff gave me the V I P treatment. Curley had special visiting privileges. He could visit me any time and stay as long as he wanted. One evening Curley got there around 8:30. He came directly from his Masonic meeting. Ah, he looked very handsome dressed up in his black suit, white shirt and black tie. About five minutes after he got there, Dr. Yellen came to the room with a tray of cheese, crackers, salami, ham, hot peppers stuffed with salmon, crab meat rolled in spinach leaves, meat balls the size of a marble, green and black olives, celery, carrots, and a bed of lettuce. He also had a chilled bottle of Herring Bone Cherry Wine. Everything was just perfect and the three of us had a magnificent time eating, talking and drinking that Cherry Wine. Curley and I were people that never drank alcoholic beverages. But that wine was a rare treat and it complemented the food and went well with it. It was unbelievably delicious.

Dr. Yellen was a splendid doctor with good humor and great bedside manners. Him and Curley sat there and talked until eleven that evening. Curley invited Dr. Yellen, to join him at his next Masonic meeting. He accepted Curley's invitation and asked if he could bring his brother, the other Dr. Yellen, with him.

I was back to work in three months and fell back into the normal routine. Nothing had changed. At first the thought of going pass the admissions desk several times a day to and from the premature ward in Maternity made me a bit uncomfortable. But I got over it on my first day back to work. I walked pass them, held my head up high and said, 'Goood morning ladies. How are you today? It's a beautiful day isn't it? I love those cheerful Halloween decorations you're putting up.'

Those three women looked at me dumbfounded and in disbelief. Perhaps they were thinking, 'I don't get it. How can she speak such kind words to us after the shameful way we behaved towards her and her husband?' I looked at them, smiled and thought to myself; 'Thank you Jesus, for giving me a heart big enough to love everybody unconditionally. I am honored to be in the shoes that I'm in. Because when I go to bed tonight, I can have sweet sleep and wake up refreshed in the morning.'

I'd say a good three years passed and I happened to be in the lab doing some last minute paperwork before I went home. I heard somebody calling me, so I said; 'Come on in I'm back here in the office.' I only had three or four more words to write down. I was trying to finish it up before I greeted my visitor.

They were approaching me quickly, so I turned around only to see a figure dressed in dark clothes and black sunglasses with extending arms. They were calling my name. I thought it was a man, the voice was heavy. Frightened. I thought; 'Who is this hideous monster coming after me?' "I screamed, threw my ink pen across the desk, scooted my chair back and ran. (Laughing). I had no ideal that I could run that fast."

I interrupted Mama's interesting story by laughing. "Mama. Please! A monster?" I knew it was rude, but I just couldn't contain myself. It was amusing and my first time hearing a grown-up taking about being afraid of a monster. I laughed at the expression on her face along with her body language as she moved her hands to help describe the monster. Anyhow she caught my infectious laughter and laughed so hard that she cried tears of joy.

But Mama didn't hesitate to tell me; 'When I'm talking, it would be nice if you didn't but in. That could cause me to lose my train of though.

If you have any questions or want to make a comment, you can bring that up when I'm through talking. Why don't you make yourself another cup of that green tea and while you're at it, make another cup of coffee for me.'

Mama continued to tell her story:

"It was shocking to find out the hideous monster was Nancy

Hatch." 'Gladys, this is me. Nancy. Nancy Hatch. Don't you know me?' I answered her; 'You don't look like Nancy Hatch and you don't sound like her either. What happened to your face and lips? Your lips are swollen and blown out of proportion like a lumpy balloon. Were you in an accident? Or do you have some kind of a disease? I don't recognize you."

"She sat on the desk and told me that she had been through hell and high water. Her husband lost respect for her and left her for a young black woman. She got a demotion on her job. She had a painful swelling mouth and throat condition and the doctors couldn't treat it, because they didn't know what it was. All they could do was push pain pills on her. She preceded to tell me that she thought she brought that condition on herself, because of the way she treated Curley and me. She admitted, that she relive that day three or four times a week and try to change the actual circumstances that took place into a positive pleasant situation. She said it haunted her badly because she couldn't change the past nor dismiss it from her mind. She asked me if I thought Curley and I could ever forgive her? I told her that we forgave her and her co-workers that same day and I got over it the first day that I returned to work from my maternity leave. I went on to tell her that I was brought up to treat people like I wanted to be treated. And when you follow that rule, surely you won't have any sick, guilty, haunting feelings following you around. And I believe the Bible when it says you reap what you sow. I also told her to forgive herself and be of good cheer."

"She admitted that she was the one who sent Curley and me those nine beautiful red roses along with that attractive heavy lead crystal vase. I still have it after all of those years. The one that's sitting on the piano. Bettye, I know you remember it. Every spring you would keep a bouquet of lilacs from the back yard in it."

"She told me that the way she got her hands on the vase was at a rummage sale. She paid fifty cents for it. And it was still in the box with the price tag on it. In return she brought it to work with the intentions of showing it to me during our lunch hour.

250

According to her, she felt terrible after making a monkey out of herself causing that devastating ordeal. She thought flowers would make up for her hateful, selfish wrongdoings. Therefore she took the vase to the flower shop on Elmwood and bought the roses and put them in it. She bought nine red roses because we had nine children. After buying them she got cold feet and decided it would be best if she remained anonymous."

With a serious expression on her face as she stared straight ahead holding the coffee cup in her right hand Mama said; "For several years, I have been receiving mail from the group of elite 'Holmes' through out the country congratulating me for being the first black woman to have a baby at Children's Hospital. They invited me to attend and participate in the recognition functions, to celebrate the extraordinary things which we have accomplished.

It was quite an honor and appreciation to receive such a letter of recognition and to know that the superior group with the last name 'Holmes' acknowledged what I did and considered me a part of them was a blessing from Heaven.

It was overwhelming! I read the first letter twenty times the same day I received it. It made my day! I couldn't stop smiling. I felt like a child on Christmas morning! Every year they have their celebration in different parts of the world and invite me. (Giving the letter to me.) This letter is from them. It came a couple of days ago. This year they are having the celebration next month (September), in Australia.

I wish Curley was living so we could attend some of these Holmes celebrations. I wrote them a letter informing them that the only thing that was keeping me from joining them on a celebration was that Curley had passed. He would have been the only person I would go with. They wrote back saying all I had to do was pack my luggage and they would make my reservations, have a car pick me up and take me to the airport. For years, I contemplated on attending at least one of those Holmes celebrations. It didn't materialize because your daddy wasn't here. I couldn't make that

251

move without him. The reason I didn't mention these letters to you all was because all of you guys would have been pushing me to go. Or you would have wanted to leave your wives or husbands and go with me. I certainly did not want that. Because that is something I would have enjoyed doing only with my husband Curley."

The April Fool Trick:

This particular April Fool's Day was on a Sunday and Mama was at work with a lot of spare time. She smiled as she contemplated; 'Um, I think I'll call Curley and play an April Fool's Trick on him.'

The phone rang, Daddy and I answered it at the same time. He was in their bedroom and I was in the living room.

Daddy: Hello.

Mama: (disguising her voice) Hello. You sound sleepy. Did I wake you up baby?

Daddy: Lady, get to the point. Who do you want to speak with?

Mama: You Baby. You are Mr. Holmes aren't you?

Daddy: Yes.   But it's eight Mr. Holmes' that live here. You'll have to be more specific.

Mama: OK. I want to speak with Mr. Curley Holmes. Is that specific enough?

Daddy: That's me. Who is this?

Mama: Hello. You fine, fine thang! My name is Pitsy.

Daddy: Wait a minute Pissy. One of my sons must be playing a

252

trick on you. They gave you this phone number and my name. To tell you the truth, I don't know which one of them did it. All of them are full of pranks. Sometimes they get a little carried away with it. You see. I am a married man.

Mama: Yes Mr. Curley Holmes. I know you are a married man with nine children. But what's that got to do with anything? Um, um, um. I've had my eyes on you for quite a while. Your sons are handsome and all. But you see. I want the daddy.

Daddy: Excuse me Pissy. I don't know where you got this phone number. But do me a favor. Don't call here again.

Mama: Oooh baby. I like the way you sound. And you got a temper too. That light my fire baby. I can't wait to see you tonight. Sugar baby! I know you can't wait to see me either. I can tell it in your voice. Um, um, um. I have something sweet that I want to whisper in your ears. Oh baby. I got something for you. I've been holding on to it since the first time I saw you. I know you want it. You can't fool me. Come on now. Confess it.

Daddy: Look Pissy! I worked last night. I'm tired. You woke me up with this nonsense. I'm not interested. Don't call here anymore dammit. A telephone is not a toy. Goodbye.

Mama: Baby. If you hang up on me, I'll call back. Be nice to me! Cause I'm a stunningly beautiful woman. Now listen to me. I'll get off the phone so you can get back to sleep, freshen up and be ready for me tonight. I'll be the fine irresistible fox in a yellow tight dress hugging my curves, at Johnny Lou's Pool Hall on William street. I'll be there at six. Be on time. You hear! I'll only be there until six thirty.

Daddy: Now hear this Pissy. My wife will be there at six. She will be the fine irresistible fox carrying the baseball bat. Goodbye and good ridden.

I waited for him to hang the phone up before I did. Then I asked

"Daddy who was on the phone?"

He answered. "Nobody."

I called Mama at work. "Hello Mama, I know that was you on the phone (laughing). I was on the other phone listening. I'm going to tell Daddy right now."

Mama: "No Bettye. Don't say anything just yet. It'll be our little secret. OK. I'll tell him when I get home from work. Remember, don't mention this to anybody."

Having a secret with Mama was awesome. And for some reason it gave me a lot of energy and put me in a good mood. It was impossible for me to keep a straight face. I couldn't stop smiling. When Daddy woke up that afternoon, I made his lunch. After he ate and joined my brothers and I in the living room to watch television, I had a difficult time keeping my mind focused on the television program. Simply because of my secret. I started to grin and stare at him while he read the newspaper.

He finally told me: "Why don't you lighten up a little and let your brothers enjoy the program." That went over my head.

And I said: "Daddy guess what? Me and Mama have a little secret."

He said, "Do you want to let me in on this little secret?" (Laughing) I answered him: "Heavens no. I can't tell you. But Mama will tell you when she get off work." I continued to laugh and put my hands over my face as I said: "Daddy it's so funny. It's about when Mama called you this morning ha, ha, ha, ha, ha it's so funny. But I can't tell you what it is"

We had dinner together when Mama got home. I was anxious for her to tell Daddy about our secret but there wasn't a hint of it at all. She talked about making a pot of vegetable beef soup for the next day after dinner. I offered to help cut up the vegetables.

Daddy mentioned the fact that he was tired and was going to stretch out on the couch, relax and watch the ball game. We had a typical late afternoon as usual. Mama and I was in the kitchen thawing out the stew meat and cutting the vegetables for the soup while we snacked on peanuts.

Daddy came in the kitchen and drank two glasses of water. Then said he was going to take a bath, get dressed and go visit his partner Henry for a while. He said Henry invited him and some more people over to meet his mother who was visiting from Stone Mountain, Georgia.

Mama didn't make a comment. She took everything in and gave Daddy a dammit to hell look. Daddy smiled and winked his eye at her. He kissed her on the cheek, then he was off to his bath. Thirty five minutes later Daddy walked in the kitchen looking good and smelling good.

He told Mama: "Honey I'm leaving now. I have to meet Henry and his eighty-five year old mother at Johnny Lou's Pool Hall. I have to be there at six. I'm not sure yet, but I probably won't be there longer than two hours.

Mama: Just a minute Curley. You know darn well that you don't have a friend named Henry.

Daddy: Did I say Henry? I meant to say Harry. I keep getting those two names mixed up.

Mama: You don't know a Harry either Curley.

Daddy: There you go questioning me and giving me the third degree. You act like I'm sneaking out to see a woman.

Mama: I don't consider two questions the third degree. Sit down. I have something to tell you. I know what you are up to. And I'm about to get mad as hell.

Daddy: I'll sit down and listen later. But I have to go right now. I hear Harry out there blowing for me. Oh yea, he's picking me up. Come on honey give me some sugar before I go.

Daddy rushed out the door and didn't give Mama a chance to tell him about the April fool's trick she played on him. That made her uneasy. All kinds of things were running through her mind. The more she thought the angrier she got.

I told her that the stew meat was completely thawed out and she said: "I ain't hardly thinking about no stew meat or soup either." She sat on the bench behind the table with a sad bewildered look, kind of like she had just lost her best friend. I sat there with her. I didn't know what else to do.

The door bell rang. Richard, Charlie, Earl and Emerson went to answer it. They returned and told Mama that a man was at the door and wanted to see her about an important issue. She asked: "Who is it?" They didn't know.

Mama and I answered the door. When we got down stairs the entry hallway light was off. Mama peeped through the window. It was dark, therefore she couldn't see anything. She was cautious not to unlock the door as she greeted the man in the hallway. "Hey you out there. I'm Mrs. Holmes. I can't see you. I think it's a good ideal if you come back tomorrow so I can see who I'm talking to. I'm not about to open this door. Come back tomorrow. OK? Bye.

The man didn't respond. We stood there momentarily whispering: "I don't hear anything in the hallway. Maybe he left before we came down here. This door will stay locked. Let's go back up stairs and look out the window. Perhaps we can see him outside."

We started to walk up the stairs and the man in the hallway opened the door that lead to the front porch and commenced to ring the door bell like a mad man. When he thought he had ranged it sufficiently, he walked back into the hallway and closed the door

256

behind him.

We were too frightened to continue to walk up the stairs. Seeing a flicker of light coming from the hallway caused panic: "He's going to burn the house down with us in it. Mercy! Where is Curley? "

The light went out and the smell of cigarette smoke found it's way to our noses. We knew that the light was for his cigarette. Mama whispered to me: "Whoever he is he need a darn good laxative. He's passing that loud stinking gas. It sounds like a double barrel shot gun. He ain't got no manners. From the smell of things he haven't used the bathroom for a long time. It smell worse than cow shit. If he don't hurry up and quit farting, he's going to blow a hole in his pants."

Mama broke the silence by asking, "Hey mister did one of my children do you any kind of harm? Throwing a rock and breaking your window or whatever? You know how children can be at times." It sounded as though he was trying to say something but it ended up in a laugh.

He laughed in different voice tones for a minute. (It was eerie.) He cleared his throat and very clearly said: "Gladys this April fool thing is wearing me out. Open the door. I have to use the bathroom. I been holding this load for a while and my stomach is cutting up something terrible."

Relieved. Mama said: "Ain't this a coincident! That man sound like Curley. But it's not him because he's visiting with Henry, oops I mean Harry."

She was overwhelmed with joy the man turned out to be Daddy. She didn't hesitate to open the door. She opened the door and Daddy rushed pass us and ran up the stairs to the bathroom. When he came out he said it was a false alarm.

Mama fixed Richard, Charlie, Earl, Emerson, Roy and me a

bowl of vanilla ice cream. Since she was serious about the laxative for the man in the hallway. She made Daddy a laxative which consisted of spices and herbs from the kitchen cabinets. Daddy drank it and said that would have saved him a lot of agony if he'd taken it a week ago when he informed Mama that he was stopped up.

Mama said he woke her in the middle of the night complaining that he was constipated. He didn't mention it again. Therefore she assumed everything was unplugged and moving along fine and dandy.

He changed the subject quick. "I declare. I don't smell any soup cooking. Usually when you make soup the aroma flows throughout the house." She gave him a song and dance about too many things happened after he left that completely took her away from finishing the soup. He volunteered to help her make it. They promised each other not to play another April fool's trick again.

While they were finishing the soup, Mama asked him how did he find out that was her on the phone! He told her that somebody let the cat out of the bag. That puzzled me. So I asked Mama if anyone else knew of our secret.

Her answer was: "No. Only you and me knew about it."

I asked: "How did Daddy find out Mama?"

She laughed until her face turned red and said: "I'll let you figure that one out." I thought that was so mean of her. She simply would not tell me who let the cat out of the bag. It darn near took a week for me to figure out that I was the one who let the cat out of the bag. I thought to myself; 'Miss Bettye you have a big mouth.' I explained what happened to Mama.

She said: "Um huh! I understand! You can't hold water!" (I think she was still warm under the collar because I blew her perfectly thought out April Fool's Trick).

I asked: "Mama what did you mean when you said I can't hold water;"

She answered me: "Honey keep on living and you'll find out." From that day until now I have a great dislike for April Fool tricks.

Daddy And Mama / My Heroes:

I thank God for every precious moment that I had with my parents. I treasure those memories and hold them dear to my heart passionately. It was a unique blessing to be blessed with two loving, understanding parents who loved my eight siblings and myself unconditionally. My father was always there and never too busy to give his advice when I had problems or just wanted to talk. Like the time when I came home from school frustrated and woke him:

"Daddy, Daddy, Daddy, (shaking him) Daddy, hi Daddy were you sleep? Do you want me to make you some coffee?"

He answered: "yes. I was sleep. You know I have to be at work in two hours. You woke me to offer me coffee?"

I commented: "No. I have some problems. I want to change my name. Why are you laughing? You're making fun of me.

Daddy, this is an absolute tremendous genuine most urgent serious need attention immediately matter of life and death situation. And I am desperately, wholeheartedly, seeking your valuable knowledge to show me how to rectify my problems."

He responded: "I see you managed to get all of your spelling words in two sentences. Exactly how many problems do you have? Two major problems. I think we can rectify them before I leave for work. But I need some coffee. I think I need more than a cup of coffee. It would be nice if you scrambled a couple of eggs and fry some bacon. Oh, cook some grits too. Yeah. A full stomach is what I need in order to function properly while I'm helping you solve your problems."

Sitting at the table eating Daddy said: "Take a seat and run those problems by me."

I told him: "The kids in school laugh at me and make fun of my name. I feel self conscious about it. That's why I decided to change my name."

In a joking way he said: "Change your name! Are you getting married?" I responded: "Daddy, I'm only eleven years old." He told me I had red blood and no yellow streaks down my back and that he was going to tell me a story. And if I still wanted my name changed him and Mama would discuss it. He proceeded to tell the story of how my name came about. After listening to him tell his story in a proud caring way I was overwhelmingly moved. I had a completely different outlook on the name 'Bettye Joe.' I simply loved it! It sounded wonderful.

The next time the teacher gave the class an assignment to write an essay I took advantage of the opportunity to write on the subject 'My Father Named Me After President Truman's Airplane:' The teacher said it was a good and unusually interesting story. She gave me an 'A.' She also took me to the side and asked, where did I get such a vivid detailed imagination?

My next major problem stemmed from a picture that a girl in my classroom drew everyday and taped it to my desk. After about a month it gave me a complex. Every time somebody would look at me I thought they were looking at my freckles. By me being extremely quiet and shy didn't help the matter at all. One day the teacher went to the office and that mean humongous lip girl turned around in her seat and told me that she had a surprise for me and to close my eyes so she could give it to me. I did. And she put red fingernail polish on two of my freckles. I took the polish from her and poured the rest of it in her hair then I hit her. The next day she drew another picture of me. That is when I went to Daddy with that particular problem.

"Daddy I want you and Mama to make an appointment for me to see a dermatologist. I need a professional opinion on what can be done about these ugly freckles. I put some Clorox Bleach on them and it burned my face like fire. I need help! These freckles have sent me to a severe stage of depression and bewilderment. Every time I look in the mirror that's the first thing I see."

"Look at this picture of me Daddy. Do you know what these dots are?"

Daddy: "measles?"

I responded: "No. They are supposed to be freckles. This girl in my class draw this identical picture and tape it to my desk practically every day. Help! I am at my wit's end."

He laughed and asked: "Is freckles really that big of a problem for you? They are so cute on you"

I told him: "I never did like these freckles! But I really don't like them now because this gigantic lip ugly girl that sit in front of me always bring them up. And everybody look at me like I have an incurable deadly disease or something."

He wanted to know if I was the only girl in my class with freckles. I was. He pointed out something to me that made a lot of sense.
"She is obsessed with your freckles. If she is that preoccupied with your freckles, it's because she is jealous of them. Why? Simply put. She want freckles too. Understand this! There wasn't enough freckles for everybody. That's why only a few very special people have them. Tell her that she is jealous because she don't have freckles and the pictures and teasing will stop. I guarantee you that." He also told me to get Mama's opinion. I did. She said the same thing only in different words.

Daddy and Mama was one hundred percent right. And from that day on when I looked in the mirror I appreciated my freckles and came to realize that they were very becoming. I was most appreciative to God for the gift of two loving, patient parents who took the time and taught me how to utilize the common sense that mother nature gave me. They also taught me to understand that there's a positive side to every situation. They were truly my *favorite* heroes!

Eventually the girl with the humongous lips and I became friendly towards one another. She wrote me a note asking if I wanted to meet in the classroom fifteen minutes early every morning to study! From studying we became friends.

She mentioned: "I think freckles are pretty. I wish I had some."

My Friend Sidney:

I had a friend that lived down the street from us. Her name was Sidney. She was a school drop-out. She had a son. I thought she was a nice person and Mama thought she was a fast hussy with no respect for herself and she used me for her babysitter. She was fond of my older brothers. That's why she was in the attic with them practically all the time while I was babysitting for her. She told me that she couldn't stay away from them. I understood that perfectly. I had handsome brothers. They were polite, respectful, and they worked.

Mama had a problem with Sidney being in the attic alone with my brothers. She would go in the attic to make Sidney leave and the door would be locked. One day Mama pulled her hair, called her a dirty name and put her out. That didn't stop her from coming around. She was there the next day.

Mama said, "I don't believe this. I yanked her hair and put her out yesterday. And she's back here today with a tulip for me. Extending her hand talking about 'let's be friends Mrs. Holmes.

After all we do have something in common: your sons.' She ain't got a lick of sense."

Mama had a talk with her about going in the attic with my brothers and their friends. She told Sidney that her actions at our home wasn't proper and they were out of order and disrespectful and it wasn't lady like. She asked her what did her mother say about her being in the company of a bunch of boys all the time.

Sidney answered, "My mother say I'm popular with boys. She let them come to the house to see me. Sometimes two or three boys at the same time. She say I'm like her and she's like her mother. She said it's in our blood like a disease and we can't do nothing about it."

She also told Mama that I was the best friend she had in the whole world. And she promised that she would stay clear of the attic. Mama showed her compassion: "Ok. Alright. That's fine. You can visit Bettye as long as you keep your word. If I catch you in the attic again I will throw you out the window. I'm sorry for getting upset and going off on you last night. It won't happen again if you keep your promise. Maybe Bettye can teach you how to make peanut butter cookies or banana nut bread."

Sidney was four years older than me but sometimes she acted my age. She used to climb upon the garage with me and pick plums and eat them with salt while sitting on the edge of the garage swinging our legs. One late Friday afternoon in January, Sidney wanted me to walk to The Busy Bee on Jefferson with her. I told her I would before getting permission from Daddy or Mama. So I decided to wait for Sidney in front of the house. On my way out the door Mama asked me where was I going. I wasn't expecting her to ask me that. She refused to let me go. For some reason she thought The Busy Bee was a bar. It wasn't. And I told her that. I also explained that Sidney's mother worked there and we were going there for some free food, a burger, French fries and a milkshake. And to play records on the juke box. I scored a lot sympathy by crying and begging please let me go with Sidney just this one time.

Daddy said, "Go on girl. And be back here in two hours."

Mama had detective fever. She put on a pair of Daddy's overalls, boots, hat and some old beat up glasses to disguise herself. She drove to the Busy Bee. When we arrived there she was sitting at a table with a glass of water. I noticed her right away. Not knowing it was her I had compassion for her.

"Sidney look at that short man wearing those seven size too big boots. Ah it's so sad. His boots are not tied and he's wearing a red sock and a white sock. I can't make out what his mug look like because that hat is pulled down too far. I suspect he doesn't want anyone to recognize him. He doesn't have money to buy food. That's why he's drinking water."

When we got our food, I gave my burger and milkshake to him. He thanked me and ate it. Sidney and I played records and ate as she showed me all the boys pictures in her wallet.

More people came in as the evening grew. Everybody was having a great time eating, talking and listening to the music. The man was still on my mind so I glanced in his direction and he was gone. According to the clock on the wall, one and a half of my two hours were behind me. Sidney walked me home and went back to hang out with the crowd and stay with her mother until the place closed.

Being hungry I went straight to the kitchen and bumped into mama. She was wearing the same outfit. I was shocked as her and Daddy laughed. I threw my hands up and shook my head in amazement. I was outdone and didn't know what to say. Finally Mama hugged me and told me that she loved me and she was very proud of me. She opened the oven and took out the three burgers topped with cheese and bacon that she went home from The Busy Bee and made for us. I took a seat and ate in silence while I attempted to figure out my mixed emotions.

Mama broke my concentration, "You're probably thinking that I spied on you and invaded your privacy because I didn't believe what you told me about The Busy Bee. You were right. I owe you an apology. I'm glad I did it because I know that The Busy Bee is a liquor free nice neighborhood place for you to go. That gives us a peace of mind. You have a beautiful caring attitude and personality towards people. I am impressed. I thought it was nice of you to encourage Sidney to go back to school. Maybe one day she will return to school. I felt terrible for taking your food but I didn't have a choice. I couldn't blow my cover."

It was difficult to be angry with Mama, because of her compliments. But in a joking way I told them that they were grounded and to go to their room. How do you handle your parents when they act like that? We laughed about her actions. I asked her why did she put on different socks? She pulled those overall legs up and was surprised and embarrassed. Mama was a knock out. We laughed about that day for years. I'm sorry because I didn't take any pictures.

As far as Sidney was concerned, I decided it was best for me to cut all ties with her. Because she was headed in the wrong direction, doing negative, disrespectful, unsafe unhealthy things to make money. I didn't feel like I was better than her, but I did feel that my values were better than her values. I wasn't a teenager yet and it was my desire to continue to grow and be around positive people and make the best out of my life.

How Did Mama Know:

The pastor of our church elected my neighbor Heather, several other kids in the neighborhood and myself to collect money for the NAACP. We met at the church at 9:00 on Saturday morning. for a brief meeting. They were scheduled to drop us off in a pair of two's in different neighborhoods, so we could work each side of the street for an hour and they would pick us up, collect the container of money which we had collected, give us an empty container and take us to a different area. It was supposed to be an all day thing. Each pair was considered as a team. The team that collected the most money would get a prize.

Heather and I worked together. The first street we worked on was our street. Every house that I went to gave money. Some people put the money in the container and some people put the money in our hand. I did the right thing. I put the money in the container. At the end of the day I had collected three times as much money as Heather. It was questioned. After we were dropped off at home, Heather came to see me and confessed that she kept a lot of the money and wanted to know if she could stash it in my room if she gave me some of it. I resented her for telling me that.

I felt guilty and responsible for her untrusting actions. I told her to take it to the church and give it to the preacher. She in return took her book bag and dumped a pile of the money on my bed and said "That's yours. You seem like a quiet girl. So continue to be that way. Keep your mouth shut."

Mama asked me to see if Heather wanted to have dinner with us. She did and we went to the kitchen. After dinner Daddy, Richard, Charlie, Earl, Emerson and Roy left the kitchen. Heather sat at the table talking with Mama while I washed the dishes.

All of a sudden my little brother Roy walked in the kitchen with money in both hands.

Excitedly Mama asked: "Roy? Where did you get that money?"

Roy answered; "From Bet Joe's room. Mama her bed is piled (holding his hands up) this high with money. Bet Joe hit the number. Mama do you need some money? Go on in there and get a handful of it. It's enough money for the whole family. I'm going to put this in the bank."

Mama hurried to my room and stood there checking everything

266

out. Then she told Heather: "Look girl. I'm sending Richard and Charlie to tell your parents to come here right now. When they get here you are going to tell them exactly what you did and how that money happen to be on Bettye's bed. You have insulted this family! There aren't any fools or dummies at this address! Do you understand me girl?"

Heather held her head down and said; "Yes."

When Heather's parents got there, she immediately began to sob. Mama told them to let her sob and get it out. Because she had something very important to tell them. She stopped sobbing and told the truth. Her parents were stunned and ashamed of what she did. Her mother hit her on the top of her head four of five times with her fist.

Then grabbed her hand and said; "Put that money back in this damn book bag. You're taking it to church and tell the preacher what you did. And just to let you know you will be in the house until you are blue in the face. I am taking that damn telephone out of your room. I am so disappointed in you that my heart is aching. We go without so you can have nice things. No more! You are going to get a damn job."

Before they left Heather looked at Mama with her red confused eyes and asked; "Mrs. Holmes how did you know I did it? It could have been Bettye for all you knew;"

Mama had a answer for her: "Um huh. It could have been her. But it wasn't. I knew that when I looked in her eyes!"

My Parents Had An Abundance Of Love, Patience And Generosity:

I admired my parents for a lot of things. But one of the things that I admired them for most of all was the tremendous amount of patience they had with us and all of our friends as well. Each one

267

of us had our own set of friends (so many children) and they all preferred being at our home. Especially in the summertime. Sometimes there would be sixteen or seventeen children hanging around on our front porch or in our back yard playing basket ball. They thought they were in our family. Sometimes they would come to our house from school before they went home.

When Daddy cut my brothers hair, some of their friends would be standing in line waiting to get their hair cut as well. It didn't start out that way. At first they laughed and made fun of the way Daddy worded things; "Richard, Charlie, Earl, Emerson, Ya'll come in the house. It's time to get your hair trimmed." 'Trim' had a different meaning for the boys in Buffalo. Therefore my brothers were often teased about getting a hair trim.

After those Buffalo boys settled down and appreciated the splendid job Daddy did on my brothers hair. The teasing ceased and Daddy trimmed their hair as well.

Love, generosity and understanding were some of the qualities my parents possessed. Daddy and Mama was always there for us. Our unique closeness bonded us. Mama was an inspiration for me throughout my life. I admired her for the honesty, strength, confidence and courage which she had. She always put us first! For instance, one time her and I went shopping to buy a pair of shoes to match an outfit she was wearing that evening.

Her and Daddy were going to Mrs. Perry's birthday party. Mrs. Perry and her husband were good friends of Daddy and Mama's. While Mama was trying on shoes and meditating on which ones to buy, I tried on a pair and kept going back to admire the beauty of them. Mama wanted my opinion on the pair she had chosen for herself and she saw the lust which I had for the shoes I tried on. So she sent me to the store next door to buy some goodies for my brothers while she purchased her shoes. When we got home I discovered the shoes in the bag were the ones which I admired.

Her budget didn't allow her to buy a pair of shoes for both of us.

Therefore she put her shoes back. I loved the shoes and thanked Mama for buying them for me. Then I did what I had to do. I took the shoes back and exchanged them for the ones which Mama chose for herself. She also got a five dollar refund back. She was gorgeous in her outfit and new shoes. Daddy said she looked like a million bucks.

General Things That Were Touching And Memorable:

I was honored to have parents like Daddy and Mama. I considered then to be my special rare gems. They had their way of saying things to teach us how to understand and use our valuable common sense. I incorporated them in my everyday life. I find myself saying them to my husband Jimmee and my children Sacha, Sancho and Malesha.

"Two heads are better than one; There is more than one way to skin a rabbit; If there is a will, there is a way; Don't put off for tomorrow what you can do today; You reap what you sow; If a dog bring a bone he will surely take one; Beware of the ditch you dig for someone else. Because you just might be the one who fall in it; Treat people like we want to be treated; Always think positive; Daddy always told us to have respect for ourselves. Because it was a necessity to have respect for ourselves in order to receive it; To be honest; To always be ourselves no matter what; To clean our house and stay out of every body else's house; To cover the ground we stand on; Not to let our left hand know what our right hand is doing; If we make our bed hard we have to lay in it. Not to let a nickel burn a hole in our pockets; And most important; Don't kiss nobody's ass! Etc."

We learned the Ten Commandments at an early age. There was a copy of the Ten Commandments on the wall above the kitchen sink. It was scribed on an attractive blue velvety background with gold lettering. Over the years it received its share of wear and tear. It came down every other year so the walls could be painted. The faded coloring, water spots and faint lettering along with the four corners turned up was no excuse to discard it, for it was part of our family. Daddy and Mama were not big on telling us that they loved us. But they were big on showing us that they loved us. They displayed their love for us each and every day. And vice versa. There are two particular things that stand out in my mind with Earl and Roy for expressing their genuine powerful 'love' for Daddy and Mama.

Roy Displaying His Love For Daddy:

One day he opened the door and invited Richard, Charlie, Earl and Emerson's friends to leave; "All right! Everybody out. Right now! Daddy have to go to work at 11:00 tonight. And he needs to get some sleep so he can function well while he's working without being sleepy. And when you all get home please refrain from calling here. Because the phone will disturb Daddy's rest."

All of those guys followed Roy's orders. They said he had a lot of spunk, ordering them around and called him a toddler. Actual he wasn't a toddler. He was a bit older. He was a serious frank five year old boy with authority who demanded peace and quiet for Daddy.

Earl Displaying His Love For Mama In An Anonymous Way:

He went to visit Mama. She was preoccupied and wasn't herself. That bothered Earl.

Earl: Mama what's wrong?

Mama: Nothing.

Earl: Nol. Mama something is wrong.

Mama: Ain't nothing wrong.

Earl: I'm not calling you a lie Mama. But you ain't telling me the truth. I know you better than that. Whatever it is, it's keeping you from smiling. You don't even look the same. Mama are you sick or something? Come clean with me. What's up? Come on. Talk to me girl.

Mama: Earl you know I don't usually bother my children with my problems. Aah. I don't know Earl. Can you hold water? I mean can you really hold water?

Earl: Mama I can hold water, coffee, milk, tea, beer, wine, whiskey, gin and vodka. Is that sufficient, or do you want me to keep going?

Mama: Alright Earl. But this is between you and me. This is our secret! You dig? Yesterday I played a number with Buela Bell Numby. The number came out. I won over nine hundred dollars. I went to pick up my money today and she told me that she didn't put the number in for me because it was too late. The woman lied. I called her at 7:00 a. m. yesterday. She called me back at 7:05 a. m. and told me that she called the number in and wished me luck. Dotta, dotta, dotta.

$900.00 is a lot of money. If she needed it for something I would have loaned it to her. I can't get over that. Mr. Howard told me that she ran a game by him like that. He cut her loose and found somebody else to play numbers with.

Earl kept his promise to Mama not to mention that incident to anyone. But after fourteen days he broke his promise. He couldn't hold it any longer. He had to confront Buela Bell Numby.

He made an important phone call at 5:30 A. M.; "Buela Bell Numby: What's up girl?"

Buela Bell: Who is this fine young man talking to me?

Earl: Buela Bell I called to give you some advice!

271

Buela Bell: Wait a minute sugar. (She left the phone.)

Earl could hear her in the background talking to herself. 'Buela Bell Numby, you still got that magic. Ha! You got this fine young man waking up at five-thirty in the morning with you on his mind. Ha! Go on with yo bad self!'

" Ok I'm back. I had to put my glasses on. I hear better when I'm wearing them. I'm always open to advice. Especially from a young man. Cup cake it's your dime. Now tell me what's on your mind, because baby I got the time!"

Earl said: "TAKE HEED! DON'T MESS WITH GLADYS HOLMES!"

Then he hung the phone up! That left poor Buela Bell Numby in jittery shambles. She went to the bathroom and turned around several times because she forgot what she went in there for. She ran to her bed, grabbed her wig and put it on side-ways. The bangs were over her left ear. She rushed to her car and took off. A block away from her house, she realized that she forgot to get dressed. She didn't bother to go back home to dress because she was on a serious mission that could not be delayed. Buela Bell thought to herself: 'Hell, I'll risk going to jail for indecent exposure! But I aint gone risk messing with Gladys Holmes. I don't know what kind of lie I'm going to tell her yet. But whatever it is I'm sure she will believe me because I'm good! Everybody say I lie real good wit a straight face too. Oh shit. I just ran that red light! What is wrong with me? I hate for my day to start off like this. I am a nervous wreck! Hell. I shouldn't have answered the damn phone.

In the meanwhile Mama was having coffee when the door bell rang.

She glanced at the clock and said out loud, "Its 5:50 a.m. Not day light yet. Who can that be?"

Mama answered the door and there stood Buela Bell Numby in her robe and slippers covered in snow. In that twenty minutes, Buela Bell Numby had developed somewhat of a nervous stutter condition; "Gla Gladys, I I I got your money rat chere in my poc pocketbook. Ca ca can I co com come in and explaaiin to you about the bi big mi mistake I made about your mon money? I just found it out last night. I, I was going to call you the first thing this morning. I, I got Goo gooood news Gladys. I did pla play your num number after all. Here here's your mon money all $999.90 of it. I, I I don't know how to explain it real good, bu but I put it in my poc ket and forgot about it. Ain ain't that som something? All of that money just slipped my mind. Trus trust me. This is the first time that happened to me. Gladys don't you know that I am a hon hon hooonest woman? Always have been and always will be."

Buela Bell continued: "I had a phone call at 5:30 this morning. I think it was one of them sev, sev, seven bo boys of yours. Who whoever it was they scared the living daylights out of me. I didn't know if I was going coming. They said; 'Don't mess with Gladys Holmes' and hung up."

I'm confused Gladys. That new medication that I'm taking make me forget about money. That's the side effect. Ain't that som something?"

Mama acknowledged the nervous, guilty, state Buela Bell was in and asked her to come in and put her slippers by the heater so they could dry. She offered her a cup of coffee to knock the chill off. She then inquired;

"Don't you know that you could come down with pneumonia by going out in this zero degree weather dressed like that? I can see through that flimsy robe. You're not wearing underwear. I have a heavy robe you can put on to cover yourself and keep warm. Where is your coat and boots anyway?"

Buela Bell ignored Mama's questions and asked her to please

273

call that young hit man and tell him that she had paid her in full. And she apologized for the dumb mistake she made. So he wouldn't come after her in a mean harmful brutal detrimental way.

Earl stopped by to visit with Mama later that day and Mama schooled him on what happened with Buela Bell. He was surprised that Buela Bell moved so swiftly on his advice. He laughed and admitted that he talked with Buela Bell briefly that morning. Mama was glad because Earl made the phone call. Her smiles returned and everything was back to normal again. She never played numbers with Buela Bell Numby again.

The First Time Mama Wore Pants: 1972

I came home from shopping and showed my outfit to Mama. She thought it was beautiful and made a comment on how the turtle neck long sleeve body suit went so well with the wide leg cuffed plaid pants. She simply loved the colors.

I was pleased that she liked it because I bought the same outfit for her. She accepted it and smiled graciously: "I know you didn't buy these pants for me. I want you to take them back and get me a skirt. I will not wear them. I ain't never wore pants before. Well, except for the time when I wore your Daddy's overalls to the Busy Bee to spy on you. And that was only for an hour or two. My mother didn't wear pants and her mother didn't wear pants. Have you noticed that women my age don't wear pants? Besides what would people say if they suddenly noticed that I took to wearing pants? I would be the talk of the town."

I answered her, "Mama, this is 1972. Things are changing fast. Pants are not targeted to a certain age group. You are always complaining about how the cold weather bother your knees. Can you think of a better way to be in style and keep your legs and knees warm, than a nice pair of knit pants that cling to you? Mama pants are in. They are here to stay. You might as well join the crowd and start wearing them too. Try these pants on and see if they fit. I know you will like the way you look in them."

I followed her around the house until she decided to try the pants on. They were very becoming on her. Her eyes lit up. She tried the body suit on too. The outfit complemented and enhanced her figure. She had enough butter to fill them out. Those dresses and skirt disallowed her figure to show. She didn't want to get out of the mirror. She tried several pair of her boots on and they looked good with the pants. I got up at 2:00 A.M. to get a glass of water and bumped into Mama. She was wearing the outfit standing in front of the mirror admiring it. Mama liked those pants so much that she told me; "Never mind taking these pants back to the store. I'll keep them. I want to go back to the same store with you and buy some more pants. I want every color they have."

Mama broke the ice by wearing pants for the first time in her life. And she loved it. From that day on she was warm, comfortable and in style where ever she went. Pants were definitely on her shopping list. Mama was a knock-out and ready to rock and roll.

Mama Did The Mashed Potatoes: 1963

I was helping Mama cook dinner when a record came on the radio. And she said: "Come on Bettye. Im-ma teach you how to do the mashed potatoes. It's similar to the Charleston. Your brothers do the Mashed Potatoes to this record. Honey I don't like you being so shy." Mama grabbed both ends of her apron and proceeded to do the Mashed Potatoes. I observed her closely. She was doing the Mashed Potatoes quite well. When the record was over she asked; "What do you think about it."

I said; "Wow! Wow! Wow!"

She said; "Do you want to translate that for me Wow girl?" I put my arms around her waist and hugged her tight.

And in my slow southern accent I responded; "Um, um, um. Whar you learn how to dance like that Mama? I declare I ain't never seen nobody dance that good.

The Taste lingers on: 1957

On a cold day in November, our first winter in Buffalo, we came home from school to the most wonderful warm hearted dinner. A pot of red beans, a pot of rice and skillet of hot corn bread. We received a package from Papa and Big Mama in Mississippi and one of the things in the package happened to be red beans. The aroma of those red beans filled the house. (If I close my eyes and concentrate I can still smell them.) There were big tender chewy chunks of salt pork in the red beans. That was the most delicious plate of red beans, rice and corn bread I ever indulged in. I am still searching for that same taste. Even though it no longer exist. The taste lingers on in my mind. Daddy and Mama said it was something they threw together in a hurry. They also admitted it was an unusually tasty dish.

Earl Got The Best Of Me: 1959

We used to fight and tease each other. My brothers would beat me up and I would beat them up. They took up for me and I took up for them. Earl got the best of me one day and I wasn't ready for it. I was washing dishes while arguing with Earl. He threw a big pretty super ripe tomato at me. I ducked and the tomato hit the wall and splashed.

Daddy walked in as the tomato juice and seeds trickled down the wall. Before he could say anything, Earl ran to him, grabbed his hand and put on an act that you wouldn't believe. He cried as he pointed to what was left of the shattered tomato on the wall. He was crying and taking deep breaths; "Daddy, look, at, what, Bet, Joe, did. She threw that tomato at me. It was coming at my eye and I got out of the way fast. Daddy that's the tomato that you said you were going to put in your lunch for tomorrow. Whoop her Daddy! She need a good whooping. Pick me up. I'm scared of her."

That six year toddler lied so good that he damn near convinced me that he was telling the truth. Daddy picked him up and before leaving the kitchen he asked me to clean the mess up and make him a cup of coffee. Well! I was devastated at the talent my little six year old brother had. I didn't know what to say. It sounded much better than the truth. It was a damn good lie. Daddy wasn't mad but I was. As a matter of fact, that was the first time in my life that I experienced the mad enough to kill syndrome. After that untruthful episode he had a good reason to be afraid of me. Yeah. He saw Daddy coming and did a damn fantastic job pulling the wool over his eyes.

When I took the coffee to Daddy he was reading a book and Earl was sitting on his lap acting like a little harmless victim. Richard and Charlie asked me why did I throw the tomato at Earl? They said I was too big to go around throwing tomatoes at little Earl and picking on him. The next day June, Doll and T. J. told me pretty much the same thing. That lie had a lot of clout going on. Everyone formed an immature opinion against me without asking me what happened. That was circumstantial evidence. So I went into a funk. And neglected to speak to the household members for four days. I needed time to think. Richard and Charlie had their field day teasing me at dinner time during those four days.

Richard teasing around; "Hey Charlie this is a nice centerpiece that Bet Joe made. There's apples, pears, bananas, oranges and tangerines. But no tomatoes. Maybe she used all of them practicing how to aim and throw better so she can hit the target next time."

Charlie said; "Yeah. You're probably right. She's been practicing for four days now. Who knows? She could be a pro by now. Ha, ha, ha, ha, ha, ha, ha. I think we better be quiet before she throws one of those apples and knock our teeth out."

Richard; "Shut. I don't have to be quiet. If she throw one of those apples, I'll jump out of the way like Earl did. I'm not about to get hit in the mouth. Ha, ha, ha, ha, ha." They laughed and thought it was funny.

After Daddy laughed along with them he said; "Y'all lay off and give Bettye a break."

I decided right then that I was tired of them teasing me about throwing that tomato. It was time to tell Daddy and Mama the truth. I did. And they wanted to know why I didn't say anything when it first happened? I had no answer for that question.

I told Daddy that I knew what Richard and Charlie said was funny, but I was hurt when he laughed along with them. He said it was a difficult thing trying to keep a straight face with them acting like that. He asked Earl did he throw the tomato at me. He admitted the truth.

Daddy asked him how long had he planned on sticking to his version of what happened? Earl hunched his shoulders and shook his head.

Daddy said; "Now I get the picture. That's the real reason why you have been running past Bettye's room every day. You didn't want her to get her hands on you for nothing. You know you will be on punishment for a while. Don't you? Are you sorry about any of this?"

Earl said; "I'm very sorry." Daddy asked him what was he going to do about it? Earl took a tiny bag out of his pocket with nine peach stones (candy) in it. He put them on the table and counted four for me and four for him. He took the last one, bit it in half and spit it in his hand. One piece was slightly bigger than the other.

And he said; "Here Bet Joe you can have the biggest piece."
Daddy told me to take my finger out of my mouth and say

something. I accepted the tiny piece of candy drenched in spit, along with the four pieces and thanked Earl. That was his way of apologizing. Because I was a sweet, loving, understanding, forgiving ,emotional, little girl that touched my heart deeply and I cried. Earl cried too. Daddy, Mama, Richard and Charlie were misty eyed too. Therefore we had a family embrace and Mama brought out the vanilla ice-cream as a treat.

From that day on Earl was back on my good list. That incident made us closer than we were before.

The Waist Line Party: 1961

My friend Peggy asked me; "Hey Bettye do you think Mr. and Mrs. Holmes will let us have a waste line party in your back yard this Saturday? If they do, I will bring the food. Our freezer is full of weiners and hot dog buns. Hot dogs and Kool Aid is all we need. Each one of us can invite ten people. Perhaps, twelve of them will show up. My records combined with you guys records will make a nice variety of music."

I didn't ask Daddy and Mama if we could have the party. I talked it over with Richard and Charlie and they thought it was a hip thing to do. So we made plans to have the party without Daddy and Mama's permission. Both of them had to work and wouldn't get home form work until 3:30 that afternoon.

The party was due to start at 11:00 a. m. that Saturday, and last until 2:00 p.m.. We planned to clean up after everyone went home. That way Daddy and Mama wouldn't know about the party. Peggy, Richard, Charlie and I agreed to split the money we made in equal parts.

I volunteered to take care of the hot dogs and Kool Aid. Earl and Emerson was going to help me. Richard and Charlie handled the admissions. They measured everybody's waist line and collected the money, a penny for each inch. Peggy played the records. Thirty five kids came to the party and we collected twenty one dollars. But they didn't start coming until 1:00 p.m.. The kids carried them selves in an orderly manner.

Everybody, except me danced. I was too shy to dance. The time flew by. While the group was rocking and rolling, we heard a horn blow while a record was playing. Simultaneously the entire crowd said they hadn't heard the horn blow in that song before and thought it was all right. So they began to sing along with the song and make the horn sounds. And before we knew what was going on, Daddy scratched the record miserably as he moved the needle across the record to stop it. Him and Mama were angry. They were tired and wanted to know what was going on in their back yard with all of those children who was trying to make sounds like his car horn?

Peggy answered that question; "Hi Mr. and Mrs. Holmes. What y'all doing home so early? All I have to say is that Y'all came home a little too early and caught us in the act. I guess you can say we're guilty of having a waist line party. I told Bettye Joe to get your permission to have this party. She said she didn't need your permission. Anyhow, y'all can't park back here just yet."

Peggy put her hands on the hood of our car and said; "Why don't y'all park on the street for a while and let us finish up back here?"

That did it. Daddy and Mama dismissed the party immediately. After everybody except Peggy was gone, we asked if we could stay in the back yard and play records while we ate some hot dogs. We got their permission to do that.

Later on I went to the kitchen to make hot dogs.

When I got to the kitchen door I screamed at the sight of what I saw Daddy and Mama doing and said; "Stop that! Both of you are too old to be fighting. That old waist line party ain't no reason for y'all to fight." Mama was kicking her legs up. I thought she was trying to kick Daddy.

So I told her; "Mama refrain yourself and keep your feet on the floor. You too Daddy. I'm sorry for having that party without asking. I promise that it won't happen again."

Mama said. "Who's fighting? We're dancing. We're doing the Charleston." I asked her was that the same dance that her and Daddy used to do in Mississippi? She said it was. I told her that was an old antique out of style dance.

Daddy said; "No it ain't either." I told them that the twist was in. After I was convinced that they were dancing and not fighting. I relaxed and while observing them. I used one of Daddy's expressions in my thoughts, (I be damn). "Is that a hot dog in Daddy's hand? Yes. It sure is. And he's eating it. Just ten minutes ago he was raising sand when Mama suggested that they have hot dogs for a snack and she would cook dinner later. He told her that he didn't like hot dogs and no way in this world a hot dog would pass his lips. He wanted some fried steak smothered in tomato gravy, rice, cabbage and corn bread. He quickly changed his mind. Because he will not part with that hot dog even while he's dancing. I can't believe it. Mama is always saying 'Never say what you won't do. Because you don't know what you'll do until you have to cross that bridge.' I learned a lesson the hard way. Everyone got their share of the money excluding me. Mama kept my share. She told me that I made my bed hard and I had to lay in it .

When Daddy Got Laid Off: 1960

One year Daddy got laid off from his job for three months. During that time he got a job working at a Chinese Restaurant as a cook. On his first day of work they taught him how to make egg rolls. He brought three dozen of egg rolls home with him. He told us to invite our friends over to have some. We did and the egg rolls were crispy, delicious and gone in no time. The next day he brought some tiny barbecue ribs they were delicious and vanished quickly.

Daddy started something. Every day our friends was coming over to see what he brought from the restaurant. They made their selves at home.

"Mr. Holmes, what did you bring from the restaurant today? Did you bring any egg rolls? When do you think you will bring some more?" Sometimes they would be in the back yard waiting for Daddy.

They would run to the car and reach for the bag: "Hi Mr. Holmes. What's in this bag? It smell good. Did you bring enough for us today? We're hungry."

Daddy alternated the bags, until he came up with an ideal; "Tomorrow, I will bring all the ingredients to make egg rolls and teach you all how to make them. Then you can bring me some of yours."

Everybody said; "Yeah. Mr. Holmes. That's a good ideal. What time shall we be here?" None of our friends showed up. Daddy taught my brothers and me how to make egg rolls and fried rice. The fried rice was easy. The egg rolls were a challenge. It was difficult to make them tight and the same size. Some of them were over stuffed and the filling were bursting out of the sides. A lot of work was involved in trying to perfect them. They were ugly crisp and delicious. After making them once a week for a year or so, we became accustomed to the concept of rolling them and it became quite an art. Daddy said; "I didn't expect any of your friends to take me up on my suggestion. Its amazing how some people want something but don't want to work to get it".

The Snow Shoveling Ordeal: 1960

My brothers and I used to pray for those no school today due to too much snow. We took advantage of those opportune times to go out and shovel snow. The money was good. For every walk way or driveway we shoveled we would get five to fifteen cents. We'd shovel snow for three people in a row. We had two shovels. Whoever got to the shovels first, had first priority.

One morning about 7:00 I called my friend Linda and invited her to go shovel snow with me. The first place we went to was the house directly across the street from us. Mr. and Mrs. Higgins and their son lived there. We shoveled the steps, the walk way and the sidewalk in front of their house.

Mrs. Higgins gave us fifty cents each. Wow! That was a lot of money. We were happy. We simply loved Mrs. Higgins. So we decided to quit for the day and take the shovels back home to Richard and Charlie. After taking the shovels home Linda and I did a dumb foolish thing.

We told Richard and Charlie what Mrs. Higgins paid us. Linda and I also decided to become partners and that Mrs. Higgins would be our only customer from that day on. Richard and Charlie thought it was a great ideal. (So sneaky.) It snowed some more that night. And the next day the schools were closed again. So after eating breakfast, Richard said him and Charlie would go shovel snow first and take Earl and Emerson with them. I stayed with Roy.

They were gone for a while. I went to the window to gaze at the breathtakingly beautiful sparkling white snow and was in for a rude awakening. (I remember this like it happened yesterday.) Richard and Charlie was shoveling the snow that belonged to Mrs. Higgins (Linda's and my customer.) I watched them for a while. Earl and Emerson were having fun, playing in the snow. Charlie was working diligently. Richard was working, but his guilty conscious was keeping him alert and on the watch out for me. He'd move a shovel full of snow and look over his shoulder at the house as though he thought I would be coming through the door any minute. Teed off! I continued watching him mainly. I was furious with him. When they were done Mrs. Higgins came out to pay them. She gave the money to Richard. I moved closer to the window so he could see me.

After he saw me he began to laugh and point at me. Then Charlie, Earl and Emerson laughed. Richard took the three dollars that Mrs. Higgins gave him and gave one to Charlie and waved the other two in his hand. Then he gave me the peace sign. I gave him the middle finger sign from both of my hands and thought to myself, 'Im-ma kill me a brother today. It's too many of us anyway.' Richard put the money in his pocket, looked at me again and put his hand to his forehead saluting me. Charlie, Earl and Emerson followed suit.

My four brothers played in the snow laughing and saluting me until they were bored. After they gathered the shovels they crossed the street on the way home and Richard yelled; "Bet Joe you and Linda can go shovel snow now. I know what you meant about this one job ordeal. I think I'll retire for the rest of the day. Ha, ha, ha, ha. Don't cop an attitude because we beat you to the punch."

Angry, I thought to myself, 'The one who laugh last laugh the loudest. I'll fix you guys. I'm going to lock the door so none of y'all can get in. At least not until right before Daddy and Mama get home from work. Ha, ha, ha.'

After thinking about it I decided to let Earl and Emerson come in because they had nothing to do with Richard and Charlie betraying my partner and me. I had a plan and it worked splendidly until the milk man showed up.

I opened the door to let my four brothers in and immediately afterwards I asked Richard and Charlie to take the trash out. They did. And I locked the door behind them. They were locked out for about one hour or so. They threw snow balls at the kitchen window, threatened to beat me up and complained about how cold and hungry they were. In return, I gave them the peace sign and saluted them. They didn't think that was funny. But I did.

The milkman showed up to deliver the milk and buttermilk doughnuts, and to collect the money for it. When I opened the door to receive the products and pay the milkman, Richard and Charlie pushed past me and went straight to the heater for warmth and comfort.

I made lunch and we sat around the table eating and talking. And before we realized it the anger we had for each other no longer existed. We made plans to go to the back yard and make a snow man.

For the remainder of that winter we continued to fight to be the first one at Mrs. Higgins' house. And the first ones always teased the others. I was unfair! Sometimes, I'd hide the shovels under my bed. Therefore I could sleep in longer.

Jimmee And Bettye / Bettye And Jimmee: (My Husband) 1992

Jimmee and I worked together in El Segundo, California. He was an Electronic Engineer and I was an Electronic Technician Specialist. He worked on the graveyard shift and I worked on the first shift. He worked overtime two to four hours a day on my shift. We became friends and talked about more than the experiments we performed and the microchips which we processed.

We started to date eleven months after we met. On our first date, February 14, 1992 we attended the movies in Hollywood, CA. And had dinner in Inglewood, CA. Jimmee was nervous and talked considerably. I was nervous, quiet and listened to him . He talked about his brothers, Sak's, Viset's, Kiki's and Det's gifted talent for drawing. He also mentioned his four sisters, Sisome, Nepaphone, Soam and Sandy.

I told him that my children and I moved to California after my husband and I were divorced. And that I was blessed with a job at an air craft company in Torrance, CA one week after I arrived in California.

Jimmee is a wonderful friendly person. His personality is awesome. He has stuck with me and been in my corner through thick and thin. He's creative in designing, building and remodeling homes. His special unique quality of work is outstanding and in a class of its own. He's well liked by everyone.

He has a special interest in magic and he does quite well entertaining our families and friends. Even though he's a superb driver, he has a bad sense of direction. That's why we get lost so much. I'd ask; "Hey babe didn't we drive past this street three times in the last twenty minutes?" He answered; "No. Why you ask? I'm the one driving. I know where I going." Minutes later he would ask me; "look in the map book and see where this freeway connects to that freeway, etc.. I think we're on the wrong freeway. We should be going east instead west. I got on the wrong freeway when we stopped to get the gas forty five minutes ago."

Somehow being lost gave us the opportunity to relax and share cherished precious memorable childhood stories.

Jimmee Telling Me About Memorable Childhood Things:

Jimmee was born in Vientiane, Laos. He lived in the country on a farm just like I did. I told him about the cow chasing me in the red dress. And he told me about the hazard with the baby chickens and the mistake in identity where the dog food was concerned.

The Baby Chickens:

Jimmee talking to me with his Laotian accent about his parents which had taken an interest raising chickens.
"One day my father decided he wanted to raise some chickens.

286

He went to town and bought five dozen of baby chickens. I think they call them biddies or something like that. He brought them home and we took very good care of them. But they began to die in a week. And all of them were dead in about nine days. My father went back to town and bought five more dozen of those chickens and brought them home. What the heck? I don't know what happened to those chickens. Maybe they were sick when my father bought them. That five dozen were dead in one week. My father said that was a minor set back. He was determined to raise chickens and went back to town and bought six dozen of chickens. Seven days went by and all the chickens were still alive.

My mom was happy. The next day five chickens died. My mom said; " That's it! No more. No more money go to buying chickens. Almost sixteen dozen chickens, dead already. Not fair! I want the money back."

My mom fried the dead sick chickens and told me to go to town and sell them. I took them to town and sold them right away. Every time the chickens died mom fried them and sent me to town to sell them until they were all gone. One day I went to town and some of the people that bought the chickens from me was calling me; "Hey little boy! Hey little boy!" I thought they were going to whoop me because I sold them the sick chickens that Mom cooked. That's why I ran. They caught me and asked; "You got any more of those chickens?" I told them no. And they said; "When you get some more, bring them to us. We will buy all of them. Those chickens were special. We never had any chickens that taste like that before. They were tender and delicious. Little boy, we will sit on the porch and wait for you to bring them. We will pay you extra money. Here take this nickel and put it in your pocket."

The Dog Food:

Jimmee (laughing) and telling me about the day when his mom gave him a pot of food to feed the dogs with. "My mom gave me a pot of food to feed the dogs. I really wasn't paying attention to what she was saying. I was a little boy thinking and daydreaming about coming to America. As I walked and carried the pot of dog food I saw my sisters and brothers playing. The first thing that came to my mind was this food is for us. I told them; "Come here. Let's eat. I have something very good to eat. Mom told me to bring it to you. They were eager to eat.

After they ate a little bit, they began to frown like they were in pain and made very ugly faces. They spit the food out and said; 'What is this nasty stuff you are trying to make us eat? It taste terrible.' They shook their heads and said: 'We're not eating any more of this food. If you think it's very good you eat it.' I didn't think it was that bad until after I took a bite of it. It tasted so bad that I almost cried. I thought for a while and came up with a brilliant idea. "Listen up. We'll give this food to the dogs. I know they will eat it. They will eat anything. Mom will think we ate it. She will feel bad if we tell her the food was nasty. No problem."

The following day Jimmee's mom asked him if he fed the dogs. He answered; "I don't know what you are talking about mom. Why are you asking me if I fed the dogs? The pot of dog food? What pot of dog food are you talking about? I didn't see any dog food. Oh! That food." Then it came back to him; "Oh shit! That food was for the dogs? No wonder it tasted so nasty. That's why me and my little sisters and brothers got sick. Yuck. I think I'm going to throw up again."

He didn't throw up again. But he took advantage of the mishap. He teased his sisters and brothers about eating the dog food. And for a long time after that when his mom made a dish that he liked, he would tell his brothers and sisters, that it was dog food and they wouldn't touch it. Therefore he ate his share and theirs' too.

The Tobacco Leaves: U S A

Jimmee talked about the time when he went grocery shopping with his parents; "My mom and dad took me shopping with them. We put meat, rice, seasonings and fruit in the basket. My mom suggested that we get some fresh vegetables. She picked up this pretty green leafy vegetable and said 'Very fresh. Look good. We'll have this for dinner.' About fifteen minutes after I ate I began to see double and lose my equilibrium. I asked my mom what the heck is going on? She said; 'I don't know. I feel the same thing.' Shortly after that, my dad and my siblings came down with the same symptoms. What the heck? Dad and Mom took the pot of vegetables back to the store and explained what happened. The owner of the store laughed and said that wasn't a vegetable for eating. It was tobacco leaves for smoking. What the heck?"

The Chinese Medicine Incident: U S A

Jimmee talking; "I got sick one night and my dad gave me the Chinese Medicine. (Vicks VapoRub applied to the skin and massaged it with a coin until the skin turns red.) Its really good. The next day in school my gym teacher saw the red marks on my neck, shoulders and back. He asked how did I get them. I told him; 'My dad did it.' He notified the Principal. The Principal called the Social Services, the Police and the President. They were going to take me from my dad and mom and put me in a foster home. They were going to put my dad in jail for a very long time.

When dad arrived at the school, he explained our Chinese Medicine Culture to them. The Principal apologized for assuming the worst and not gathering substantial information before involving the law. My dad was mad as heck! But he accepted their apology anyway."

My Sister Attempted to Cook The Cat: Mississippi

We grew up listening to our parents tell the story about my sister and Tula. (Tula was a cat that adopted the Jackson and Holmes family.) This story was always amusing, no matter how many times we heard it.

One wonderful Friday afternoon, Mama was cooking supper. The radio was on. She was singing along with the songs and switching her hips from side to side while she stirred her cornbread mixture. She poured the cornbread mixture in the iron skillet and it was ready for baking. She switched something terrible to the stove and opened the oven door with the intentions of placing the skillet on the rack in the oven.

Surprise! Surprise! Surprise! Tula sprung from the roasting pan in the oven over Mama's right shoulder. Her feet barley touched the middle of the kitchen floor. She ran like the dickens. She was hot and in a hurry.

Tula's actions scared Mama and caused her to drop the skillet of cornbread on her foot. That left her in a state of doubt. She shook her head and walked to the table and took a seat. She commenced to re-think. "What in the hell just happened? Where did that cat come from? I thought she came from the oven. But that is just impossible. I fired the stove up way over an hour ago. And I know good 'n' well that cat couldn't stand all of that heat. Oh shit! My mind must be playing tricks on me. Unless, maybe, I'm dreaming."

She looked down at her foot which was covered with raw cornbread and aching and swelling from the heavy iron skillet falling on it. She bent down and rubbed her foot and rotated her ankle and said to herself; 'Shit nol! I ain't dreaming. My mind is not playing tricks on me. This is for real. How in the world did that darn cat get in my stove in my new roasting pan?'

She went back to the stove and took another look. She removed the roasting pan from the oven. It seemed like all of Tula"s hair was in it and withered. Mama was out-done, mad and wanted to see which one of those little rascals decided to bake Tula the cat. They had some tall explaining to do! They were outside playing when she called them, "June, T. J., would you all come in here please?"

They came and sat on the bench at the table saying; "Mama, we just saw a funny ugly looking thing run by us real fast." (That was Tula.) Mama asked which one of them decided they wanted cat for supper? June and T. J. was in left field and had no clue as to what Mama was talking about . My sister jumped off the bench and went to the back porch and stuck her head back in the door and said; "Mama, I remember what happened now. June and T. J. told me to put Tula in that brand new roasting pan that Daddy brought you when he came home from work yesterday:" that's why I did it." Mama went to the door to talk with my sister about what she did; "Tula is a good cat. She keep the barn clear of mice. That was a very mean," Before Mama could finish her sentence, she threw her hand up to swing at a bee, preventing it from landing on her and possible stinging her. But in return my sister ducked, bumped her head on the door and took off running because she thought Mama was swinging at her. She ran to Papa and Big mama's house. Big Mama told Mama that my sister was her little girl, and not to whoop her just because she tried to cook Tula.

June and T. J. helped Mama clean up the mess. She put the roasting pan in the trash. And her attitude was cheerful by the time Daddy arrived home from work. Laughing, mama informed him of that day's unexpected distasteful activities.

He had a good laugh and teased my sister; "Your mother told me that you darn near cooked Tula today. I didn't know you could cook. What kind of seasoning did you put on her? I like chicken. Why didn't you cook a chicken? Etc.."

Papa and Daddy looked for Tula but had no luck in finding the slightest trace of her. So they assumed that she either adopted another family or died in the woods. For the next month they had breakfast, dinner and supper at Papa and Big Mama's house.

Mama made sure that the stove was clean, disinfected and aired out before she used it again. She also limped for a couple of weeks. Daddy bought her another roasting pan. June and T. J. teased my sister for years about the cat; "Mama, did our sister help you cook today? What kind of meat is this? It look funny. It don't taste right. Is this the cat that we saw in the field the other day

Emerson The Wine Maker: Buffalo 1997

In September 1997, Emerson called Jimmee and me at 6:45 a. m.; "Hey, what's up? I'll be up there in fifteen minutes. I have some grapes for you guys." He brought a shopping bag full of concord grapes and said; "Hey Bettye take a look at these grapes. Aren't they big? They're sweet too. Hey I got them from the back yard where the Renfroe's used to live. (Laughing) I got a bag for myself yesterday. I'm thinking about making some wine for the holidays with mine. Check this out. I can make some wine for you guys too? I have everything we need to make it."

We started making the wine the next day after he took my sister in law, (Nickie) to work. He washed the grapes and divided them equally in six wide mouth glass gallon bottles. He took the potato masher and mashed them, while adding sugar. He had it in control. He seemed to know exactly what he was doing.

My mind began to wonder and I started to laugh and asked him if Mama ever told him about Papa's corn liquor making days? He laughed and nodded his head yes. I laughed and told him that he had inherited Papa's bootlegging genes. We joked about that momentarily.

We had a blast when he brought up the incident that happened when Mama, Roy and him were visiting me when I lived in California. Mama's long time friend, Jonnie whom moved to California from Buffalo. Jonnie came to visit us with her nineteen year old daughter, Jalea who was a model for local department stores. Jonnie wanted to show Mama her home, the town and take her shopping. Jalea wanted to stay home with Roy and kick it. So we were off with Jonnie for the day.

Roy and Jalea listened to music and watched television. He made some Buffalo Chicken Wings with blue cheese dressing and celery sticks. He brought it to the living room where they were watching television. He went back to get some cherry soda and she followed him to the kitchen and saw two quarts of Mama's peach wine experiment. She picked up one of the bottles and inquired about it. Roy told her; "That's some kind of an experiment that Mama is trying out. I think its a combination of peaches, water, sugar and yeast. It's been there for about two and a half weeks. If it goes well it should turn into wine and be ready to drink in a month. Mama got the recipe from a magazine on the plane when we were flying out here. I believe it's supposed to be good for rheumatism." Jalea opened it and was impressed with the fragrance of it.

She told Roy; "Pour that cherry soda out and put some ice in the glass. I'd rather have a glass of this half made wine if you don't mind." Roy gave her the glass of ice and she filled it up to the brim with the in-mature wine and gulped it down fast. She had three more glasses before she felt the effect. Directly after that all hell broke loose. Jalea was too advanced and hot for Roy to handle. She threw her chicken bones towards the fireplace. Then she threw the crystal glass that she was drinking from towards the fireplace. She took her blouse off and threw it at Roy and said she was hot and wanted to dance for him in the nude. Her hands were all over him.

Poor Roy! He didn't know what to do. He went to pick the chicken bones up and talked; "Aahhh. I'll get them later. It's more important to get the broken glass first. Aahhh, doggone.

293

She's taking her bra off? That's too extreme. She's not leaving anything to my imagination! Whew! I'll get the glass later. I have to prevent her from disrobing any further. I was thinking about asking her if I could give her a teeny weeny kiss on the cheek. But I think she wants to give me the cake and the ice cream too. On one hand I'm flattered and on the other hand I'm offended. What kind of guy do she think I am?

I have morals. I am a nice respectable teenager who just turned sixteen yesterday. I'm still wet behind the ears. I am not ready to be a father. I would find it difficult to look in the mirror if something happened between us today. Yeah. She's cute, but her chest is flat as mine. Her legs are gorgeous. Um, um, um. Darn. If she was sober I wouldn't be having this conversation with myself."

"Jalea! What is wrong with you girl? Here. Put your blouse back on. Get it together. I'll bring you some ice water so you can sober up before your mother gets back. I told you not to drink that stuff. And it was aimed for medicinal purposes only. You should have listened to me. I traveled three thousand miles to baby-sit a drunk nineteen year old."

When Roy got back with the water Jalea was on the couch out cold. Roy was scared and didn't know if jalea was in danger of dying from an overindulgence of in-mature home made wine. So he did what he had to do. He called her mother and explained what happened. Jonnie was mad. We left her house after she talked with Roy. Jonnie was speeding and blowing the horn at people telling them to get out of her way.

Jalea had managed to straighten up and put her blouse back on. But it was inside out and unbuttoned. The wine gave her a sense of humor. She was cracking jokes, laughing, cutting up, and being silly. She looked in the cabinets for something else to eat. That's when Jonnie approached her and told her that she smelled awful and asked what had she been drinking. Jalea told Jonnie, "None of your damn business." And laughed hysterically as saliva ran from her mouth. Jonnie was upset with Mama for making the wine. She was upset with Roy and accused him of giving Jalea the wine and getting her intoxicated so he could take advantage of her.

Mama was angry with Jalea for disturbing her wine while it was in the makings. Roy was disturbed with Jonnie for leaving Jalea for him to babysit. He was very outspoken; "Your daughter's hot pants are too tight. And the dog is biting her. Next time you want to leave her with a sixteen year old guy to baby-sit, make sure she is dressed properly and stays away from home made wine."

Jonnie and Jalea stormed out of the house and we never heard from them again. After we had fun reminiscing, Emerson told us that he would keep a close eye on the wine for three weeks because that was the crucial stage. Then he'd bring it upstairs and instruct us on what to do with it until it was ready to drink. The wine turned out beautifully. Our company enjoyed it immensely during the Thanksgiving and Christmas holiday.

Richard's Plumbing Experience: Buffalo

Emerson and I laughed about the time when Richard worked diligently for about an hour unstopping the bathroom sink. His face was covered with sweat when he finished. He bragged while rubbing his hands together and cracking his knuckles. He proudly said; "That was a tough job to master but with my steady persistence I finally unstopped that darn thing. I still don't know what the devil was stopping it up."

We were relieved that Richard unstopped the sink because it was an inconvenience. Emerson went to the bathroom, turned the water on and started to laugh while Richard was still in the kitchen bragging.

This is what happened. Richard inadvertently punched a quarter size hole in the pipe under the sink. And the bucket that he left under the sink was catching the water. Actually the sink wasn't unstopped like he presumed it was.

Thanksgiving Dinner at School 53: November 1997

I will especially remember that day, when Emerson asked me to put off going on my diet for one day. Because he wanted Jimmee and me to accompany him to a Thanksgiving dinner at School 53, the elementary school which my siblings and I attended.

We simply had a wonderful time. There were a group of children from different elementary schools in Buffalo that put on an outstanding performance, singing gospel songs. City officials made speeches.

They saved the best for last. The dinner was much more than what we expected. Juicy turkey with moist dressing, ham, roast beef, fried chicken and a variety of vegetables, desserts, beverages etc. We enjoyed eating the awesome food and mingling with people that we went to school 53 with. I acquired recipes from some of the people who prepared the food.

After dinner Emerson and I took Jimmee on a tour of the school. We told him of memorable events that took place there. We attended classrooms and recalled things from way back. We played games in the gym. We also sat in the auditorium enjoying positive gossip until the doors were ready to close. It was one of the nicest Thanksgiving dinners I have ever attended. I was honored that Emerson invited Jimmee and I to join him for that pleasurable occasion.

October 4 2004 Emerson's Funeral

Emerson was in a peaceful sweet sleep. His long eyelashes seemed to move at times. His lips gave an impression of a faint smile. His straight brown hair had grown considerably during his stay in the hospital. His hands were well manicured. His blue suit, blue shirt, and blue stripped tie matched the silver/blue casket which he was displayed in. I believe Jesus met him at the end of his road.

While standing at the casket watching Emerson, thoughts entered my mind; "Hey Bettye! Don't cry! I have a request for you. Smile and laugh when you think about me. There is a lifetime of fun, joyous, crazy, witty, memories of me stacked in your memory bank that will keep me alive in your heart.

I know you cried and prayed and kept up the faith because you didn't want me to leave. But I was tired and it was time for me to vacate that good looking, rugged body which I occupied. I am complete now. I can jump up and clap my feet. Don't look back and worry about what I went through or what I didn't have or places I never went. That's torture! If you must look back and think about me, look at the times when I was happy. You know, kidding around, playing pranks or teasing you about something. Think and talk about the enjoyable times I had with the family and friends. And break into a sweat laughing. It will uplift your spirit and put you in a good mood sis.

Hey. Check this out! I am tickled here. Everything is bright and cheerful here! There is soft sensational music everywhere. Daddy, Mama, June, T. J., Richard and Earl met me with open arms. There's no hospitals, no sickness, no pain, and no suffering here.

Hey, I love y'all. But if I could come back to visit for one hour, I would have to decline. There ain't no way that I will ever entertain that ideal. You can still talk to me. I will be with you and around you forever. You just won't see me sis. Don't be sad. Be happy instead."

Family, friends and neighbors attended the funeral. It was short and sad. Reverend C. Roads spoke; "Good morning. My name is Reverend C. Roads. I have known Emerson Holmes for years and years. I worked with him and his late brother June for many years and we became close friends. I got to know the rest of their family and they considered me as family. Emerson was very nice and on the quiet side with a sense of humor. He was a mess at work. He had something funny to say every day that kept us laughing. One day his joke had me in an uproar and our supervisor came by and asked me what was amusing? All I could do, was point at Emerson. But Emerson was looking serious and working diligently.

Emerson, June and myself loved to cook and often talked about how we seasoned whatever it was that we cooked. Each one of us swore that we were the best cook of the three of us.

We will truly miss Emerson. He's in a better place now. And God knows best.

The preacher from Emerson's church did a weak eulogy. He knew Emerson well. He often visited him in the hospital. But he referred to Emerson as 'this young man' A lady sang the same song twice without the company of a piano or organ. I wanted them to sing, 'I Won't Complain.' It's a beautiful song.

The preacher was wearing a wig that didn't cover the back of his head. It was obvious therefore, attracting a lot of attention. I wasn't pleased with his mannerism and the way he conducted the funeral. A member of his church read the obituary:

Emerson Holmes born October 5, 1954. He departed this life on Tuesday October 1, 2002 at 6:45 a. m. after a lengthy illness. His pet name was **"M"**. Born in Gloster, Mississippi. He was the sixth son of his loving parents, Curley and Gladys Holmes. He moved to Buffalo, New York with his family in 1957. He became a member of Walls Memorial A. M. E. Zion Church at an early age.

He attended Elementary School 53 and East High School. His special interests in food and cooking inspired him to attend

O' Neal School Of Culinary arts. Emerson was employed by Niagara Machine and tool shop as a machinist for twenty seven years.

On October 27, 1987 he was united in holy matrimony to Essie King (Nickie). Leaving to cherish his memory are: his loving wife **Essie**, daughter **Tachica**, one grand daughter, **Jada**, two sisters, **Dolly (Robert) Gilchrist** and **Bettye (Jimmee) Chansamone.** two brothers, **Charlie (Charlene) Holmes** and **Roy (Rochelle) Holmes, One** aunt, **Lottie Holmes Moore**; and a host of nieces, nephews, cousins, and friends.

"A tribute to our brother Emerson Holmes"
God saw the road was getting to be a burden for you to climb
He gently closed your loving eyes
And whispered, "Come with me Emerson, Peace be thine."
The weary hours, the days of pain,
The restless, sleepless nights which you endured will cease
At last you will have glorious sweet rest and glorious sweet sleep.

God saw you were getting weary, weary, weary,
Because He loved you passionately, He did what He thought was best
He stood beside you
And whispered, "Come and rest in peace."

Emerson, you were gone before we knew it
And only God knows why

Sleep on my dear precious Emerson and take your rest,
We love you dearly, but God loves you the best
now you will have sweet, sweet, sweet, sleep, Emerson!
Your loving sisters and brothers
Doll, Bettye, Charlie and Roy

My mind began to wonder; 'Emerson I remember your first words. They were complete sentences which started our neighbors to talk and exaggerate; 'Did y'all hear about Curley and Gladys's boy? He done went to talking. Done waited till he got five years old before he uttered a word. He is pro-noun-cin words I ain't never heard. He decided to git off the pot. Take yo hat off scratch yo head and listen to this. The way it was told to me is that old maingy dog done teached that boy how to talk. It seem like that happened yesterday. But it was a lifetime ago.'

'I remember the times when Jimmee and I would get home from work at 12:30 a. m. and find a pot of warm delicious food on the stove which you prepared for us. You were kind and generous Em.'

'What about the time when Charlie and Marlon (Charlie's son), had Jimmee get ready to go to Canada with them to see the topless dancers and one hour after they were due to stop by and get him Marlon called and canceled out. You took him instead. And he said; "M", My brother. Charlie, not my brother. Marlon, not my brother."

'What about the time when Sacha, Malesha and I came home for Christmas in 1991? You and I played a trick on T. J.. That was hilarious. (A faint smile possessed my lips as my mind continued to wonder).'

'T. J. was drinking and rudely demanding that somebody fix him something to eat. That upset Mama. In return she made corn beef and eggs for him.

That burned me up: "Mama, I don't think you should run around and wait on T. J. when he drink and act like a fool. Mama go crazy! Take that baseball bat from behind the door in your bedroom and beat him over the head with it. That'll straighten him up."

Mama said; "Aah, I like to keep peace. I don't mind fixing him something to eat. You know your brother has a heart of gold and he's one of the nicest people in the world when he's not drinking. Besides I don't want him in the kitchen burning any more of my

Tupperware. During the summer he decided to warm the meat loaf in the oven. I put the meat loaf in my Tupperware bowl and refrigerated it the day before. T. J. put the bowl in the oven on 400 degrees. Then he went next door to visit Hexton.

I'd been gone for about an hour. When I returned home T. J. was sitting on Hexton's porch and they were lolly gagging. Girl as soon as I opened the back door I could smell rubber burning. I didn't know what it was. All sorts of things ran through my mind as I rushed up the stairs and into the kitchen. Smoke was coming from the oven. I turned the oven off and opened the oven door. And my beautiful Tupperware bowl was on the floor of the oven bubbling looking like a pile of you know what. The meat loaf was on the rack burned to a crisp.

T. J. rushed in. He knew I was mad! Are you ready for this Bettye? T. J. had the nerves to grab his chin put his other hand on his hip and say; 'Gee! I thought that bowl was oven proof! I can't believe this!'

I went down stairs and talked to you M, about playing a trick on T. J. . We hoped it would make him think twice before indulging in his liquor. M, you came up stairs and walked through the dining room where T. J. was eating and watching television.

We sat in the living room and you said; "Hey Bettye, what time did you say the hospital is picking T. J. up tomorrow morning? At eight. Good. (In the meanwhile, T. J. turned the television off, so he could do what we wanted him to do. *'Listen'*). Me, you Doll, Charlie Earl, and Roy have to be here so we can sign him in that place. Its for his own good. You're right. That's the only choice we have.

They said if he give them any trouble they'll put him in a straight jacket.

Mama made a comment: " I called Doll, Charlie, Earl and Roy. They will be here at seven. (T. J. sat in the dining room, so quiet like a perfect gentleman. Our talking made him sober and took his appetite.) They suggested that after the hospital pick T. J. up we can go out to breakfast."

Mama had a difficult time trying to stop laughing long enough, to tell us that T. J. wasn't as drunk as he pretended. Because half of the liquor he was drinking was Lipton tea.

Later that evening I was washing dishes when T. J. came in and looked out the kitchen window and said; "Look like we're going to have a white Christmas, sis. Gee. Look at that snow come down." I made some Spanish rice and chicken and we had a good conversation while we ate.

While taking the trash out he said; "Its a good western coming on in about fifteen minutes. You want to watch it with me? Order a pizza. I got it covered."

The pizza arrived halfway through the movie. We enjoyed it and the movie as well. He asked; "Hey Bettye aah, aah, what was y'all talking about earlier? Seem like y'all was talking about locking somebody up! You were the one doing most of the talking. I can't believe this. My baby sister want to hang me."

I laughed and responded; "T. J., we love you with a passion. And it's tearing us apart to see you drink. I know you can do better. If you can go without drinking at work you can do the same thing at home. T. J. don't worry and be nervous about what you heard us saying. We were jiving. See you in the morning."

He said; "Darn straight! I'm nervous and worried. Hell. My own family want to ship me off to a strange hostile dangerous place two days before Christmas. Gee! I can't trust none of y'all. Getting together behind my back and plotting against me just because I want to have a little Christmas drink. I want you to call those people in the morning and tell them never mind. I'm not going anywhere with them."

The phone rang the next morning. T. J. answered it disguising his voice to sound like a woman.

It was Roy; "Hey T. J.. What's up? Hey, I'm on my way to pick up Bettye. We're having breakfast. Do you want to accompany us? T. J. hung the phone up.

M, you came upstairs after taking Essie to work and asked T. J.; "Hey T. J., you want to take a ride with me to the mall. I going shopping to buy my wife a Christmas gift."

Being suspicious, T. J. replied; "Ain't no way in hell you will get me out of this house today Emerson. I heard everything y'all said last night." You were holding your coat across your arm as you walked in T. J.'s direction.

T. J. Jumped out of his chair and ran to the living room saying; "You ain't about to put that damn straight jacket on me. You better hurry up and believe that." That was some kind of funny. M, you told him that we set him up hoping to physic him out about drinking.

A beautiful glow came over T. J.'s face and he smiled and faked it; "Gee! I knew that. You got to get up pretty early in the morning to pull the wool over my eyes."

T. J. stayed away from liquor. If he had a drink he kept it from us. That incident virtually made our Christmas a beautiful one.

Reverend Joe L Fisher talked with me immediately following the funeral. Smiling, he inquired; "Do you live in Moreno Valley. CA? This is a small world! My sister and my brother-n-law live there too. John and Dorthy Metcalf. They live on Smoking Flame Gun Drive. Do you know where that street is? I'll give you her phone number so you guys can acquaint yourselves. Yes. She's a very nice person. I'll call and let her know to expect your phone call.

I joined Pleasant Grove Missionary Baptist Church right then. Reverend Joe L Fisher, Reverend Michael J Robinson, Mr. and Mrs. Stenhouse and F. Martin welcomed me with warn open arms.

After the funeral our family, relatives and friends, mingled in the church parking lot. My daughter, Sacha talking fast: "Mama what kind of wig wearing preacher is that? Where did he get his credentials? Everybody in church laughed at his wig. It only covered the top of his big head. Mama, stop trying to keep a straight face. You know that was funny.

Why didn't he ask anybody to say complimentary things about uncle Emerson? I was waiting for him to ask. I wanted to say Uncle Emerson loved the Wayne Brady Show! I talked to Uncle Emerson a week before he went in the hospital. He was in a good mood. He stopped smoking. He was going to join Uncle Charlie, Aunt Charlene and Aunt Doll's church. He said he was ready to walk the narrow straight line."

Sacha continued to talk; "Look Mama, Reno wanted me to read this letter. She read it. "Uncle Emerson, I'm thankful for the encouraging talks you had with me trying to make me do the right thing. I will never forget your kind compassionate generous heart. I'm appreciative for the lessons you taught me, especially this one.

We had a snow storm and Mama told me to shovel the driveway and sidewalk. I went out side to do it and was sidetracked. I went across the street to talk with some girls and stayed there with them until it was almost dark. The driveway and sidewalk was done when I got back. Mama looked out the window and was pleased. She gave me ten dollars and made a grill cheese sandwich and a mug of hot chocolate to warm me up after shoveling the snow. Uncle Emerson, you asked me to ride to the steak house with you. You sent me in to order three steak sandwiches. I told you it would be six dollars and held my hand out for the money. You said; 'You have the money. Pay for it.' I told you that all I had was the ten dollars mama gave me. You answered me; 'I know. That's the money I'm talking about. The way I see it, that's my money. How do you think the driveway and sidewalk got shoveled? Did you think the man on the moon did it? I darn near froze to death shoveling that snow. And you took credit for it. I don't think so! Check this out man. I'm teaching you a valuable lesson for misleading your mother and accepting money for work that I did. The three sandwiches are for Bettye, my wife and me. When we get home you are going to tell Bettye what you did. I hope you remember this lesson for years to come. Go pay for the sandwiches. Oh. Bring my change back.'

Although you gave me half of your steak sandwich Uncle Emerson, I was perturbed. But after thinking about it, I came to the conclusion that you were a cool uncle for doing that and for stepping in front of me to keep Mama from breaking the broom handle over my head." Peace be with you Uncle Emerson!

Sacha continued; "Malesha wanted me to read this; 'My dear Uncle Emerson: It's hard to believe that you are gone. Your witty sayings, phrases and laughter will truly be missed tremendously. Rest in peace Uncle M!'

Junior Renfroe shared something with my sister; "You know how close me and Emerson were when we were growing up. Emerson was a comedian from the time he was a little boy. I remember the time when he decided to take June's car and teach himself how to drive. I was in the car with him. He drove down East Utica very slow. He rode the brakes. We didn't go over ten miles per hour. It took twenty minutes to get to East Utica and Jefferson. The signal light changed eight times before he got the nerves to make that right turn onto Jefferson Ave.

His turn was too short therefore, he ran over the sidewalk and drove (one block) down Jefferson to Glenwood. We sat there ten minutes before he made the right turn onto Glenwood and discovered a police was driving behind us. Emerson drove a little faster fifteen mph. Every time the meter went up to fifteen mph Emerson stepped on the brakes. When we parked in front of the house the police parked his car, got out and asked Emerson how old was he and if he had a driver's license:

Emerson was twelve. He told the police that he was sixteen. And he was attending A B D Mechanic school. And his assignment was to fix the brakes on the car which belonged to his brother June.

The police said, 'You have a baby face. You look to be ten or eleven years old. I believe you know what you're doing. Good luck on those brakes.'

After he drove off Emerson said; 'That cop scared the devil out of me. I thought I was going to jail. Ay man you know why June gave me these keys? To wash his car. I better hurry up and wash it before he comes out here and suspect something. If he ask me if I been monkeying around trying to drive his car Im-ma tell him no.' June never found out"

Everyone congregated at my sister and Bob's house to eat afterwards.

Mama's Last Visit to California: 1987

The last time Mama visited me in California was the most treasured of all! I sent for her to come spend some time with me after I underwent surgery on my feet. She was there for six weeks and every day was a joy to behold. We indulged in shopping two or three times a week. We went to dinner on the beaches twice a week. We stayed in Vegas for eight lovely days. We pampered ourselves. We had the pleasure of having room service every morning. One evening she and I were admiring the beautiful lighting and decorations on the strip from our room on the twentieth floor.

We had a limousine come get us and drive us around the town. Mama said; "I feel special. All I need now is something to snack on." We indulged in submarines sandwiches while seeing beautiful Vegas during the evening.

After returning home to California, before retiring to bed Mama and I continued to utilize the Jacuzzi to rid the stresses that was bestowed upon us during the day.

She accompanied me to my doctor's appointments. She also accompanied me to the examining room. She and Dr. Mc Cannon talked about the good old days living in the country. He was from Kanfield, Arkansas. He smiled frequently giving Mama and I the impression that he had a romantic interest in her. He also said; "I love a plump woman."

Two days later he called; "Hello, Bettye this is Dr. Mc Cannon. I'm calling to see how your feet are progressing. I'm glad to hear that. You'll be back to work in no time. How is your mother? She's a fine looking plump woman. I'd be honored if she would go out to dinner with me. That's if you give your permission."

I asked him if he was married? He was a widower.

Dr. Mc Cannon parked in my driveway. Mama was looking out the window as she said: "Come here Bettye. What kind of car is that? It sure is pretty. A Rolls Royce? You mean to tell me, that I'll be riding in a Rolls Royce! Honey hush! Can I handle that? Dr. Mc Cannon had a crush on Mama that wouldn't wait. And she knew it. She was shy and lost for words as she approached the front door to let him in. I thought it was kind of cute.

She wore a navy blue suit trimmed in red. Her black hair with a touch of silver gray was combed to the back in a bun. Her complexion was smooth with a hue of deep pink rouge. She was stunning.

Mama returned home with her untouched food in a spirited way. She began to talk excitedly; "I didn't get a chance to eat because we were involved in conversation and the time flew by. I Had a lovely time. Remember the expensive camera that we were admiring in the gift shop at the hospital? He bought it for me yesterday. This is lovely Isn't it? He bought a beautiful plant for you Bettye. I'm liking this! Luke Mc Cannon is a gentleman with a big soft heart. He has sixteen siblings. He served in the Army the same time Curley did. I enjoyed talking with him. We have a lot in common."

I had a barbecue for Mama and invited Dr. Mc Cannon, some of my co-workers and members from my church. Mama mingled and made lots of friends. Dr. Mc Cannon brought barbecue goat. Mama said it was so-so, and it was something that she would have to acquire a taste for. Dr. Mc Cannon took Mama to a play, dinner in Hollywood, dinner in Beverly Hills, dinner in Redondo beach, a dinner cruise, etc.. He also accompanied us to church.

The Park:

Mama and I checked out everything, while visiting Willowbrook Park. It was a gorgeous, well kept park. People were barbecuing, fishing, jogging, bike riding, swimming, etc.. We sat on a bench that had a shade tree over it, protecting us from the sun's rays.

Mama talked; "Um, um, um, this is really nice. This park is here because Earl thought of an idea and wrote it on a piece of paper. And now it has materialized. I remember when Earl told me about this park. It was the year 1979 when I was visiting you all. He, his twins, Troy, Paul and their mother, Roberta were with him and we came here. The city was demolishing some projects (pointing) over there. He told me; 'Mama, this is going to be a park one day!'

Earl had confidence that the city would accept his proposal to make these grounds a park. He was concerned about having a place of recreation within the community for the community. (Smiling) Um, um, um. This park is full of people. If Curley was alive, he would be a proud, happy man. All of our boys are smart! Me and Curley did alright! Oh yeah Bettye, that goes without saying, my girls are smart too. You better believe it.

Maybe we can come back here before I leave and do a little fishing. Girl, this country scenery takes me back many years. This place reminds me of Mississippi at noon."

Our reminiscence was quite fulfilling and enjoyable. Mama talked; "The first time Doll and I came to California, Richard was stationed at the Army base in Orange County. He took us somewhere every day. We got lost one day and stopped at a gas station to use the pay phone to get directions. The operator was no help.

On the way back to the car with a map, Richard was interrupted; 'Hello! Mister, were you on the pay phone a few minutes ago? The phone is for you." Richard ran to the phone.

He came back to the car and said; 'I was just asked out on a blind date. It was the telephone operator. She said I sound so good on the phone that she had to call me back. She want to take me out tomorrow. Her name is Harmony. She wanted my address. I told her that I live on the base. I got her phone number. I'm not familiar with aggressive women. What if she kidnap me? Or something worse?'

Mama continues to talk; "Yeah. Richard called Harmony the next day. She took the three of us to a restaurant in Long Beach. We had a table overlooking the beautiful blue Pacific Ocean. She ordered steak and lobster for us. The food was sooo good! We had a ball.

Harmony was a well established good looking woman four months older than me. Her personality was friendly and down to earth. Doll and I liked her from the jump. She said Richard was the finest man she ever saw. She asked him to marry her that same day!

Harmony owned three houses in Redondo Beach, California and three houses in Torrance, California. She and Richard dated until he was shipped to Germany."

"You know Earl took his first trip to California on the bus. (Laughing) He had a two hour layover in Salt Lake City, Utah. He played pool with some white guys that live there.

One of them asked earl; 'Man where are you headed to?'

Earl said; 'L.A.'

Thinking Earl was white he said; ' L.A? That's a black man's town. What the hell are you going there for man?'

Earl became conscious of the surroundings and observed. After observing he realized that he was the only black person in the vicinity. So he excused himself and went back to the bus station to await the bus going to California."

Breakfast on the bus: Mississippi

One spring school morning In Mississippi, Mama was still combing my hair when the bus driver arrived fifteen minutes early. She told June ,Doll and T. J.; "Y'all go on and get on the bus and tell the bus driver to wait for Bettye. Im-ma finish combing her hair and make her a sandwich and she'll be on her way."

She hurried to the kitchen. My heart was happy as I watched her crack the egg on the side of the iron skillet and drop it in the hot bacon grease, saying; "Darn! I forgot to tell Mama and Daddy (Big Mama and Papa) to bring me some black pepper from town yesterday." As she sprinkled chili powder on the egg she said; "I guess this chili powder will have to do."

She made a ham, bacon and egg biscuit sandwich, with a little of her homemade apple jelly. It was looking good.

Daddy was sitting at the table popping his fingers to the music on the radio. His broken foot (which was in a cast), was propped up on a pillow on the bench. He broke his foot the previous day at work. Therefore he had some free time to be at home and chill out.

Mama was just about to wrap my sandwich in a white cloth so I could go when Daddy said; "Honey cut that sandwich in half. She can't eat all of that. I'll eat the other half."

I said; "Daddy, I can eat all of that. Mama please don't cut my san-mich in half."

Daddy responded; "Come here." He pinched my earlobe. "You can eat all of that. Huh?"

I assured him: "Yes sir"

Smiling. He questioned me; "How do you know that?"

I answered; "Because I helped Doll milk the cow and make the bed. And I washed my face two times. And you better believe I'm real hungry rat now."

After laughing, he asked: "Was your face that dirty?"

I answered: "No sir. When Doll was milking the cow, I asked her to squirt some milk in my mouth and she missed my mouth and got it all over my face. Ain't that something Daddy?" They laughed and I followed suit.

Mama didn't cut my sandwich in half. She wrapped it in the white cloth, gave it to me and said; "Honey eat this on the bus. Put this cloth across your lap to catch the crumbs. When you get off the bus at school. Shake the crumbs to the ground. Fold the cloth and put it in your book and bring it home." She pinched my cheek and said; "Thank the bus driver for waiting for you."

I sat on the seat behind June and admired my sandwich from all

311

angles. Then I kissed it before I took pleasure in demolishing it. I relished everything about that sandwich. I closed my eyes while I chewed each delicious bite. The sandwich went so fast that I had to look around to see if any was left. It was gone, crumbs and all. The only thing left, was the awesome lingering taste on my lips.

Roy And His Friend:

One evening Daddy told my seven year old brother, Roy a bedtime story about when June and T. J. was growing up in Mississippi and how well they handled their B.B. guns. And how much fun they used to have. Roy was moved; "Daddy, all I want for Christmas is a B.B. gun." Daddy said; "Well, we'll see what Santa Claus say."

Roy made comments; "Daddy! Man to man. I'm a big boy! I've been knowing about Santa Claus for a long, long, long time! You're the man! That's why I'm asking you."

Later that evening Daddy was in the living room reading the newspaper when Roy started to talk in his sleep; "three, six, eight, three ,six, eight, three, six, eight." Daddy wrote that number on the news paper. He played it the next day and it came out.

Roy was happy. He got his B.B. gun before Christmas. Richard, Charlie, Earl and Emerson taught Roy how to shoot it. Roy started off shooting soda bottles, luggage, Mama's can fruit, Mama's uniforms on the clothes line and everything else until he was banned from shooting in the attic.

Roy went through ten B. B. guns within eight years. He was a good shooter. He directed his attention to moving targets in and around our back yard: dogs, cats, squirrels, birds and sometimes my brothers' friends.

Roy's friend, Mickey often came over with his B.B. gun. They would hang out in the back yard for hours and shoot those poor

defenseless animals and laugh and joke about it.
Mickey: Hey Roy, look at that bastard hop. I shot him in the ass.
Ha, Ha, ha!"

Roy: (Laughing) Yeah that's the same bastard I shot between the eyes yesterday. I'm tired of his vegetarian fat ass hopping through Mama's garden and taking a bite of every vegetable and leaving leftovers for us. Mama work hard in this garden. If he hop through this yard tomorrow, I'm going to ice him and throw him on the grill.

Mickey: Don't ice the fat heavy ass bold squirrel man. Those B.B.'s are weighing him down. That's why he's hopping. Tomorrow he'll be crawling. Anyway, what do you think will happen if you put him on the grill and he's loaded with undigested BB's? Man, we'll be running for cover. Let's wait for him to kick the bucket.

A few years later:

They Faked It: 1982

One Saturday evening Roy and Mickey, two twenty two year old fancy free, good looking guys were on their way out to a night club. They drove pass a young couple that was fighting. Mickey was the driver. Therefore he backed up and stopped the car in the middle of the street.

They got out of the car leaving the doors open and stopped the fight. Mickey flashed his library card and identified himself as ' Detective Mickey. 'Roy flashed his driver's license and identified himself as 'Detective Holmes.'

After they saw how big the guy was they walked back to the car and talked; "That's a big ass dude! What did we get ourselves into? He's huffing and puffing like a bear. He's mad as hell."

Roy said; "Daddy always told us to clean our house and stay the

313

heck out of everybody's else house. I knew I should have drove tonight! This is how people get killed. Putting their nose where it doesn't belong. Damn. My night is spoiled now."

Mickey talked; "Ah man! Be cool. It ain't that bad. Come on. Let's talk to him. Maybe we can apologize." (Mickey was 5'4" and barely weighing 120 lbs. Roy was 5'11" and possibly weighing 130 lbs).

They asked the guy his age. In a squeaky high pitch voice he said; "Fifteen." Mickey asked his weight? Trembling as he responded; "Three hundred and twenty eight pounds. And I'm six feet six inches tall."

Mickey took advantage of the big guy's fear; "You big clutz. What were you beating on that girl for? She's cheating on you? Big deal. It's a free country. Girls cheat on their boyfriends. Dummy. That don't give you the right to beat on her. You sorry ass sissy. A real man will not hit a woman. He'll walk away first. I should kick your ass. That is a serious offence. You scared, sad, sorry ass, simple giant. I should throw you in jail. Where do y'all live?" Both of them lived on the same street but in different directions.

In the meanwhile Roy talked with the girl. "You're twelve years old? Do your parents know where you are? What? You slipped out of the window while they were in the bed sleep? That was a dumb thing to do. You slipped out of the window to get your little fast ass kicked. Are you happy now? What are going to tell your parents about your black eye? I hope you don't tell them you got beat up in your dreams. Well. It's time for you to take that journey home and face the music. What? No! I'm sorry. We're policemen. Not taxicabs. Oh yeah. You wasn't too scared to walk after dark when you sneaked out of the window. I hope you learned a lesson from this. Start running. You'll be home in no time. And pray that your parents are still sleep."

Mickey teased; "Roy, check this out. This big jack ass sissy is

314

crying. I think he's going to piss on himself next. Ha! Don't you want to hit me big boy?"

Roy and Mickey talked among themselves; "Let's get the hell away from here before a real policeman drive by."

Mickey approached the guy. "Hey you! Me and my partner talked. This is your lucky day. We're going to let you go. Start walking and don't look back unless you want to go to jail."

The girl took off running in the direction of her home. The guy started walking in the opposite direction and tripped over his feet.

Mickey made a comment; "Hey clumsy. One more thing, If I hear of you hitting a girl again I will whoop your ass from one end of this street to the next. Do you comprehend?" The guy nodded his head and continued to walk.

Mickey started again; Hey you. One more thing, I'm placing you on a 8: p. m. curfew until you're eighteen." The guy said; "OK" and kept walking.

Roy and Mickey laughed; "Whew." We pulled that one off. But check this out man! We performed a Good Samaritan Act. Ha. Ha. Ha. Ha. We deserve a medal!"

Mickey: One day I will become a policeman. That's what I really want.

Roy: Not me. I want a comfortable job sitting behind a desk. Not a job jumping over fences and building chasing all kind of crooks.

They continued on with their night club plans. And Roy specified; "One more thing, absolutely no more stopping on the way to the club. Do you comprehend?"

Mickey became a 'policeman.' And he simply loves it.

Roy became a 'State Trooper'. He's enjoying it.

He had his comfortable job working as a Psychiatrist in a prison located in upstate NY. He worked with disrespectful juveniles who had no appreciation for him or anybody else.

Roy was a caring person. It was his goal and desire to make a difference in the juveniles lives. The stubborn juveniles had goals and desires of their own. Therefore they gave Roy a difficult time. They were comfortable with their gangster ways and didn't want to make a change.

One of Roy's patients, Dan, an in-mature angry fifteen year old boy, inspired him to make a decision to change his career.

"Good morning Dan. Come in and have a seat. Are you feeling better than you were last week? Alright. Let's talk about why you slapped your mother, shot your father in the foot and kicked the dog breaking his ribs causing him to go to heaven."

Dan answered; Yo. It's like this Dr. Holmes. My mama wouldn't give me no money. My daddy put his two cents in it. That chump should be happy that I shot him in the foot. Cause that ain't what I was aiming for. The damn dog tried to bite me. That's three counts of self defense. It's an open and shut case. I'm innocent!"

Roy didn't like Dan's attitude. And Dan said; "Crystal ball, crystal ball, show me some future. Dr. Holmes, I see me and my boys, shaving your head, jacking you up and leaving you for dead."

Roy got up from his desk and walked to Dan, putting his hand on Dan's shoulder. He remarked; "You're right Dan. I see the same thing! Wait a minute. There's more. Um. I see me dragging your sorry ass across my desk by the collar. And slamming you on the floor and putting my foot on your neck. Yo. Dan, um, um, um. (Shaking his head.) That's a shame! I see four guards carrying you out of this office face down and you are spitting your teeth out. Your boys, Iron Head, Steel Fist and Bullet Proof are laughing

316

and calling you a fool. Steel Fist is wearing your new shoes. And that ain't cool. Wait. There's more. Um. It's a number. But it's not clear. Crystal ball, crystal ball, don't fade on me. Um. It's getting clear. Twenty-five thousand dollars? I think its connected with the lottery."

Dan smiled saying: "Yo, Dr. Holmes I play the numbers all the time."

Roy interrupted; "No. It's not that. Its twenty-five years attached to the fifteen years that you are serving now. (Laughing) That's kind of like hitting the lottery. Don't you think so Dan?"

Dan: Dr. Holmes you psyching me out talking like that. There ain't no such thang as a crystal ball showing the future.

Roy: Are you sure Dan? Cause I really did see all of that stuff. Yo Dan. Remember this. Anything is possible.

Dan forced himself to smile; "Yo Dr. Holmes I like you. You cool wit me. Any thang you wont Doc I ken git it for you. Jus name it. Yo, Dr. Holmes I got some real issues I want to discuss wit you. I trust you Doc."

Roy interrupted Dan when he opened the door; "Your time is up. I'll see you next week."

Dan: Yo. Dr. Holmes, you're cutting my time short today.

Roy: Yo. Dan yo. The crystal ball took up your time showing the future.

As Roy took that long drive home from work he thought; "As much as I hate to do it, I'm going back to school and acquire another career. I'm going to take this job and shove it. Those hard core gangsters don't appreciate me, they don't value their life and they are not interested in making a change. And I ain't going to jail for murder."

You Are Too old For Baby Dolls:

I did not want to grow up. I wanted to stay a child and continue to get baby dolls for Christmas. Mama and I were Christmas shopping . The shopping basket was loaded with toys for Richard, Charlie, Earl, Emerson and Roy. There was one toy missing. I strolled down the isle until I found a cute baby doll. I put the doll in the basket.

Mama was observant. While we were standing in the line waiting to be checked out. She took the doll inspected it and said; "This is a cute little ol doll. Somebody done put it in our basket by mistake. Here Bettye, run back there and put it on the shelf." I took the doll and said; "Look Mama, its half price. I want Santa Claus to bring me this doll."

Excited and not aware of the loud tone of her voice, she called me Bettye Joe. (Usually Mama called me Bettye.) "Say what? Bettye Joe. You got to be kidding! Now let me get this straight. You want Santa Claus to do what? Oh Lord! You are twelve years old. You will be a teenager next month."

Everybody in the line were staring at us and Mama wouldn't stop talking; "I was planning on buying you a suit and some boots for Christmas. This doll business has to stop. You been helping me and Curley put Christmas toys out for years. Go back there and get three or four puzzles and some games. You managed to talk me into buying you a doll last year. But you better believe, you ain't gon do it this year! You are too old for baby dolls!"

Mama And Her Boys: 1992

Mama had a doctor's appointment at the hospital. I helped her get dressed. Earl, Emerson and I were going to take her to the appointment. Emerson and I helped her down the stairs and to the car.

As soon as she got situated in Emerson's car, Earl drove into the driveway and said; "Y'all can ride in my car." Mama directed Earl; "Park on the street. I'm already in Emerson's car. As soon as Earl backed out of the driveway, Charlie drove into the driveway, blew his horn, got out of the car and said; "Hey Mama I'm going to the hospital with you too."

Mama said; "Come on y'all. Help me out of this car. I want to ride in Charlie's car. As soon as she got her left foot in Charlie's car Roy drove into the driveway and got out of his State Trooper's car dressed in his uniform and said; "Ay. I caught you all just in time. I'm going to the hospital with you guys."

Mama said; "Wait a minute y'all. I think I'll ride in Roy's police car." After she got settled in Roy's car, out of the clear blue sky she became a spirited sassy knockout as she gave orders. "Earl you and Emerson ride with Charlie. Bettye you can stay home and cook dinner and finish painting. (Smiling.) I'll be alright. My boys are going with me. (Looking at Charlie.) Charlie follow Roy! "

"Roy, I'm running late for my doctor's appointment. This is the opportunity I been waiting for. To ride in a speeding police car with the siren on. Turn the siren on before you back out of the driveway. If somebody is driving down the street they will have a chance to pull over to the curb and stop. And remember you don't have to stop at the red lights. Just slow down a bit to see if its clear then zoom on through."

Roy laughed and made a comment; "Mama I can't speed and put the siren on unless it's legitimate. If I do that I'll have to call it in. Then I'll be in trouble."

Mama looked at Roy and reiterated; "I'm running late for my doctor's appointment. That's a legitimate reason. Let's not get logical Roy. We won't discuss the matter any further. We are

319

wasting time. Turn the siren on and let's boogie. Or as Bettye say: 'Let's rock and roll.'"

That was a positive pleasant switch from the irritable attitude she had earlier that morning towards going to the doctor; "Call the doctor's office and tell them I won't be there for my appointment. Nol. I don't need a reason. OK. Tell them I'm in a bad mood."

"All they are going to do is poke my legs and feet with a needle and ask me if I can feel it. Those doctors act like they don't know how to do nothing but write prescriptions. If I tell them I feel good they write me a prescription. If I tell them I feel bad they write me a prescription. I have a mind to flush all of that medicine down the toilet."

"Bettye put this shirt back in the drawer and give me the one that you brought me from California. That's not the one. The one that say **'I'M The Boss.'** Bring me the mirror. I want to see how you're styling my hair. Why don't you put a part in the middle and brush it to the back. Alright. Its looking good. I just want to sit around the house and look my best. I have a feeling that somebody is coming to see me today."

Roy didn't speed or put the siren on. Mama was on time for her doctor's appointment. She was overwhelmed because her beautiful sons accompanied her to the doctor. She was a proud *mother*; "These are my sons. Yes. All four of them. Um huh. Ha, ha ha. Thank you. No. I hate to disappoint you. But all of them are married."

"Dr. August this is the most you ever said to me. I thought you were uppish! You're the one that's always pushing prescriptions on me. Yes. Didn't I tell you earlier that all of my sons are married? Aren't you engaged to Dr. Sanders? I see. You still have playing the field in your blood. I declare there are a lot of young single men out there. What you want with a married man? Dr. August I thought this was a prescription. This is your phone number. Thank you. I will call you if I have any problems. What?

You got to be kidding. I have four lovely daughter in laws. And I love all of them! You better give this darn number to a single man. Mama's boys accompanying her to her doctor's appointment was good medicine for her and it lasted the entire summer. She mentioned it practically every day. And she always had a big smile as she reminisced.

The Magazine:

I was a thirteen year old girl sitting in the kitchen reading a True Love Magazine when Richard and Charlie came in; "Bet Joe you're not supposed to read a magazine like that. Put it back under the bathtub before T. J. come home. That's his magazine." I told them; "It's mine now. I found it under the tub when I was cleaning the bathroom. Get out of my face."

They told Mama and she snatched the magazine out of my hands; "You ain't got no business reading this kind of magazine!"

I answered; "Yeah. I know Mama. I'm sorry. But that was a good story I was reading. Besides Mama I need to exercise my brain. I read in the encyclopedia that the only exercise your brain get is by reading."

Mama said; "Oh yeah. Well get busy exercising your brain by reading the encyclopedia, the newspaper, some comic books, etc."

I made a comment; "Mama, Please. I declare. If I don't find out the ending to that story I will have a migraine headache and sleepless restless nights."

She responded: "Don't worry you'll get over it."

The Process:

When Earl was twelve years old he gave his fourteen year old friend Henry Henry a process because Henry Henry kept begging him to do it. The guys in the neighborhood raved about it. Some of them wanted processes as well.

When Henry Henry sat down to dinner that evening his mother noticed his hair; "Henry Henry, what is wrong with your hair? Its slick! And it has waves from your forehead to your neck.

He answered her; "Mother this is a process. Earl gave it to me. (Smiling and patting his hair) This is nice! Isn't it mother?

She talked; "Henry Henry don't bother to eat. Take your ass to the bathroom. I'm going to wash that process out of your hair with some Tide! Tell that young man, Robert Earl Holmes to keep his damn hands out of your hair."

He asked; "Mother are you going to wash the process out of Father's hair too? Because he's at Earl's house getting a process as we speak. Mother, Father loves my process! That's what influenced him to get a process. Earl and I are contemplating on going down town after school tomorrow to Grants Department Store's picture booth and take pictures of my process.

Henry Henry's mother washed his hair faithfully every day and finally one day the process was gone.

Our Lovely Family Has Deceased Dramatically:

322

Smiley Jackson (Papa) October 20.1976. He got sick and drove himself to the hospital and departed his life there. My brothers were his pallbearers.

Mary Ellen Jackson (Big Mama) Had a stroke in 1959. Never recovering from it, she departed her life in January 27,1961.

Curley Holmes (Daddy) He was mis-diagnosed and treated for pneumonia. One week later he was hospitalized and after further testing, it was established that he had a heart attack a week prior that. (not pneumonia) A third heart attack five days later took him from us on January 31,1969.

Two months prior Daddy's death, we had thanksgiving dinner at June and Dolly's (June's second wife). house. It was a lovely occasion. The family worked diligently preparing that awesome meal.

Daddy expressed himself several times; "I am so happy that I could jump up and clap my feet. All of my children, except Richard, are here with me. And he would be here if he wasn't in the Army. June, you and Miney blessed us with four beautiful grandchildren. I'm eager for you and Dolly to continue on. Doll, you and Bob blessed us with two wonderful grandchildren. I see that Geritol worked wonders! T. J., you and Sue blessed us with two lovely grandchildren. Bettye, you and your husband blessed us with two gorgeous grandchildren. I don't know if I'll ever be able to pronounce my grandson's name. How do you say his name again? 'Sancho Sereno.' Charlie, you and Charlene blessed us with this (holding her in his arms) precious little bundle of joy. Gladys take a look at this baby! She look just like Bettye. She has dimples. Oh boy. She can't stop smiling at me. Janine, I like your name. Miss Janine, Charlene and your Aunt Bettye had a bet going on. Charlene went to the hospital with false labor several times. So your Aunt Bettye made a bet. She betted Charlene that she would have Sonho Sobecho first. Charlene won. You came one day before Senoho Satreo."

Daddy continued; (Looking around) "I'm so happy! I hope I don't get sick or anything. We moved to Buffalo in 1957 with eight children. And twelve years later we have nine children and twelve grandchildren. I wouldn't trade this for nothing!"

I often think of that lovely Thanksgiving Day which my family shared felicitously. I thank God for that most *precious* day!

Gladys Holmes (Mama) She was a diabetic the last fourteen years of her precious life. She also had a stroke in 1992, and her left leg was amputated twenty two days before she slipped away to be with Daddy. September 22,1994.

I dreamed Mama's death three days prior her death. The dream was extremely vivid. Her hospital room, and the surroundings, were sparkling white. There was a sense of peacefulness and joy. Her face was bright, cheerful, and flawless, as she laughed and spoke these words; *"Bettye, I am alright. I am happy. I want you to stop crying and worrying about me. Curley is with me. He came to get me!"*

I began to laugh then. There was a lot of laughter and happiness. It was a most beautiful dream. After awaking from the dream, I was bewildered.

Doll, Charlene, (Charlie's wife) and I was with Mama when she made her transaction. At the same time my Husband, Jimmee, was driving to Sandy, Utah. (He left for Utah, after taking me to the airport in Los Angeles, CA to go to Buffalo, NY.) And something happened that made him sit up straight. He said; "I was very sleepy and looking for a place to pull over and park so I could take a nap. That's when a white figure appeared in your seat and remained there for several seconds. I kind of a sensed it was your mom's spirit. Therefore I wasn't afraid. When I got to my parents house in Sandy, Utah, my dad met me at the door and told me your mom had passed. I told him: "I know!"

Doll, Charlie and Charlene, Earl and Geneva, Emerson and

Essie, Roy, Rochelle and I were in Mama's room with high hopes: "She will wake up now that Bettye is here". We planned what we would do for her when she came home from the hospital. We talked about humorous old times and laughed. Doll, Charlene- and I wanted to stay longer. I whispered in Mama's ear; "Wake up my sweet baby. Let's rock and roll. We have places to go and things to do." I held her hands and pinched her cheeks.

After reading the Bible to Mama, Charlene sat in a chair by the window and nodded.

Mama was lying on her back unconscious and her head was turned to the left. The sole of my feet became extremely hot as I stood at the foot of Mama's bed staring at her. Mama opened her eyes and turned her head only to stare into my eyes momentarily. I was overwhelmed with joy as I ran to her saying; "Mama, you're awake!"

She closed her eyes and turned her head to the left again. I began to plead; "Mama open your eyes." She opened them again but they immediately closed! Doll and the nurse rushed back to the room. Mama was very still. A clear fluid began to escape her mouth and the nurse said; "This is beautiful! Both of Mrs. Holmes daughters and her daughter in law are here with her while she is making this beautiful transition. You are blessed to be here with your mother and your mother in law! Bettye, I'm one of the nurses whom you talked with many times when you called here from California. Looks your mother was waiting for you to get here!"

I heard what the nurse said. And I tried to think of another definition for transition, but my mind wouldn't produce anything. Therefore I did the most difficult thing I ever did in my entire life. 'Hug Mama and listen to the death rattle in her throat and accept it!' That was a hell-of-a-lump to swallow! And a hell-of-a-lump to digest!

We purchased a gorgeous pink dress trimmed in white pearls for

Mama to be displayed in. But the dishonest undertaker switched it with a two hundred fifty dollar cheaper pink dress trimmed in white lace. The white pearls on the dress was to match Mama's white pearl earrings. I noticed it immediately. But due to the fact that he did an excellent job on Mama, I didn't mention it to my siblings. I wonder if the undertaker have sweet sleep?

Edward Jean Holmes (June) June was diagnosed and treated for having diabetes for six months. But his condition continued to deteriorate. After complaining profusely of having excruciating pain, the doctors ran further tests and performed exploratory surgery on him. He had spider cancer of the liver. He departed this life three weeks later. He took pleasure in and relished the fact that so many people came to the hospital to pray for him. He told Edward Jr. that he saw the beautiful light.

His children from California, Joyce, Denise, Renee, and Edward Jr. along with his youngest daughter Nicole, his loving wife Dolly, and his siblings were at his bedside, doing whatever they could to make him comfortable until he took his last breath. December 9,1986.

In July of 1986 June had attended Edward Jr's wedding and had a ball. He enjoyed himself to the fullest. His children made a big fuss over him and he loved every minute of it. They cooked for him They took him out to dinner, Hollywood, Universal Studios, Magic Mountain, Disney Land, a play and Lancaster. He simply loved being in Lancaster. It was difficult for him to leave them.

Thomas James Holmes (T. J.) was a diabetic the last eight years of his life. He was never able to digest the fact of losing June. At the time of June's death he was working in Georgia. And wasn't able to attend the funeral because he was in the hospital. He inadvertently took an over dose of insulin when Mama called to inform him June had cancer.

T. J.'s doctor told Mama that she would let him know of June's death when he was stabilized. He was extremely emotional about

June being sick. T. J. was totally shattered and blown away when he heard of June's death.

My daughter Malesha spent some time with T. J. in January of 1992. She drove and he directed her where to go. "Stop at the liquor store on East Ferry. Me and June went there, practically every week-end. Hey girl. Take this money, go in there and buy me a bottle.

Do you Know how to get to Clinton street? Alright. Lets roll. We're going to Mozza's pizza joint. Wait a minute. Don't park yet. When that red truck move, I want you to park there. That's the spot me and June parked in. You can see everything when you park here. Do you want some of this drink? That's good. You don't need to drink anyway. Its not good for you. I'll buy you a pop.

Get what you want and bring me one slice with everything on it. You better believe it. Mozza make the best pizza in Buffalo. Ha, ha, ha. I heard the pizza in California sucks. The first thing y'all want to do when you come back to Buffalo is get some pizza."

After laughing talking and joking around, T. J. became extremely quiet. Malesha questioned him; "Uncle T. J., are you going to sleep on me? Hello. Hello. Hello. What is your problem?"

Crying, he answered; "I miss June so much, that I can't stand it! We used to have a lot of fun when we came down here. We always had three slices of pizza, that was our thing. It seemed like every time we came down here, we'd have an argument about something stupid. But we looked forward to that. That's the way it was and I miss it. Do that sound crazy? Alright. Hey lets go get another slice of pizza."

They had their three slices of pizza and headed for home just like him and June always did. T. J. was most appreciative to Malesha, for sharing those precious hours with him. T. J. departed this life the following month. February 4,1992.

Richard Noble Holmes: Richard was grief stricken at the death of June. He felt guilty, because it was June that passed instead of him. (He loved June better that he loved himself).

He said: "It should have been me! It hurts. I 'm crushed when I look at June's kids. They love him so much. He was a good man, a superb father and a loyal brother. He had so much to live for."

June's death left Richard depressed   mentally and emotionally drained. He didn't take care of himself anymore. He was in and out of the hospital. And one day he went into cardiac arrest. The doctors brought him back and he blessed them out; "If that happens again do not attempt to interfere again. I am in unbearable pain from you insane doctors beating on my chest. I think you all broke my ribs. I like where I was! It was peaceful!

Richard departed his life thirteen months after June's death. He was hospitalized and diagnosed as a diabetic three weeks after he was discharged with a clean bill of health from the United States Marines.

A couple of days after Richard's funeral, a package from the United States Army and the United Sates Marines arrived in the mail. Emerson brought it upstairs, and opened it. Mama and I were in her bedroom, she were relaxing in her bed and enjoying the pedicure I was giving her. Contained in the box was a letter and a wooden picture frame with a certificate in it.

Emerson read the letter; "Dear Mrs. Holmes we were sorry to hear of the death of your son Richard Noble Holmes. We were proud to have Richard serve in the United States Army and the United States Marines. Etc

The certificate mentioned duties Richard accomplished during his ten years in the service. He operated the heavy duty equipment. (The Army). He was a Military Policeman. He utilized his gifted talent as a Calligrapher and an artist by making signs and posters

328

for The United States Marines. Etc.

Mama held the certificate to her chest as she talked; "I don't know how Curley and June convinced Richard to change his mind and go to the Army when he was drafted. I remember how hot and spicy Richard was when he was drafted. He said; 'I am not going to the damn Army! Shit! I'm moving to Canada!' Curley would have been so proud of Richard for serving his country. Who would have believed that he would have served two years in the Army and eight years in the Marines?"

Robert Earl Holmes: (Earl) Earl departed this life thirteen months after Mama passed, in the same hospital and the same hospital Room. His death was caused by a blood clot in his artery.

Earl's wife, Geneva said; "One day when I was visiting Earl in the hospital, he looked up and smiled saying: 'Daddy! Mama! June! T. J.! Richard! All of you guys are here!'

Sweet peace was upon his face. And in a couple of days, he stole away.

A unique thing happened during Earl's funeral. There was an unusually beautiful bouquet of flowers positioned near Earl's casket and the flower pedals kept falling. Earl's daughters and Jimmee saw the pedals falling.

After the funeral was dismissed, Jimmee and Earl's daughters, Kamilah, Tiffaney, Veronica and Le Rondra approached the bouquet and Tiffaney grabbed one of the flowers and commenced to shaking it. Nothing fell from the stem!

Jimmee and my nieces assumed it was Earl saying: "Cheer Up! Be Happy! I Am At Peace;" Or something of that nature. It was Earl's character to do something like that!

Emerson Holmes: (M) Emerson became a diabetic in his mid

329

twenties. He departed this life four months after having his right leg amputated due to diabetic complications.

The surgery was intended to be a solution that would prolong his life. But complication after complication set in and he slipped into eternal sweet sleep!

An unusual thing happened to me during Emerson's surgery in Buffalo, NY! I was living in Moreno Valley, CA. It was my day off from work. I took a walk early that morning and everything was fine. Forty five minutes after the walk, I was forced to get off the computer due to excruciating pain in my right leg! It was ongoing for the entire day. I soaked in a hot bath, I massaged my leg with Tiger Bond, I took pain pills. I tried elevating it.

Nothing relieved that sudden excruciating mystique condition that possessed my leg. My doctor gave me an emergency appointment to see him.

I didn't know Emerson was having the surgery. Two days prior that, I talked with him and he told me that the doctors were trying everything they could to avoid the surgery.

I talked with him after Doll called and informed me of the surgery.

He was the conversationalist: "I'm alright. I'm glad its over. I can still feel my foot. Its itching real bad. The doctors say that's normal.

I'm hungry. I don't usually like hospital food but I ate everything they brought me today. I'm waiting for Roy. He always bring me a steak sandwich or submarine. Chucky, (Doll's nephew in law) visited me yesterday. He said he was going to bring me something good to eat. I hope he bring pizza. Hey Bettye you ever eat at Wendy's? Me and Doll went there one day last week. We had an awesome baked potato. Maybe she'll bring me one of those when she come to see me. Sunday Charlie brought me a platter of barbecue ribs and some collard greens. Check this out. It tasted better than mine. Anyhow I woke up hungry about 1: a. m., and asked the nurse to heat it up for me. She brought it back saying; 'Ooh. Mr. Holmes these ribs and greens smell so good. Can I sneak one of these ribs? Please? I'll die, if I don't.' She sat on the bed and ate more than I did."

When I got off the phone my painful leg episode was gone. But I didn't realize it until the middle of the night. I woke up and was preoccupied with what Emerson went through. And I suddenly remembered my leg pain. I got out of bed and walked. I examined my leg. Everything was painless and back to normal. I believe it was an act of one sibling sharing the pain of another sibling miles away. I know the pain and agony he encountered with his leg. I encountered it too!

There are only **four** of us left in the fourth generation: Doll, Bettye, Charlie, and Roy.

The End